ORDNANCE SURVEY

Plan *of the Instrument.*

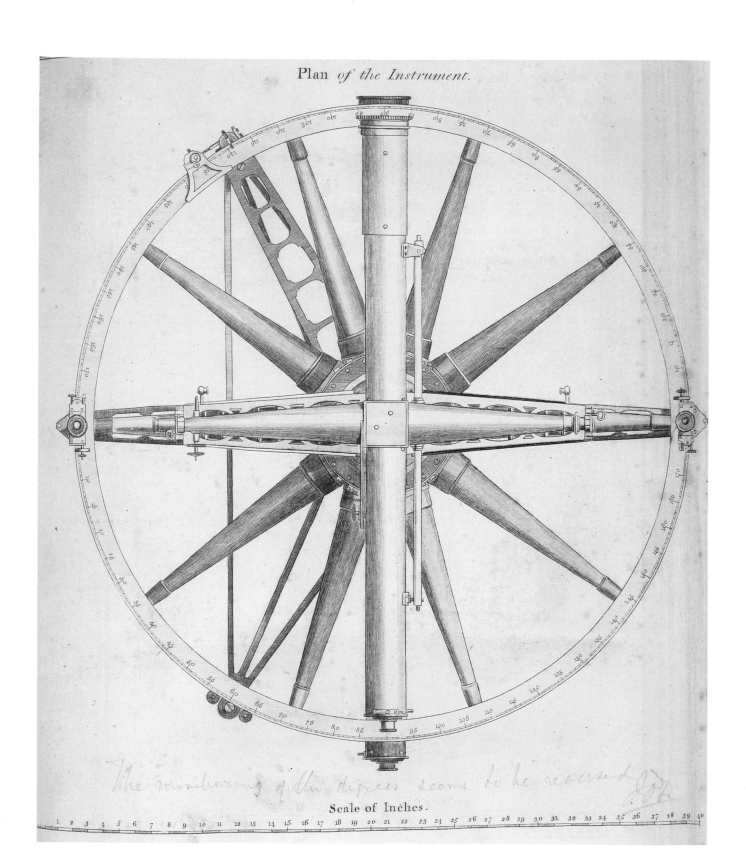

The numbering of the degrees seems to be reversed.

Scale of Inches.

1 2 3 4 5 6 7 8 9 10 11 12 13 14 15 16 17 18 19 20 21 22 23 24 25 26 27 28 29 30 31 32 33 34 35 36 37 38 39 40

ORDNANCE SURVEY

Map Makers to Britain
since 1791

Tim Owen and Elaine Pilbeam

Ordnance Survey, Southampton
London: HMSO

Maps and text © Crown copyright 1992
First published 1992 by

Ordnance Survey   and   HMSO
Romsey Road   St Crispins
Maybush   Duke Street
Southampton   Norwich
SO9 4DH   NR3 1PD

Designed by Alison Beaumont, HMSO Graphic Design

ISBN 0 31 900249 7 (Ordnance Survey)
ISBN 0 11 701507 5 (HMSO)

British Library Cataloguing in Publication Data

Owen, Tim, *1946–*
    Ordnance Survey: map makers to Britain
    since 1791.
    I. Title II. Pilbeam, Elaine, *1961–*
    526.0941

HMSO publications are available from:

HMSO Publications Centre
(Mail, fax and telephone orders only)
PO Box 276, London, SW8 5DT
Telephone orders 071-873 9090
General enquiries 071-873 0011
(queuing system in operation for both numbers)
Fax orders 071-873 8200

HMSO Bookshops
49 High Holborn, London, WC1V 6HB   071-873 0011 (counter service only)
258 Broad Street, Birmingham, B1 2HE   021-643 3740
Southey House, 33 Wine Street, Bristol, BS1 2BQ   0272-264306
9–21 Princess Street, Manchester, M60 8AS   061-834 7201
80 Chichester Street, Belfast, BT1 4JY   0232-238451
71 Lothian Road, Edinburgh, EH3 9AZ   031-228 4181

HMSO's Accredited Agents
(see Yellow Pages)

and through good booksellers

Front cover
A composite map of Maidstone comprising nine extracts of maps held by Ordnance Survey's Record Map Library. All extracts are reproduced at their original 1-inch scale, except for the last two which are reduced to 1-inch from 1:50000.

Starting from the earliest map at the top, brief map details are as follows: Mudge map of Kent, 1801; New Series, sheet 272 of Chatham, 1876; 'Brown Hills' map of Maidstone, sheet 288, 1905; Third Edition (large sheet series), sheet 117, 1909; Popular Edition, sheet 116, 1921; New Popular Edition, sheet 172, 1946; Seventh Series, sheet 172, 1957; 1:50 000 First Series, sheet 188, 1972; 1:50 000 Second Series, sheet 188, 1990

Back cover
Observations being made from the top of St Paul's Cathedral during the 1848–50 Survey of London (Illustrated London News, 21 June 1848)

Frontispiece
Plan view of Ramsden's 3-foot (Royal Society) theodolite

Chapter-heading boxes
ch 1 (p 3): *Ramsden's 3-foot (Royal Society) theodolite*
ch 2 (p 15): *the small (18-inch) Ramsden circular instrument, built in 1795 and in use until the 1850s*
ch 3 (p 27): *Colby's compensation bars*
ch 4 (p 37): *Casella 8-inch level, c.1850*
ch 5 (p 45): *Troughton and Simms 12-inch vernier theodolite, 1846*
ch 6 (p 53): *Airy's zenith sector*
ch 7 (p 67): *Troughton and Simms 12-inch theodolite, c.1870*
ch 8 (p 80): *Smith magnetometer*
ch 9 (p 93): *Troughton and Simms 4-inch theodolite, c.1914*
ch 10 (p 105): *diagram of strip-flying used for mapping purposes in the 1930s, showing how overlap of aerial photographs was achieved*
ch 11 (p 119): *Tavistock 5½-inch theodolite, c.1935*
ch 12 (p 134): *Wild T2 Universal Theodolite*
ch 13 (p 147): *Kern DKM 2-AE theodolite with Aga Geodometer*
ch 14 (p 163): *Desktop computer*

For the staff of Ordnance Survey, past and present,
makers of 'the best maps in the world'.

CONTENTS

FOREWORD
BY THE DUKE OF RICHMOND

My predecessor, the 3rd Duke of Richmond, has always appeared to me to be the most visionary of all my nine predecessors, and he is certainly the one who left the strongest imprint on the life and history of our nation. He sympathised with the inhabitants of the American Colonies, and advocated universal male suffrage in 1780; his roles as Ambassador to Louis XV, army officer, minister and politician, head of a ducal family, magistrate, sportsman, landowner, builder, patron of the arts, planter of trees – even mender of local roads – kept him in touch with, and often ahead of, national developments throughout his life. He was a notably independent man and worked very hard to improve the British army as a fighting force. Able officers saw him as a means of curing incompetence in the service. 'Do you therefore, my good Lord, persevere and move the Country usefully and Honourably; urge the Ministers . . . ' General Wolfe wrote to him in 1757.

He founded Goodwood Racecourse some five years before his death. Generations of racegoers have watched an annual race at Goodwood Racecourse called The Drawing Room Stakes. It took me some years to realise that this name did not refer to a room in Goodwood House, but recalls the Map-Drawing Room of the Ordnance Survey which was founded by the 3rd Duke in 1791.

During his 'reign' the 3rd Duke increased his estate from 1100 acres to 17 000! So it is transparently clear why he was so interested in having accurate surveys. He employed (and even paid for extra tuition for) the best surveyors he could find – a measure of his thoroughness and his own deep interest in surveying. That the requirements were very similar for both land acquisitions and military campaigns will not have surprised him in the least. He was, all his life, aware of the need for good maps.

Under his guidance as Master of the Ordnance (1782–1795) the Ordnance Survey (officially launched in 1791) was begun, and it is indicative of his determination that the two men who surveyed his own 72 square mile estate at Goodwood, and produced the exquisite maps still in the archives here, were earlier employed by him at the Ordnance. In 1782 he brought Yeakell and, two years later, Gardner into the Ordnance under the direction of William Roy and they remained for the rest of their lives.

It can truly be said that the Duke harnessed together the civilian surveyor and the military engineer and created the national survey of Great Britain.

Richmond.

CHRONOLOGY

===== Charles Lennox, 3rd Duke of Richmond, Lennox and Aubigny KG, PC, FRS, FSA =====

1735   Born London 22 February: Earl of March.

1745   Enters Westminster School as a Town Boy.

1750   Succeeds to the title of Duke of Richmond, Lennox and Aubigny (8 August).

1752   Sets out on the Grand Tour, visiting among other places, Paris, Vienna, Rome, Naples, Hanover, and Geneva. Returns to England in 1756.

1753   Gazetted Captain in the 20th Regiment of Foot, now Royal Regiment of Fusiliers.
Graduated from University of Leyden.

1755   Elected Fellow of the Royal Society.

1756   Colonel, 33rd Regiment of Foot, now Duke of Wellington's Regiment (West Riding).

1757   Marries (1 April) Mary, youngest daughter of the third Earl of Ailesbury.

1758   Opens an academy at Richmond House for 'any painter, carver, sculptor or other youth to whom the study of statuary might be useful'.
Colonel, 72nd Regiment of Foot (disbanded five years later, at the end of the Seven Years War).

1759   Serves with distinction at the Battle of Minden (1 August) in support of Prince Ferdinand of Brunswick.

1760   Lord of the Bedchamber to King George III, but resigned in the same year.

1761   Carries the Sceptre and Dove at the Coronation of George III.
Major-General.
Lord Lieutenant of Sussex.

1765–66   Ambassador Extraordinary and Minister Plenipotentiary to the French Court.
Admitted to the Privy Council.

1766–67   Secretary of State for the Southern Department in the Marquis of Rockingham's first administration.

1770   Lieutenant-General.

1770–75   Tables eighteen resolutions directed at threats to dissolve Colonial assemblies in America if they would not accept certain propositions sent to them in the King's name.

[1774   Death of Louis XV]

1775   Opposes Lord North's Prohibitory Act forbidding New England Trade and Fisheries.

1776   Formally registers his seigneury of Aubigny in the French parliament.

1778   Moves address in Parliament for the recall of British troops from America.

1779   Supports Rockingham's motion for the removal of the causes of Irish discontent 'by a redress of grievances'.
Proposes (unsuccessfully) reduction in the Civil List.

1780   Formulates proposals for universal adult male suffrage as part of his 'Declaration of the Rights of Englishmen'.

1782   Invested as Knight of the Garter.

1782–95   Master-General of Ordnance (out of office April–December 1783).

1793   Elected Fellow of the Society of Arts.

1795   Colonel, Royal Regiment of Horse Guards, now the Blues and Royals (Royal Horse Guards and 1st Dragoons).
Field Marshal.

1796   Death of Duchess Mary.

1797   Colonel, 2nd Battalion 35th Regiment, now the Queen's Regiment.

1804   Publishes his *Thoughts on National Defence*.
Speaks in the House of Lords for the last time (25 June).

1806   Dies at Goodwood (29 December).

ACKNOWLEDGEMENTS

Numerous people have generously given their time, knowledge and memories and our grateful thanks are due to them all. Space does not permit us to detail the help given by each and we hope that the alphabetical list that follows is considered sufficient thanks. As well as those named a large number of people have provided snippets of information and to them we give collective thanks.

J H Andrews, John Bear, Geraldine Beech, Denis Bill, the Bloggs family, Paula Broomfield, Colonel W H Bond, 'Jim' Bowhay, Patricia Boyne, Sheila Caine, Alan Carey, Gerald Chamberlain, Rex Chilman, Peter Chausseaud, John Clift, Julian Cooper, Charlie Dawson, J J Dawson, Betty Drewitt, Dave Earley, Major General R C A Edge, Elaine Foote, Martin Green, Ian Greenway, Francis Herbert, Rod Hatch, Albert Hicks, Yolande Hodson, Major General B St G Irwin, Reg Jerrard, Doug Lacey, Dr R Leech, Bob Lindley, John Moxon, Peter McMaster, Tim McCann, John Maynard, Ian Mumford, Brian Nanson, Richard Oliver, Jim Page, John Philpott, Richard Porter, Pat Poppy, Alex Robinson, Andrew Rochelle, Matt Saunders, Bill Seymour, Peter Seden, Douglas Shatz, Tony Smart, Graeme Smith, Pete Smith, Norrie Smith, Walter Smith, Peter Staniczenko, David A Trippier RD JP MP, Mike Trimboy and the members of Staff Records, Brian Unwin, Louise Warwick, Peter Wesley, John White, and the staff of the OS Record Map Library.

The map series charts were compiled jointly by John Paddy Browne and Drs Chris Board, Roger Hellyer and Richard Oliver.

Special thanks are due to John Paddy Browne without whose encouragement and practical help we may never have finished, and to our families and friends who have patiently accepted our absence from social events. Our thanks are also due to Brigadier A B Clough who, before he died in 1989, aged 100, gave us an insight into Ordnance Survey under MacLeod's Director Generalship.

Lastly, we are grateful to the following individuals and organisations for permission to reproduce the illustrations which appear in the book: Les Auckland; British Library, London; J R P Browne; Peter Chasseaud; Civil Aviation Authority, London; *Daily Mirror*, London; G A Dawson; Geological Society of London; Guildhall, London; Roger Hellyer; Yolande Hodson; *Illustrated London News*; David Kingsley; National Gallery of Ireland, Dublin; Tim Nicholson; V Orford; Public Record Office, London; Punch Publications Ltd, London; The Duke of Richmond, by kind permission of the Duke of Richmond; The Royal Collection, St James's Palace, London, copyright reserved, reproduced by gracious permission of Her Majesty The Queen; The Royal Irish Academy, Dublin; The Royal Library, Windsor Castle, copyright 1992 Her Majesty The Queen; The Royal Society, London; Science Museum, London; Survey of Kenya, Nairobi; Tom Weir. Copyright for all other illustrations resides with Ordnance Survey.

Introduction

The past 200 years have seen vast changes in society ranging from the industrial revolution, the development of the internal combustion engine to space travel. Over this period our society's awareness of, and need for, maps has steadily increased. In Ordnance Survey, we are indeed fortunate to be providing a service which is truly needed by society and for which there is a growing appreciation.

By its nature, map-making, which is about the world we live in, is interesting, as it gives people the information they need to make proper use of the land. It is therefore not surprising that those involved in map-making become absorbed by their work and highly skilled in its execution. Also, through the necessary teamwork involved, they develop a strong identity with their organisation and comradeship with colleagues. It is on this basis of committed staff that the present pre-eminent position of Ordnance Survey among map makers is founded.

It is fitting that Ordnance Survey should take a pause to mark this 200th anniversary, with the publication of this colourful and informative history, detailing important and intriguing insights into our past, and as a statement of the skill and dedication of its staff.

Peter McMaster
Director General, 1985–91

1 ORIGINS AND EARLY MAPS

An insignificant event

On 21 June 1791, a small entry was made in the Expense Ledger of the Board of Ordnance recording the payment of £373.14s, to Jesse Ramsden for a 3-foot theodolite. The purchase was made at the instigation of the Master General, the 3rd Duke of Richmond, and this insignificant entry is now generally accepted as the founding action of the Ordnance Survey.

Cartographic sophistication had been growing for centuries, the pattern being set by Saxton who produced thirty-four county maps and one general map of Britain between 1574 and 1579. These were published in an atlas which represented a great step forward as the first complete set of maps of the country. Beyond this venture support for mapping was locally organised, mainly by a system of subscriptions taken from purchasers to fund each survey. This resulted in many grand schemes failing due to lack of support, and although large numbers of maps were published only a few were of an exceptional quality.

By the 1750s, official mapping in Britain had begun to fall seriously behind some other European countries and the Society of Arts noted that British maps were 'wholly destitute of any public encouragement' and 'extremely defective'. They attempted to pressurise the Government into taking action, but when this failed the Society itself offered in 1759, 'a Sum not exceeding one hundred pounds, as a Gratuity to any Person or Persons, who shall make an accurate Survey of any County upon the Scale of one Inch to a Mile'. This award not only stimulated the production of maps to county boundaries, but also laid down the tradition of the 1-inch scale.

As a result, towards the end of the century much of Britain had been resurveyed on a county basis. However, these new maps did not suit military purposes, being particularly ineffective in their depiction of relief, an essential cartographic ingredient for an efficient military map, and being at a scale inadequately small for field engineering. Military needs were therefore satisfied by augmenting available maps with local military surveys undertaken by trained army surveyors, whenever the need arose.

By the 1790s Britain still had no accurate national map, or survey on which one could be based.

The founding of the Ordnance Survey on that midsummer's day in 1791 combined the interests of military surveyors, commercial map makers and scientists, after a period of increasing cartographic activity.

William Roy

Whilst the founder of the Ordnance Survey must be acknowledged as the Duke of Richmond, the credit for the idea of a national survey must be given to William Roy, who had died in 1790.

William Roy, who was both son and grandson of Factors to the Lairds of Milton, was born on 4 May 1726 at Miltonhead, Lanarkshire. He received a good, solid education, at Lanark Grammar School, being 'soundly drilled in the elements of Latin and Mathematics', but did not go on to further education, unlike his brother James who became a minister. It is possible that Roy first learnt about surveying by

Extract from the accounts of the Board of Ordnance.
Public Record Office

helping his father, on the estate surveys with which the factor was bound to be involved.

Some time after 1738, he moved to Edinburgh and gained experience of surveying and making plans, probably as a civilian draughtsman at the office of the Board of Ordnance in Edinburgh Castle.

The Jacobite uprising, culminating in the bloody battle of Culloden in April 1746, highlighted the need for accurate military maps. A battle was won by more than sheer force of numbers or quality of weapons. Great advantage could be gained by surprise and tactical placing of troops, by knowledge of the enemy numbers and position and, importantly, the lie of the land. During the rebellion both the Duke of Cumberland's commanders and the Young Pretender, Prince Charles Edward Stuart, had access to copies of the best map available. This had been compiled by John Elphinstone in 1744 and published in early 1745 at a scale of 1 inch to 13½ miles (1 : 855360). It was far too small a scale for the detail needed by military commanders.

This was apparent to Lieutenant Colonel David Watson of the Engineers, the Deputy Quartermaster-General of the forces in northern Britain, who had taken part in the Battle of Culloden. Watson recognised the need for better maps of Scotland and put forward proposals for a survey to the Duke of Cumberland who, with his generals, had 'found themselves greatly embarrassed for want of a proper survey of the Country'. Cumberland returned to London in July 1746 and obtained authority from his father, George II, for the survey to proceed. The King, who was keen to continue with the pacification of the Highlands, saw the importance of having the country mapped and agreed to the scheme.

Watson had seen Roy's work and had identified him as a cartographer of suitable ability to take on the mapping of Scotland and, to alleviate the problem of a young clerk having seniority over the soldiers who were to work for him, he appointed Roy to the post of Assistant Quartermaster. In his *Account of the Trigonometrical Survey*, Roy recalled that Watson 'being himself an Engineer, active and indefatigable, a zealous promoter of every useful undertaking, and the warm and steady friend of the industrious, first conceived the idea of making a map of the Highlands'. He continued 'As Assistant Quartermaster, it fell to my lot to begin, and afterwards to have a considerable share in the execution of that map.'

Roy started work on his own at first, on an experimental basis, at Fort Augustus. He was joined between 1748 and 1750 by more Engineers, eventually totalling six surveying parties. At the same time that the survey was taking place Marshal Wade was developing his project for road construction through the Highlands. Watson laid out the roads and supervised their construction.

Colonel David Watson, drawn by Paul Sandby, c.1760.
Royal Collection

Watson's original scheme was to survey the Highlands, but by 1752, when this was nearing completion, the decision was taken to extend the survey to cover the whole of Scotland.

A nephew of Watson, David Dundas, joined Roy and was placed under his tuition. He later took command of one of the two parties surveying the southern part of Scotland. According to Dundas 'each Surveyor was attended by a Non-commissioned Officer and Six Soldiers as Assistants – one carried the Instrument – Two measured with the Chain. Two for the fore and back stations – one as Batman.' Dundas later became Commander-in-Chief of the land forces in Britain and probably the most brilliant military tactician of the century.

Roy, perhaps, saw that parallels could be drawn between the English need to contain the Highlanders after the '45 uprising and the Roman control of clan movements during their four hundred years occupation of Britain, but whatever first fired his imagination, he became increasingly interested in antiquities as the evidence of Roman invasion fell under his surveyor's eye.

*'View near Loch Rannoch',
showing a surveying party at
work, c.1749. Drawn by Paul
Sandby RA, chief draughtsman.*
British Library

Occasionally he was able to pursue his interest as the survey proceeded. As Roy put it, the Antonine Wall 'was observed in the ordinary way' but 'without the Wall itself becoming the principal object'. He continues: 'It was therefore judged proper, in 1755, to survey accurately the line of this old intrenchment.' In later years, Roy became an expert on Roman military antiquities in Scotland and a Fellow of the Society of Antiquaries of London in 1776.

In 1755, the survey of Scotland was abruptly curtailed and operations were brought to a close, as officers were recalled during the build-up to the Seven Years War. The maps and documents were rolled up, the work never to be resumed.

Roy joined the army in 1755 and was appointed a Practitioner Engineer, the lowest commissioned rank in the Corps of Engineers. He left Scotland with Dundas, and with Colonel Watson they reconnoitred the south coast in preparation for the expected French invasion.

Britain was at war with France, not for European gain, but ultimately for supremacy in America. With an enemy only 20 miles away across the English Channel, invasion was always considered a threat but, in the event, no attempt was made by the French. During the war, Roy experienced active service in France and Germany, where his skills were exploited to produce sketch maps, notes and plans, and he received rapid promotion.

Roy recognised the vulnerability of Britain to invasion and, in 1763, made his first proposal for a national survey. It was, he said, a plan for defence, to be made 'during times of peace and tranquillity'. The plan for a 'general Survey of the whole Island at public cost' was considered by the government but the scheme, with Roy as its Director, was finally dropped on the grounds that it 'would be a Work of much time and labour, and attended with great Expence to the Government'.

Roy refused to let the matter rest, and in 1766 prepared a less ambitious plan, complete with a detailed analysis of the probable cost. It was again not taken up. The seven years of war with France and Spain had taken its toll on the national purse, and, with the sense of stability that peace brings, preparation for war, albeit for defence, proved too hard to reconcile. By that time both of Roy's allies in the mapping field had died, David Watson in 1761, and the Duke of Cumberland in 1765.

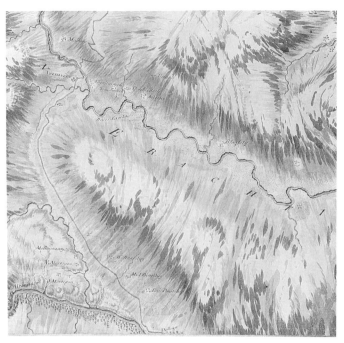

Part of the fair drawing of the Military Survey of Scotland.
British Library

Barometer experiments

The relatively simple technologies used in the mapping of Scotland had stirred in Roy a curiosity to investigate the application of scientific techniques, as an aid to more accurate survey. The use of the barometer as a means of determining height, using it, in effect, as an altimeter, interested Roy because he knew that better knowledge of the height of the surveyed point increased the accuracy of its position in relation to other surveyed points. In 1775, Roy calculated the height of Snowdon as 3568 feet, which stands comparison with the modern accepted value of 3560 feet above mean sea level.

Barometers were also used by Roy in a more complex experiment with Dr Nevil Maskelyne, the Astronomer Royal, in an attempt to find the density of the earth from the determination of 'the figure and dimensions of the hill'; the hill in question being Schiehallion in Perthshire. The task of the mathematical calculations was entrusted to Dr Charles Hutton FRS, Professor of Mathematics at the Royal Academy, who, while doing this, reported in 1778 that he 'fell upon' the method of 'connection together by faint line all the points which were of the same altitude'. This idea is now well known to all map users as the familiar contour line.

For his own amusement

The start of the American War of Independence in 1776 diverted the attention of the nation and any remaining thoughts of national mapping were put to one side. However, as soon as peace was declared in 1783, Roy's incurable enthusiasm for survey came once again to the surface and in that same year, for his own amusement, he measured a base across the fields between 'the Jews-Harp, near Marybone, and Black-Lane, near Pancras', in London. It was the foundation for a triangulation scheme, carried out 'for determining the relative situations of the most remarkable steeples, and other places in and about the capital with regard to each other, and the Royal Observatory at Greenwich'. Roy hoped that the activity might 'serve as a hint to the public, for the revival of the now almost forgotten scheme of 1763'.

It was a shrewd move, or a fortunate one, but either way Roy was ideally placed to capitalise on the opportunity that followed, and to forge ahead with his dream for a national survey.

A curious event on Hounslow Heath

In 1784 numerous distinguished visitors, including the King himself, and large numbers of curious bystanders were drawn to observe the strange operations taking place on Hounslow Heath. Sir Joseph Banks, who was President of the Royal Society, 'ordered his tents to be continually pitched near at hand', so that the visitors could be received and given refreshment.

They were watching the placement of long wooden boxes, laid precisely end to end, and supported on trestles. Soldiers would remove one from the end and carry it carefully to its new position at the front of the line. After adjustment, checking and examination of its position, another box would be brought forward, and in this way gradual progress was made over the Heath. This measurement (for that's what it was), is acknowledged as the beginning of accurate trigonometrical survey in Great Britain.

It was the first step in an important scheme to connect the observatories of Greenwich and Paris. The initiative had come from the French, who believed that the latitude of Greenwich was in doubt, and that, in order to find its correct value, it would be desirable to connect Greenwich, geodetically, with Paris. Dr Maskelyne was convinced, however, that because the true dimensions of the earth were still uncertain the connection with France would not solve the argument.

Early triangulation

William Roy lavished a previously unheard-of amount of time and money on the measurement made at Hounslow Heath, but he knew that an accurate survey had to start with a precisely measured line. Once the length of this line was known, it could be used to form the 'base' of a triangle. The two ends of Hounslow Heath Base, King's Arthur and Hampton Poorhouse, were connected with a third point at St Ann's hill to form such a triangle.

By measuring the internal angle at each point of the triangle, the length of the two unmeasured sides could be calculated using simple trigonometry. Mapping is based on triangles, hence triangulation (station) and the early name for the Ordnance Survey – Trigonometrical Survey.

Each side of this 'launch pad' triangle was then used as a base for others, and the procedure repeated until the desired network was built up. The triangles had an observing station at each point, with one side length and two stations common to any adjacent triangle.

Ramsden's 3-foot theodolite, was capable of observing more than 70 miles with no more than 2 seconds of arc error. The theodolite was really little more than a telescope that could be accurately and consistently pointed at a target, and a reading made of the angular difference between one target and another. Once observations had been made at the three points of a triangle, the internal angles were added together and Roy could be satisfied, if the total equalled 180 degrees, that the observations

were good. (In fact, the instrument proved to be so accurate that observations within large triangles introduced an apparent error, and the summed angles often, by a very small amount, came to more than 180 degrees. This error, known as spheroidal excess, was caused by the observations being affected by the curvature of the earth.)

The beauty of the triangulation system was that it combined a minimum of actual measurement on the ground with the application of sound mathematical theory, and the result was a highly accurate framework for map making. The same principles of base measurement and triangulation remain, in many instances, in use today, only the equipment used for taking the measurements has changed.

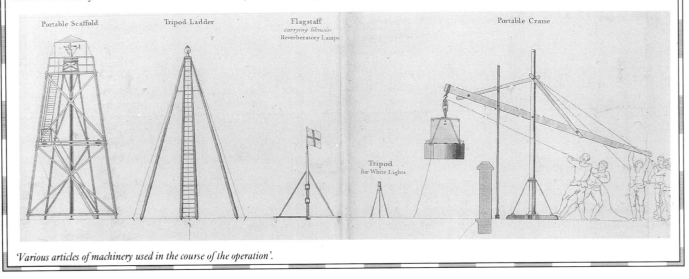

'Various articles of machinery used in the course of the operation'.

George III was anxious to oblige the French, and, being greatly interested in astronomy, agreed that the connection should go ahead under the direction of the Royal Society (of which he was patron) and 'soon supplied the funds that were judged necessary', generously paying for essential instruments to be made. The 'great Theodolite' which was to observe the angles of the triangulation was ordered in 1784 from Jesse Ramsden, the foremost instrument maker of the day. While the instrument was being constructed, the measurement of the base was made.

The importance of the accuracy of the base measurement cannot be over-stressed, and Roy, who was put in charge of this operation, made the most thorough preparations. First, using soldiers, who Roy thought to be more readily controlled than ordinary labourers, the ground was cleared of obstacles and vegetation along the intended base

line. Then, in June, the base was roughly measured using a steel chain. The same soldiers were placed as sentinels to prevent any accidental interruptions to the proceedings and provided the overnight guard for 'such parts of the apparatus, as it was foreseen must remain carefully untouched'.

The final measurement was to have been made using wooden rods, deal being chosen for its straight grain. Although widely used on the continent, deal was found to be less suitable for Britain's damp atmosphere. Any variation in humidity made the wood swell or contract slightly, affecting the length of the rods and this system was abandoned after more than half the base had been measured. Roy looked for an alternative, and, after rejecting cast iron as too heavy to handle, he accepted the proposal made by Lieutenant Colonel Calderwood, a member of the Royal Society, for using glass tubes.

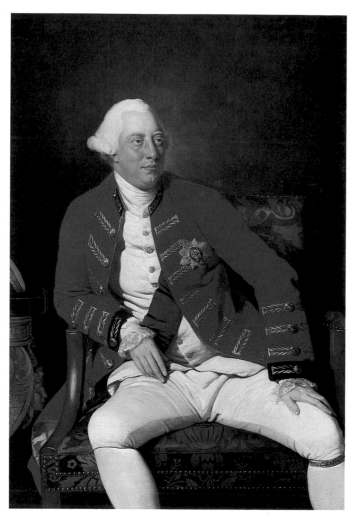

King George III, 'a generous and beneficent monarch, whose knowledge and love of the sciences are sufficiently evinced by the protection which he constantly affords them' (Account of the Trigonometrical Survey, 1784–1796). Royal Collection

After some experimentation, three glass tubes were drawn. They were 20 feet long and 1 inch in diameter, a remarkable achievement. Roy was delighted, they were so straight that 'the eye, placed at one end looking through them, could see any small object in the axis of the bore at the other end.' The rods were accurately measured for length and placed in specially designed, lightweight wooden cases from which their ends protruded, constituting a bulky and fragile but practical measuring device.

Ramsden meanwhile had constructed a new, more accurate, steel chain and the opportunity was taken to test this against the glass tubes. Both proved satisfactory, and Roy ideally would have preferred to measure the entire base using

the glass tubes and the steel chain, as added security against error, but as the weather was worsening and the wooden coffers holding the chain were found to be defective, the base was completed using only the glass tubes. The measurement was completed on 30 August 1784, each end being carefully marked by wooden pipes, the lower end of which passed through the centre of a buried cart-wheel.

The precision of the measurement obtained with so much care was ranked as an achievement of great scientific importance in the century, and for his work Roy received the Copley Medal for Science from the Royal Society.

Hounslow Heath was only the beginning of the project to connect Britain and France geodetically. From this base line, a network of triangles was planned to extend down to the south coast of England. Each point of a triangle was carefully chosen for its visibility to and from others, using, where possible, high vantage points such as the tops of hills and church towers. The selection of these 'stations' and purchase of the necessary equipment was soon completed, but nothing could begin without the theodolite. Roy was hopeful of starting the triangulation in 1786, but the summer passed without the instrument being delivered.

The delay caused great frustration to Roy who, now aged sixty, was no longer in good health. He found it an ever-increasing strain keeping interest in the project alive when, inevitably, it waned during this long period of inactivity. At last, the theodolite was delivered in July 1787, almost three years after the date it was ordered.

The cross-Channel connection

Winter was now approaching and the chances of completing the planned triangulation network in 1787 were slim. It was agreed that Roy would commence the triangulation, breaking off at a point convenient to the French to co-operate in the cross-Channel observation, and then resume the English triangulation afterwards. The first ten stations were in this way fixed before removal of the instrument to Dover.

Observations were made at night, using 'white lights' (a luminescent compound, burnt in a copper cup set on a tripod), as the distance across the channel was too great for daylight sighting of targets. The weather was, in general, extremely bad, but there were sufficient clear nights to enable the cross-Channel connection to be firmly established.

Roy now backtracked to fill in the gaps, but two stations had to be left until the following year because the weather 'at length became so tempestuous that it was utterly impossible to continue'. The winter was spent in calculating the observations that had been made so far and operations were completed the following year.

With such a man as Ramsden

Jesse Ramsden was an ingenious inventor and maker of fine astronomical instruments and his unique skills achieved international recognition. Even with a staff of some sixty men employed at his London workshop, he still found difficulty in meeting the demand for the intricately constructed and 'incomparable instruments'.

The order for the first 'Great Circular Instrument' was placed in 1784. Without it the trigonometrical connection with France could not be made. Ramsden took three years to construct the instrument causing Roy, when questioned about the delay, to exclaim 'with such a man as Ramsden there is no help for it'.

Despite its great 200-lb weight and 3-foot diameter, it was sometimes necessary to raise the theodolite, up 16 feet on to its own portable scaffold, to give a clear view to targets. The instrument, with its assorted apparatus, was 'transported from place to place, in a four wheeled spring carriage, drawn by two, and sometimes by four horses', with the scaffold carried in a second wagon. A steel surveying chain was also made by Ramsden to supersede the glass tubes used for accurate base measurement, as well as many other instruments for survey work.

Ramsden, with his perfectionist eye and unhurried genius, and Roy, who was ever anxious to make progress, eventually fell out, after Roy openly criticised Ramsden's 'remiss and dilatory' conduct. His legendary disregard for time is amply illustrated by the occasion when Ramsden arrived at Buckingham House to be informed by the King that he was 'punctual as to the day and the hour, while late by a whole year.'

The original 3-foot theodolite survived until 1940 when it was destroyed in the blitz at Ordnance Survey's Southampton headquarters, but the second great theodolite, which Ramsden completed in 1791, may be seen at the Science Museum in London.

Jesse Ramsden, by Robert Home. The fur-lined coat was introduced by the artist, 'to the disgust of his sitter, who said that he had never worn such a thing in his life'. Royal Society

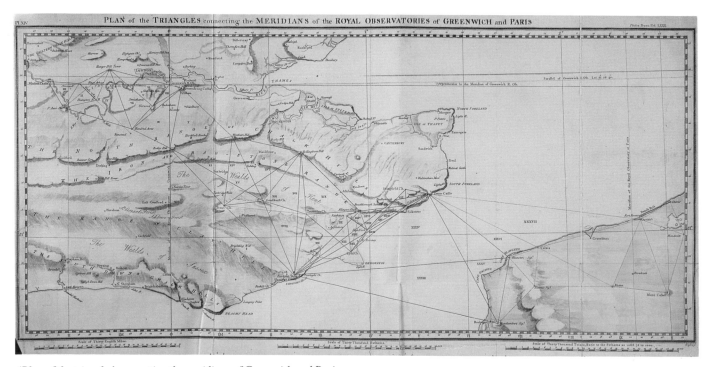

'Plan of the triangles', connecting the meridians of Greenwich and Paris.

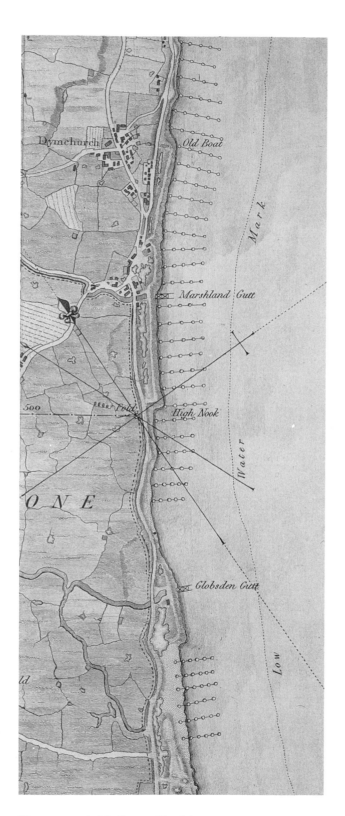

The eastern end of the Romney Marsh base.

A cold, wet, corner of Kent

A second base had to be measured to provide verification of the results, and Romney Marsh in Kent was selected as a suitable, though damp, location. The work was entrusted to Lieutenant Fiddes of the Royal Engineers as Roy was now 'in very indifferent health'. Being satisfied that Ramsden's new steel chain was just as accurate as the glass tubes used at Hounslow Heath, Roy elected for this to be used instead, a decision which overcame the difficulty of transporting the long, delicate, glass tubes, which if broken would have been difficult to replace.

The measurement was carried out despite recurrent bad weather and was completed on 4 December, 'with the most unremitting labour and perseverance'. This time there was no encouragement from distinguished visitors, who were noticeably lacking in this cold, wet corner of Kent.

The measured length was compared against the length computed from the triangulation originating at Hounslow Heath. Roy wrote, with evident pride, to his friend Dr Lind 'It will give you pleasure to be informed that our trigonometrical operation answers to a wonderful degree of exactness. The base in Romney Marsh . . . deduced from that on Hounslow Heath, agrees with the measurement within less than a foot.' Thus, after four and a half years, the first triangulation of this part of the country was complete, providing an accurate framework for map making.

The original question of the latitudinal position of Greenwich was almost completely overshadowed by the usefulness of the framework, but Maskelyne had been correct when he said that he did not think the connection would resolve the dispute. The results offered no immediate solution at all.

The loss of Roy

Roy's health was deteriorating and the row over the late delivery of the theodolite widened to include claims of faults in the measuring apparatus used on Romney Marsh. The vilification from Roy was quite out of character, as he always had the greatest regard for scientific achievement, and Ramsden's work was of the highest calibre. Roy included his complaint in his draft paper on the results of the triangulation, which he submitted to the Royal Society, but Ramsden's detailed vindication of his case eventually resulted in some of the more provocative passages being erased from the paper.

Roy now suffered from a lung complaint, which demanded a warmer winter climate. In November 1789, he went to Lisbon leaving Isaac Dalby, a mathematician who had been employed on the triangulation since 1787, to continue correcting the proofs of his paper. Roy returned the following spring, but, with only three pages of the proof left to check, he died on 1 July 1790 at the age of sixty-four.

Roy had never married and left his house, money, gold watch, the Copley medal from the Royal Society and many manuscript maps and drawings to Thomas Vincent Reynolds who had worked for Roy since the measurement of the Hounslow Heath base in 1784. By 1797 Reynolds was Surveyor-General of the coasts of Great Britain and Ireland, no doubt due in some part at least to Roy's tutelage. Roy also left a substantial annuity to Reynolds' mother, Mrs Mary Hayes, who lived in Poland Street close to Roy's own house in Argyll Street. Reynolds was the natural son of Baron Ducie of Tortworth, Gloucestershire.

Roy's paper was published posthumously in the Philosophical Transactions of the Royal Society, and with it he left a legacy of standards in mapping not previously seen. During his life he had continually tried to persuade the government that mapping of the whole country should be undertaken, and he always considered his current work in the broader context of this greater plan.

In the conclusion of his paper for the Royal Society, he advocated the extension of the triangulation to cover the whole country and asserted that 'The honour of the nation is concerned in having at least as good a map of this as is of any other country.' The pity is that he was denied the opportunity of founding the national mapping organisation that he had striven for over a quarter of a century to establish.

The second great theodolite

Roy's censure of Ramsden had not prevented him giving credit where it was due and, as a result of a paper Roy had earlier read to the Royal Society, Ramsden received an order for a second 3-foot theodolite. Roy's paper, which described the chain of triangles for the connection with France, also suggested that the East India Company would be interested in such an instrument for a trigonometrical survey of India and, in so doing, to ascertain latitude and longitude measurements, ultimately improving navigation for its fleet of ships.

Not content with expressing this idea, Roy had made sure it reached its target by forwarding a copy of the paper to the Court of Directors of the East India Company. They, in turn, consulted two experts, one of whom was James Rennell, the first Surveyor General of India. This brought the idea full

circle, as Rennell had returned to England, was a member of the Royal Society and was familiar with Roy and his work. He gave Roy's suggestion every support, which led directly to the East India Company ordering a duplicate of the theodolite Ramsden had built for Roy.

The instrument was completed in 1791, but Ramsden, being the perfectionist he was, could not resist incorporating a number of improvements based on Roy's experience with the original. He demanded a higher price for the improved theodolite which the East India Company, unexpectedly, refused to pay. Ramsden was left with a very valuable instrument and no obvious customer in sight.

The founding of the Survey

Charles Lennox, 3rd Duke of Richmond, had a strong interest in cartography and some knowledge of geodetic techniques. He was unusual in that he had employed his own surveyors on the Goodwood Estate in Sussex since 1758.

Between them, Thomas Yeakell, an engraver who had served under Richmond in the army, and William Gardner, a Sussex surveyor, produced maps of the Goodwood-owned estates and manors. They also undertook private work and in 1770 they set out to survey the whole of Sussex at a scale of 2 inches to 1 mile. The money was raised by subscription, but only the four southern sheets, out of a total of eight, were completed.

Appointed Master General of the Board of Ordnance in 1782, Richmond had, naturally enough, been viewing Roy's work with ever-increasing interest. The plans for mapping on a national scale complemented his own ideas for national defence policy and Richmond assisted considerably the Hounslow Heath and cross-Channel connection project, by making men and equipment available to Roy.

The headquarters of the Board of Ordnance was at the Tower of London, its role being fortification, military defence and small arms and munitions. The Master General was military adviser to the Cabinet and in that position Richmond became aware of the advanced state of mapping in such countries as Austria, Denmark, France, and parts of Britain's Colonial possessions, notably India and eastern North America. Britain itself, although having some excellent piecemeal surveys, had no national map.

Since Roy's death, no further progress had been made towards the establishment of a national survey. Richmond, on hearing of the availability of the Ramsden theodolite, immediately saw the opportunity for furthering Roy's project, this time under his own control, and he authorised the purchase of the theodolite by the Board of Ordnance.

Charles Lennox, 3rd Duke of Richmond, in uniform as Master General of the Board of Ordnance.
Duke of Richmond

The Duke of Richmond

Charles Lennox, 3rd Duke of Richmond, is popularly famous for being the founder of the Goodwood racecourse. Each July there is a race called the 'Drawing Room Stakes' which commemorates his twelve years as Master General of the Ordnance. The Drawing Room (literally, the room where the maps were drawn) was at the Tower of London, the headquarters of the Ordnance Survey which Richmond founded in 1791.

He was a man of wide and varied interests which included science, politics, fine arts and the theatre; he was also a soldier of distinction. He loved Goodwood and was responsible for transforming it to the splendour evident today. Well liked and respected for his fairness by his estate workers, he did, however, sometimes succumb to a rashness of temperament and impetuousness which marred his judgement.

His position as Master General of the Ordnance provided Richmond with the opportunity to indulge his love of innovation and invention, particularly in the modernisation of artillery. He had less success when it came to coastal fortification, which many considered unnecessary for an island nation. Richmond expressed the opinion that the Navy could well be dispersed overseas when attack came, leaving the country open for invasion. This same view had been given by Major General Roy when he put forward his proposal for a survey of the whole country in 1766.

Richmond's influence in the Cabinet was reduced by the French declaration of war in 1793, when war strategy, rather than defence, became the key issue. He retired in 1795 but never lost his interest in maps and enjoyed playing war games, studying local maps and using them to plan the defence of Sussex. He died in 1806 at the age of seventy-one.

The following day, Isaac Dalby was appointed to the Drawing Room of the Board of Ordnance. He was the first formally appointed Ordnance Survey employee, and his experience strengthened the mathematical side of the draughting and surveying staff that already existed for drawing the plans of military fortifications. Richmond was quite clear in his motives in employing Dalby: the furtherance of Roy's plan.

Richmond recognised the need for further mathematicians, who would also take the part of instrument observers.

On 12 July 1791, on the advice of Dr Hutton, who named the best mathematicians in the two Corps, appointed Major Edward Williams and Lieutenant William Mudge. Major Williams became the first Director of the Ordnance Survey, or, as it was called at the time, the Trigonometrical Survey of the Board of Ordnance.

Richmond had brought Yeakell into the civil side of the Board of Ordnance in 1782, and Gardner followed two years later. These two men helped to lay the foundation for the distinctive style of finished Ordnance Survey maps.

Early days of the Survey

The accuracy of the survey work depended upon the exactness of the Hounslow Heath base-line measurement, raising concern that it had only been measured once. It was thought possible that the glass tubes may have sagged in the middle, or not been truly aligned, so it was decided to measure the base again. Steel chains were used, and a small difference found. This result and Roy's earlier calculations were then averaged to give a mean value which was used for all subsequent calculations. The wooden pipes at each end of the base line had rotted, and were replaced with decommissioned cannon. Triangulation then continued along the south coast, with a further base of verification measured in 1794 on Salisbury Plain.

The trigonometrical survey formed the framework for the general map of England. The great primary triangles were divided into smaller secondary triangles, and these were further broken down into tertiary triangles. The points of all these triangles provided the surveyor with exact references to which he could, by measurement or angular observation, relate the position of buildings and other detail on the ground.

Shortly after the founding of the Survey, instructions were received from 'his Grace the Duke of Richmond, to be minute in our Survey of Sussex; and to furnish Mr Gardner chief Draftsman to the Board of Ordnance, with materials for correcting a Map of that county'.

William Gardner was back on home ground and incorporated into this work, duly corrected, the four earlier sheets of the map of Sussex he had completed with Thomas Yeakell. This time, he worked with Thomas Gream, another Sussex man employed by the Board of Ordnance, using the information supplied by the Trigonometrical Survey. The map was published in 1795 by W H Faden, Geographer to his Majesty, under the patronage of the Duke of Richmond. Although funded by Richmond, the methods, style, staff and printer used to produce this map, are the same as the map generally recognised to be the first Ordnance Survey map: the 1-inch map of Kent, published in 1801.

The Kent map was started in 1795, 'in conjunction with Mr. Gardner, from which a very fine Map has been since formed, containing all that part of the county, which, from its proximity to the coast, may in the process of time, become the seat of military operations'. This military significance was the main reason for its priority. The survey was started at 6 inches to the mile but work went on so slowly that it was finished at 3 inches to the mile and was then 'fairdrawn' in the Drawing Room of the Tower to the scale of 1 inch to 1 mile.

Ramsden's second (Board of Ordnance) 3-foot theodolite.
Science Museum

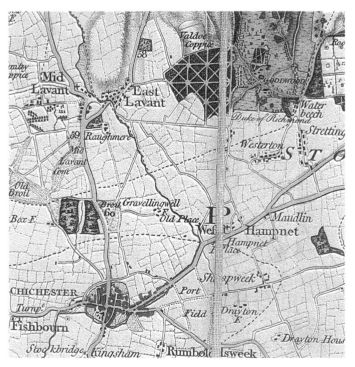

Extract from the 1795 1-inch map of Sussex showing the Goodwood Estate.
David Kingsley

The scale of survey of the Kent map was found to be immensely time consuming, as at 6-inch scale there had to be accurate survey of the boundaries of every field. It was therefore agreed that the next map, that of Essex, should be carried out as 'a proper military map, exactly similar to that of Sussex' but surveyed at a scale of 2 inches to the mile and reduced for publication to 1 inch. This less accurate survey allowed a speedier result. Essex was started in 1799 (as Kent was completed), and published in 1805; Kent and Essex together providing a military survey of the Thames Estuary. The Essex map was the first to be actually surveyed, engraved and published by the Trigonometrical Survey and was the first to use the national sheet-numbering system.

Williams died in 1798, one year before the Kent survey was completed. No known likeness or portrait exists of him and he was considered by at least one of his colleagues to be ineffective. He was heartily condemned in 1821 by Isaac Dalby, who said:

Truth compels me to drop eulogy in noticing our colleague Col. W who nominally was the principal; I say *nominally*, because he never made an observation, or calculation, nor did he write a line of any of the printed accounts; in fact, he proved a dead weight in the undertaking by frequently retarding its progress: and the only time he benefited the service, was when he took his departure to the next world.

This damning picture is disturbing from such a respected man as Dalby, and although it is wrong to accept one opinion as fact, simply because it has happened to survive to the present day, it is apparent that Williams lacked the enthusiasm and drive shown by Roy before him, and Mudge and Colby after. He died in service to the Survey and may have suffered from ill health for some time prior to his death, with Mudge in effective control.

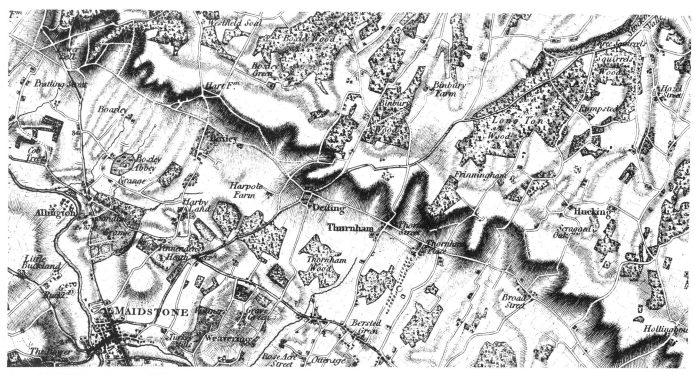

Part of the 1801 1-inch map of Kent.

2 MUDGE AND COLBY

Mudge as Director

William Mudge came from a Devon family, being born in Plymouth in 1762, the ninth of twenty children. His father, who married three times, was a celebrated physician of the day. William Mudge expressed a desire for a career in the army and became a cadet at the Woolwich Royal Military Academy. He was commissioned as 2nd Lieutenant in the Royal Artillery and then sent out almost immediately to South Carolina and the American War of Independence. On his return and promotion, he was posted to the Tower of London and began to study mathematics and mechanics which he applied to the construction of clocks for a hobby. Mudge sought assistance from Dr Charles Hutton, who was one of the most highly regarded teachers of mathematics at the time, and in due course and with some perseverance became a first-rate mathematician. It was because of this that Mudge's name was put forward in 1791, by Dr Hutton, as a suitable officer for the newly formed Trigonometrical Survey.

After the death of Williams in 1798, Mudge was appointed as Superintendent of the Survey on the grounds of his 'zeal and ability' for the task. Although he had already carried much of the responsibility for the day-to-day work of the Survey, here at last was his chance to speed up the pace of work. One of his first actions was to apply to the Royal Society for the loan of the original Ramsden 3-foot theodolite which had been lying unused at their apartments for some time. The instrument needed some updating and adjustment but, once ready, it enabled the survey to progress at a faster rate and was used right up to 1853. Ramsden was also asked to complete the zenith sector which had been ordered three years earlier in 1795.

The same year that he was appointed Superintendent, Mudge was elected a Fellow of the Royal Society; an honour which had not been extended to Major Williams, his predecessor. Mudge made his home within the Tower of London and lived there until his marriage. A devoted father of four sons and one daughter, he became especially close to his eldest son, Richard, who was to follow his father into the Ordnance Survey. Mudge was noted 'as a man of great amiability of disposition and evenness of temper; ... an excellent chief, kind and considerate; upright and scrupulously attentive to the public interest'.

'We have ten officers of engineers . . . I have ten surveyors under them.'
'Is that the whole force?'
'Yes the whole force'
Major General William Mudge, 1824.

The retirement of the Duke of Richmond as Master General of the Ordnance in 1795 had robbed the Survey of its most enthusiastic patron, and although the desirability of a national survey was obvious to his successors, they did not possess the degree of active interest that Richmond, as founder, had shown.

The demands of war came before all other military considerations and Mudge was sensitive to the fact that the Ordnance Survey was considered to be a low priority. The survey continued during this period as a low-key operation whose few trained officers were often diverted to duties not relevant to it at all and 'the public expected much more from the conductors of the Trigonometrical part of the Survey, than it was possible for the number of individuals to perform.' Mudge appeared reluctant to make application for further assistants to his senior officers who might well consider them unnecessary or impossible to appoint because of the War. As well as having the direct effect of slowing down the work, shortage of staff and extraneous duties overburdened Mudge and his officers so that they were unable to make much time available for scientific experiment and advancement.

The progress of the survey continued to be directed by military need, so the triangulation spread westwards, along the vulnerable south coast, reaching Land's End in 1796, and only then spreading north. Two national survey operations were in fact in progress. The scientifically orientated trigonometrical survey was carried out first, laying down the network of triangles, and this was followed by the topographical or, as it was known, 'interior' survey from which the maps were drawn.

In 1800 the surveyors and draughtsmen at the Tower were formed into a military unit, the 'Corps of Royal Military Draftsmen' and became 'subject to the Rules and Disciplines of War'. They were supplied with blue uniforms similar to the Corps of Royal Engineers. Although they were exclusively employed on cartographical duties, these could be anywhere that the military need arose, at home or abroad, and the domestic survey was carried out by only nine or ten persons 'in the field' at any one time. In 1805, the title of the Corps

A Tower Draughtsman and a Gentleman Attendant.
Royal Library, Windsor Castle

was amended to include Surveyors, which could be taken as recognition of the evolvement of the separate roles of draughtsmen and surveyors. A few of the men were employed continuously on the domestic survey, mainly those who had been with it from earlier days, prior to the Corps being set up.

A geographic labourer

The adventures and achievements of the early trigonometrical surveyors drew admiration from those who understood the nature of their difficult task. William Wordsworth, in this poem written in 1813, described an incident which happened to one of the trigonometrical surveyors on the Mountain of Black Combe in Cumbria. The poem was originally written on a stone on the side of the mountain, perhaps to serve as a warning to those contemplating the ascent.

Stay, bold Adventurer; rest awhile thy limbs
On this commodious Seat! for much remains
Of hard ascent before thou reach the top
Of this huge Eminence, – from blackness
   named . . .

Know, if thou grudge not to prolong thy rest
That on the summit whither thou art bound,
A geographic Labourer pitched his tent,
With books supplied and instruments of art,
To measure height and distance; lonely task,
Week after week pursued! – To him was given
Full many a glimpse (but sparingly bestowed

On timid man) of Nature's processes
Upon the exalted hills. He made report
That once, while there he plied his studious
   work,
Within that canvas Dwelling, colours, lines,
And the whole surface of the out-spread map,
Became invisible: for all around
Had darkness fallen – unthreatened,
   unproclaimed –
As if the golden day itself had been
Extinguished in a moment; total gloom,
In which he sate alone, with unclosed eyes,
Upon the blinded mountain's silent top!

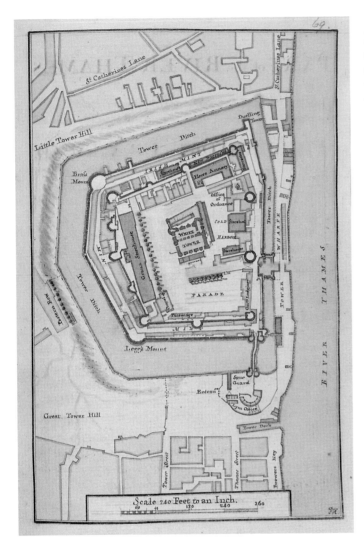

Plan of the Tower of London c.1750.
British Library

As well as his duties relating to the Survey of Great Britain, Mudge was also given responsibility for training new cadets in practical surveying. These cadets comprised partly of new recruits for the Survey of Great Britain, but largely they were potential new officers for the Royal Engineers. This took up a great deal of Mudge's time and that of his best surveyors, at the expense of the survey. Mudge applied himself to the duty of overseeing the training with enthusiasm. He often personally supervised their progress and certainly, at times paid closer attention to their training than the work of the Ordnance Survey. Mudge enjoyed extending the hospitality of his own home to the cadets, treating them more as friends than perhaps was usual for a senior officer. Royal Engineer cadets continued to be trained with Ordnance Survey cadets until 1833, after which a survey school for Royal Engineers was set up at Chatham. Mudge's success with the training programme later led to his being made Lieutenant Governor of the Royal Military Academy in Woolwich in 1809, as well as still retaining his post as Superintendent of the Ordnance Survey. Mudge was also given a third post in 1810, that of public examiner of the new East India Company college at Addiscombe, and the following year described the pressure he was under: 'I have more business on my hands than I have strength for, or if I had strength, even time to perform, and this has always been the case.'

The curriculum for the cadets was drawn up by Robert Dawson, a talented teacher, who although only twenty-seven had been employed in the Drawing Room of the Tower since he was eighteen and his detailed instructions helped to create a standard method of military survey. Dawson, though, is best known for his influence on the depiction of relief on maps, pioneering a method of drawing hills and mountains which gave the maps a degree of realism and a three-dimensional quality.

One cadet trained by Dawson was exceptional. Thomas Colby was born in 1784 at Rochester in Kent, but was from a well connected military family with an estate in south Wales. He joined the Royal Military Academy at Woolwich and received his training in practical surveying from Dawson, where he came to Mudge's attention. Colby was commissioned as a Second Lieutenant of the Royal Engineers in December 1801 when he was still seventeen, and was appointed, at Mudge's request, the following year to assist with the Trigonometrical Survey on a permanent basis. He was the first officer of the Royal Engineers to be appointed to the Survey, and from then on all military directors of the Ordnance Survey were taken from this corps. A tremendous rapport grew up between Mudge and Colby and, recognising in him a kindred spirit, Mudge soon made him his personal assistant.

Listed as '1st Class surveyors and draftsmen' were Thomas Yeakell, Robert Dawson, William Stanley and Charles Budgeon (Dawson's nephew). Edward Metcalf, William Hyatt and Henry Stevens were listed as 2nd Class. Other surveyors from the Corps worked on the domestic survey for shorter periods.

Although the Trigonometrical Survey continued to extend northwards without a pause, Mudge had to obtain separate permission from the Board of Ordnance before he could authorise the interior survey of each county. Progress was slow and Mudge ruefully calculated that at this rate it would take fifty years to cover the whole of England and Wales by 1-inch mapping.

However, in 1803 both Colby's career and his life were almost abruptly ended by a serious accident. Mudge described what happened:

> On Monday last, Lieut. Colby in the act of placing an over-loaded Pistol on the Ground, was severely wounded from it going off unexpectedly:– His left hand grasped the Barrel, and was so violently injured, that amputation became necessary:– It accordingly was taken off just above the wrist the same Evening. The loss of his hand is not the only misfortune to be deplored, as his Skull received a violent blow, producing a Fracture in the Forehead . . . The Brain it seems remains free from any injury: nor any future evil apprehended beyond a scar.

Colby was perhaps lucky that the surgeon decided against a further, most dangerous operation to remove part of his skull and chose instead to trust to Colby's strong constitution to pull him through. The deep scar of this injury remained visible all his life but otherwise full physical recovery was made and Colby overcame the loss of his hand to continue to take his part in making theodolite observations. By 1805, Mudge gained so much confidence in Colby's ability that he wrote:

> Glad that I am that I have a man with me, who can think and act as you do . . . I wish you in all things to consult your own will, convenience and happiness, requiring you only to be punctual in writing me about all you do.

An increasing amount of work was delegated to Colby by Mudge as his own responsibilities increasingly took him away from Ordnance Survey duties. Both men showed a remarkable energy, drive and enthusiasm for the Ordnance Survey, putting the work above their own comfort. In 1811 Mudge wrote:

> I shall have shortly to look back on the long dream of twenty years, and at the time I exclaim in truth how it has flown, with the mortification to know that I have toiled to every purpose but that of growing rich.

The failure of the Board of Ordnance to post enough trained military surveyors to the Survey drove Mudge to resort to the employment of local civilian surveyors to carry out much of the 1-inch mapping. In time, this unorthodox solution was sanctioned by the Board of Ordnance, but they limited the number who could be employed to four persons. The civilians were paid by results according to the number of square miles surveyed and drawn, and although the specification they had to follow was strictly laid down, the temptation to sacrifice accuracy for speed, and thereby increase their income, proved irresistible to some.

Mudge was aware of the problems and in 1816 informed the Master General that more time was needed for superintendence of the civilian surveyors than either he or Colby could find. He found that his work at the Academy prevented him from overseeing the surveyors on a day-to-day basis and Colby was equally busy engaged on the Trigonometrical Survey in Scotland. As a solution Mudge advocated the appointment of an officer who could regularly visit the surveyors who were by that time spread 'across the whole breadth of the Isle', adding apologetically that 'I have for some time delayed this application that it might not interfere with the many services for which Engineers were required during the War.' The request was granted and in the same year Mudge's son, Lieutenant Richard Mudge, was appointed to supervise the surveyors in the field. That Mudge had delayed so long could cynically be interpreted to mean that he was waiting for his son to be ready to take up such a post, or perhaps Mudge simply found it difficult to delegate this essential task, and felt he could keep vicarious control over it through his son.

Richard Mudge had passed through the Woolwich Academy and had been employed on the Survey, in charge of the Drawing Room, since his return from the War in Portugal. His father issued a ten-point circular to try and rectify the worst surveying abuses and hoped that, armed with this, Richard Mudge could bring the surveyor's work into line. Although improvements were made, the civilians proved somewhat resistant to a number of the instructions, resenting at this late stage the change in working practice.

In 1817 these problems were overtaken by events when the Corps of Royal Military Surveyors and Draftsmen was disbanded. Mudge was allowed to retain only the four '1st Class Surveyors and Draftsmen', Yeakell, Dawson, Stanley and Budgeon, who had served with him for so long, plus Stevens, a '2nd class' man from those days, and two other officers. The troublesome civilian contracts were each terminated as soon as this could be conveniently arranged.

The reduction in staff inevitably slowed down the progress of the 1-inch mapping, just at a time when public awareness of it was beginning to grow. Demand outstripped the resources of the Ordnance Survey with individual counties each claiming that their need for a map was more pressing than their neighbours.

Extra resources were requested from the Board of Ordnance, but before these were granted it had to be proved to them that the maps would sell, particularly as the sales of existing Ordnance Survey maps were poor. The only means of doing this was to resort to a subscription system and, in the case of Lincolnshire, for example, an arrangement was made that the survey there would receive priority on the condition that '500 impressions of the Map at a price not exceeding four Guineas and a half each map' were subscribed for.

The Ordnance Survey therefore was guaranteed sales of the map and was led to survey first those counties where demand was greatest. The disadvantage was that the mapping proceeded in a piecemeal fashion across the country. By 1820 subscription lists for Ordnance Survey maps were opened in a number of county towns.

Restriction on publication

In 1811, after only a few maps had been published, the Master General ruled that the Ordnance maps should be withdrawn from sale to the public. This decision was apparently taken because of the regular invasion scares along the south coast and the hope that withdrawal of the maps would prevent them from falling into enemy hands. However, as commercial maps were still available, and the Ordnance sheets already published were still in circulation, it is doubtful that this would have been a very effective security measure.

A contributory pressure behind the prohibition may have come from the Commission of Military Enquiry which descended, without notice, in 1811 to question Mudge about the running costs of the Ordnance Survey. The Commissioners were under an impression that the expenses had exceeded £10 000 per annum and in Mudge's words, 'I believe they thought some great secrets were hidden.' But Mudge had anticipated just such an inquiry and, with some self-satisfaction, he laid before them an account of every shilling expended on the survey from 1791; from which the true cost

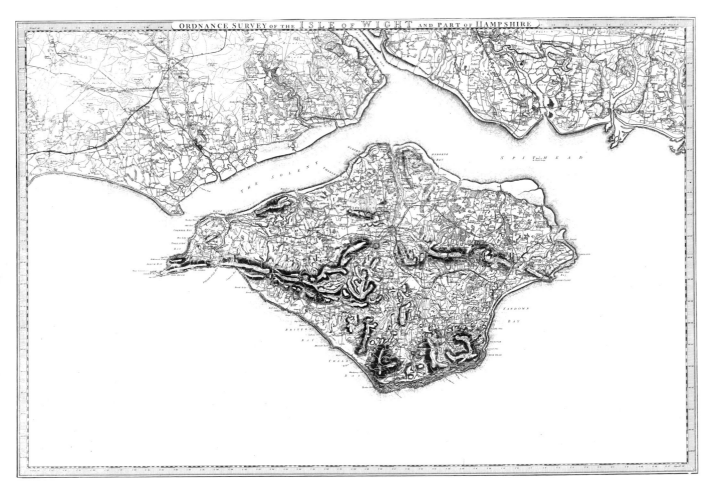

'Ordnance Survey of the Isle of Wight and Part of Hampshire', sheet 10, 1810. The first recorded use of the name Ordnance Survey.

Triangulation

The work of the trigonometrical surveyors followed a regular pattern with a 'hill season' and a 'close season' within each year. The former extended through the summer months until such time as increasingly bad weather forced the men to return to headquarters. The close season was spent in computing and adjusting the season's observations, experimenting with new equipment and making repairs and modification to instruments, before planning for the next hill season's tasks.

The following extracts from an account by Lieutenant Robert Kearsley Dawson (son of Robert Dawson the draughtsman) give a vivid contemporary description of one such hill season under Captain Colby.

On the following morning, Thursday 17th June – the really laborious part of the business commenced, that of conveying the camp equipage, instruments and stores, to the top of the mountain. Horses were hired for the purpose, and made to carry the packages slung like panniers over their backs, so far as the ground proved tolerably even and firm: but when it became broken and hummocky, . . . or springy and wet, there was no alternative but to unload the horses, and carry the things on the men's shoulders . . . After encouraging the men for a while at the outset of their laborious undertaking, Captain Colby went on, taking [Lieut.] Robe and myself with him, to the summit, where he selected a spot of ground for the encampment as near as practicable to the station.

Tuesday, 29th June – It was no uncommon occurrence for the camp to be enveloped in clouds for several weeks together . . . And then in a moment the clouds would break away or subside into the valleys, leaving the tips of the mountains clear and bright above an ocean of mist . . . And although nothing could, under favourable circumstances, exceed the good nature and patience which

Captain Colby showed even to the humblest of his visitors . . . so on the contrary nothing appeared to worry him more than the approach of visitors when we were really at work, and whatever might be their rank, he would scarcely speak to them.

Friday, 23rd of July – Captain Colby took me and a fresh party of the soldiers on a station-hunt . . . Our first halting-place was to be Grant Town, at a distance of twenty-four miles; and Captain Colby having, according to his usual practice, ascertained the general direction by means of a pocket compass and map, the whole party set off, as on a steeple-chase, running down the mountain-side at full speed . . . Sometimes a beaten road would fall in our course, offering the temptation of its superior facilities to the exhausted energies of the weary members of our party; and in such cases freedom of choice was always allowed them. Captain Colby would even encourage such a division of his party and the spirit of rivalry which it induced, and took pleasure in the result of the race which ensued. Arriving at Grant Town in about five hours and a half we dined there, and proceeded afterwards along the valley of the Spey, by the high road, to the Aviemore Inn to sleep. The distance travelled by us that day was calculated at thirty-nine miles.

Monday, 26th of July – Arriving at Cluny we found it to consist of only a few miserable mud hovels, one of which, being a public-house, was to be our abode for the night.

Thursday, 29 July – made an attempt to reach the summit of the Coolin Hills, but were completely foiled in the attempt, and that was probably the only instance in which Captain Colby was ever so foiled.

Saturday, 14 August – . . . returned to the camp on Corrie Habbie, having walked 586 miles in twenty two days, including Sundays.

Wednesday, 22nd of September – . . . we had frequent and violent storms of hail, rain, and wind, which occasionally threw down some of the tents; but in the intervals the atmosphere was clear, and allowed of the instrument being constantly at work. September is in fact considered one of the best months for the Trigonometrical Survey . . .

Wednesday, 29th of September – After seeing the instruments safely packed, the keys of the provision chests were, according to established custom, given to the men, who received also from Captain Colby a carte blanche to provide themselves with a farewell feast. The chief dish on such occasions was an enormous plum-pudding. The approved proportions of the ingredients being, as we were told, a pound of raisins, a pound of currants, a pound of suet, &c to each pound of flour; those quantities were all multiplied by the number of mouths in camp, and the result was a pudding of nearly a hundred pounds weight . . . A large brewing-copper was borrowed to boil it in, – the pudding was suspended by a cord from a cross-beam to prevent its burning, and it was kept boiling for four and twenty hours – a relief of men being appointed to watch the fire and maintain a constant supply of boiling water. A long table was spread in three of the marquees, pitched close side by side and looped up for the purpose – and seats being placed also for Colby and his subs, we partook of the pudding, which was excellent, and withdrew, after drinking 'Success to the Trig'.

The *esprit de corps* portrayed by Dawson still exists today in the triangulation and geodetic operations of the Ordnance Survey, although, sadly, the plum pudding ceremony has been allowed to lapse.

was reckoned to be about £4300 per annum. Mudge was also able to give an estimate of the income from sales of maps over the next year. The Commissioners noted that 'Colonel Mudge believes that not only the expense of the engraving will be altogether defrayed by sale of them, but, in a course of time, a portion also of the original expense of the Survey.'

Their conclusion, however, was disappointing, and instead of giving praise for economy of public monies, they suggested that the provision of published maps should be left to private enterprise. This was also the opinion of the commercial map sellers who saw the publication of Ordnance Survey maps as a threat to their trade.

A Colby camp of the 1840s, on Creach Bhein, near Fort William, revisited by Ordnance Survey staff during the retriangulation. A surveyor said: 'The camp was established in the nearest position to the pillar that afforded any shelter, i.e., in a shallow saddle about 100' away – a well-laid footpath connecting the two and running through the camp to the cook-house. Low stone circles surrounded the larger tents in which the labourers and sappers were accommodated.'

At the end of the war in 1816 the prohibition was lifted and Mudge was instructed to once again publish the maps. In October 1816 a printed Bill of Prices, which listed all available sheets, was circulated to the trade. The following year advertisements were drawn up and placed in the appropriate county newspapers and the Ordnance Survey took the first small step towards commercialisation.

Colonel Mudge's maps

The Ordnance Survey now began to establish its position within the existing map trade, at this time a relatively small industry with only a handful of major businesses.

William Faden, who had published the first Ordnance Survey map of Kent in 1801, as well as the scientific reports of the Trigonometrical Survey, continued his close relationship with the Ordnance Survey. He was a supplier of maps to the Board of Ordnance, who themselves needed commercial maps where their own did not yet exist, both for military purposes and to enable the surveyors to plan their work. Faden also coloured, mounted and repaired maps for the Ordnance Survey. It was then perhaps natural that he should be allowed to sell the newly published Ordnance Survey maps, but, with hindsight, it could be considered that it was a mistake to award him the sole rights. The public could always purchase maps at the Tower, but Faden was the

ORDNANCE MAP
OF
GREAT BRITAIN.

THE Master-General and Board of Ordnance having granted their Authority for the Sale of Impressions taken from the Plates engraved at the Tower, for the General Survey of Great Britain, performed under the Superintendence of Colonel WILLIAM MUDGE, of the Royal Artillery, on a scale of one inch to a mile; The Public are hereby informed, that the following Plates are already finished, and may be had by application to Mr. BAKER, Principal Engraver, at the Drawing Room, in the Tower of London, and of most of the Principal Map and Book Venders in the Kingdom.

		Price £ s. d.
PART I.	Containing the County of ESSEX, with portions of SUFFOLK, CAMBRIDGESHIRE, HERTFORDSHIRE, SURREY, KENT, and MIDDLESEX; comprised in Plates No. 1, 2, 47, 48.	3 3 0
PART II.	Containing nearly the whole of DEVONSHIRE, part of SOMERSETSHIRE, part of DORSETSHIRE, part of GLAMORGANSHIRE, and the Eastern part of CORNWALL; comprised in Plates No. 20, 21, 22, 23, 24, 25, 26, 27..............................	6 6 0
PART III.	Containing the Western part of CORNWALL, and part of DEVONSHIRE; comprised in Plates No. 29, 30, 31, 32, 33............... Or, with Three additional Sheets from Part II. to complete the County of Cornwall, £4 10s.	2 2 0
PART IV.	Containing nearly the whole of DORSETSHIRE, with portions of SOMERSETSHIRE, WILTSHIRE, and HAMPSHIRE; comprised in Plates No. 15, 16, 17, 18..............	3 3 0
PART V.	Containing nearly the whole of SUSSEX, with portions of KENT and HAMPSHIRE, including the ISLE of WIGHT; comprised in Plates No. 4, 5, 9, 10, 11, completing the Southern Coast......................	4 4 0
PART VI.	Containing the greater part of SURREY, with portions of HAMPSHIRE, WILTSHIRE, BERKSHIRE, MIDDLESEX, and SUSSEX; comprised in Plates No. 8 and 12................	1 17 0

MR. BAKER will shew an Index Map of the Survey, and Gentlemen wishing to procure Maps of the Country adjacent to their own Estates, may select any sheets they please for that purpose. Several other Plates of this Work are now in an advanced state of engraving.

Early advertisement for Ordnance Survey maps.
Yolande Hodson

only map seller allowed to sell them on behalf of the Ordnance Survey. Other map sellers found this arrangement objectionable claiming that the restriction was hurtful to their business and eventually the Board of Ordnance agreed to widen the arrangement. However, the prohibition on map sales intervened, nothing was done and a substantial amount of bad feeling towards the Ordnance Survey was generated in the trade. In 1816, shortly after the publication of the maps was resumed, it soon became apparent to Mudge

> that an idea has gone abroad among the Mapsellers of London that as a portion of the Public, at whose expense the Ordnance Survey is carried on, they have a right to reduce from and publish, Copies of the Ordnance Survey on Scales to their own convenience'.

Mudge explained that copies of the maps would affect sales of the Ordnance Survey originals and, by way of underlining the seriousness of the problem, he quoted an example:

> I know for certain that the Map of Cornwall which has not been published more than a fortnight, is now reduced to the scale of ½ inch to 1 mile and is about to be put into the hands of an Engraver for publication.

The Board of Ordnance took legal advice and it was found that maps were indeed protected under the Copyright Acts for 28 years after publication, provided that the date of publication and the 'name of the proprietor' were printed on each map.

Interior survey

The techniques employed by the Ordnance 'interior' surveyors generally followed the pattern of field surveying adopted by civilian land surveyors. The establishment of a national triangulation framework on which to base their survey was, however, new.

For the interior survey to progress, the large triangles provided by the trigonometrical survey had first to be broken down into a network of smaller triangles, nowadays known as a 'secondary' or 'lower order' triangulation. The theodolite used was the 'Small Circular Instrument', 18 inches in diameter, which embodied many of the features of the 3-foot theodolite, but was considered to be of 'portable size' which 'may very readily be taken to the tops of steeples, towers, etc.' This instrument still survives and is in the care of Ordnance Survey.

The surveying took the form of traverses, chain survey and sketching, the method used depending on the circumstances in which the surveyor found himself. A traverse consisted of a series of measured lines between temporary observing stations, at which magnetic bearings were taken to adjacent stations, starting and finishing at an existing triangulation station. The result was a series of points whose position could be plotted accurately on to the surveyors working map.

Traversing was useful where a chain was slow to use, such as through winding country lanes. Magnetic bearings were taken to points that could not be measured to, such as church spires, and these 'intersected points' were plotted on the map graphically, using a protractor. One of the instruments used was a plain theodolite, also known as a circumferentor, which had a graduated circle and compass, with an alidade for pointing.

When chaining, the surveyor would measure along a perfectly straight line between two previously surveyed points, perhaps down the centre of a road. Details to be shown on the map, such as houses, were measured to as a right-angle offset from the chain line. A measuring wheel (cyclometer) was sometimes used for this.

When enough accurately measured points had been added to the map the last detail to be mapped was sketched, either by eye or using box sextants or azimuth prismatic compasses. Distances were estimated or paced, an accurate enough method for the scale of mapping being produced.

Each surveyor carried a sketching portfolio, 12 inches by 10 inches, attached to which was drawing paper, cut to the same size. All measurements were carefully noted down in a field book.

These methods of survey were tried and tested and should have given a satisfactory result, so inaccuracies found by Mudge on the early maps could be fairly considered as laxity or inconsistent application of techniques.

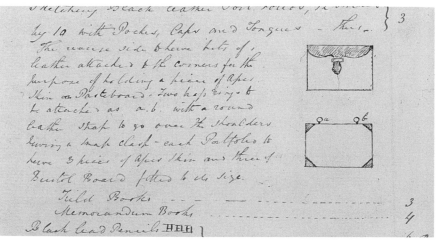

Extract from a return of stationery requirements for apprentice surveyors, listed by Robert Dawson in 1821.

Published 1.ˢᵗ June 1810, by Lᵗ Colᵗ Mudge, Tower. *Price 2/6*

From the margin of the 1810 map of the Isle of Wight and Part of Hampshire.

This last point landed Mudge in rather hot water, as his own name had been added to the maps in the form 'Published . . . by Lᵗ. Colᵗ. Mudge, Tower'. The map sellers argued that Mudge had no ownership of the map and therefore was not the proprietor, concluding that, as no proprietor was named, then all persons were free to copy the maps. Mudge, from being the complainant suddenly found the tables turned and had to defend his own action. He explained that he had copied the form of words from that used by Captain Hurd, the hydrographer, on Admiralty Charts and 'naturally took it for granted that if I followed his example I should give equal security to the Ordnance Survey Maps'.

Mudge was a notably cautious man, but on this occasion his personal pride in the idea of his name being printed on each and every map made him, for once, forget to double check that his actions were correct. This could have been disastrous, but to his immense relief the Attorney General decided that he had acted within the spirit of the Copyright Acts, and that the signature of the employee was acceptable on behalf of the company. Once this had been decided it only remained to quash the map sellers objections by taking a tough line on offenders and prosecuting them for breach of the Copyright Acts.

But Mudge could see that this would only do more harm to the Ordnance Survey in terms of commercial relationships, and through his intervention no writs were issued. Instead it was agreed that a notice should be published in the newspapers cautioning map sellers that the copying of Ordnance Survey maps was prohibited. The notice was carefully worded to avoid offence, implying that at least some of the map sellers had perhaps inadvertently broken the law, but it was quite explicit that any future offences would result in prosecution.

This solution was altogether most satisfactory and no map seller took the risk of copying the Ordnance Survey maps for some years.

The arc of meridian and the zenith sector

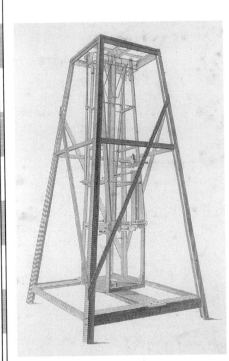

Ramsden's zenith sector.

For geographers and cartographers, the accurate positioning of land masses in relation to each other is of prime importance. It was this that had prompted the connection, carried out by Roy in 1787, between the Observatories of Greenwich and Paris.

Mudge was receptive both to the needs of the scientific community, and to the lobby from the Admiralty, who needed better latitude and longitude figures for nautical charts and the positioning of offshore islands. He also considered that the national mapping would benefit, making it possible to place the maps of Britain in their correct geographic position on the earth's surface.

In 1802 Mudge took delivery of the zenith sector ordered from Jesse Ramsden in 1795. This astronomical instrument was designed to observe celestial bodies (mainly stars) in a zenith position (vertically above an observer). Observations had to be made close to the zenith to avoid distortion from atmospheric refraction which increasingly occurs near the horizon. By observing the same stars from places some distance apart, the difference in latitude between observing stations could be calculated. In daylight, on a clear day, the zenith sector's 8-foot long telescope could observe a third-magnitude star within a limit of 7½ degrees either side of the zenith.

A meridian can be described as an imaginary line joining the north and south poles designated by degrees of longitude from a reference or zero meridian. Mudge's measurement of arc was taken on a line from Dunnose, Isle of Wight, to Clifton, South Yorkshire.

Twenty-seven stars near the zenith were observed at Dunnose, seventeen of which Mudge was able to observe again later at Clifton. From this, Mudge calculated that the length of 1 degree of the meridian at the latitude of approximately 52 degrees north of the equator was just over 69.1 miles. Mudge's series of results suggested that the earth would be a sphere flattened at the equator and this was known to be wrong. He correctly concluded that 'the plumb-line of the sector has been drawn towards the south at all stations' thereby suggesting the opposite to the established oblate spheroid theory for the shape of the earth! (A sphere which has been slightly flattened at the top and bottom.)

However, the observation of the arc of meridian did provide an accurate spheroidal alignment on which to base the 1-inch maps and geographical coordinates of the trigonometrical stations, throughout the country.

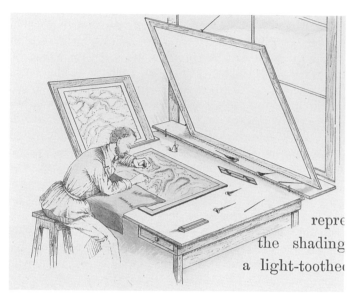

Engraver at work in the 1830s.

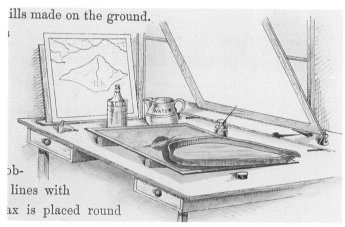

After a protective waxy coating had been applied to the copper plate, hill-features were marked by a needle which removed this 'etching ground'. Acid was then used to bite in the lines to the required depth.

Engraving

It was logical for the Ordnance to develop its own engraving service within the Tower of London. Although the Kent map was published by Faden, it was probably engraved by his staff at the Tower. This would have satisfied the need for security, both in a national military sense and in terms of the unique original material from which the engraver worked.

In any event, the decision was taken in 1801 for two engravers to be formally employed by the Ordnance for the purposes of engraving the Essex map. Thomas Foot and a Mr Knight were duly appointed to work from ten in the morning to four in the afternoon for a payment of 3½ guineas and 2½ guineas per week respectively. Thomas Foot was the same accomplished craftsman who had engraved the Kent map for Faden and the Sussex map for the Duke of Richmond. Within a couple of years the work required four full-time engravers.

The surveyors made sketch maps as they worked, plotting the detail at a scale of 2 inches to 1 mile, and later reducing this at the Tower to a 'fair drawing' at 1 inch to 1 mile. The engravers worked from the fair drawings.

The copper plates were planished and polished to a mirror-smooth finish by a junior engraver who then heated them and applied a coating of virgin white wax. The map was traced on to the wax and cut, in stages, and in reverse, on to the plate using a small, sharp-pointed, chisel-like tool, known as a burin.

There were three distinct stages of building up the map detail which allowed for a division of labour, according to ability, within the engraving team. Firstly, the coastline, roads, buildings and outlines of woods and vegetation were incised. This was the least difficult operation. Then names, the vegetation itself, rock depiction and other ornamentation were added. Finally the hills, whose skilful depiction gave the map its third dimension, were carefully engraved. Individual craftsmen became specialists at different tasks. One Ebenezer Bourne, for instance, engraved all the lettering on the early maps.

For Mudge to keep an eye on progress, proofs could be pulled from the plates at intervals and these were circulated to the county concerned so that the spelling of place names and other detail could be checked. Proofs were also demanded by the military who could not always wait until the final publication of the map.

Shetland will be written on my heart

The culmination of Mudge's career was to have been the extension of the west European arc of meridian, northwards through Britain, an achievement of international scientific importance. As a symbol of improved relations between England and France since the end of the War, co-operation was encouraged by the Government and the French scientist Biot arrived in Britain in 1817. The British arc of meridian at this time extended from Dunnose to Clifton and it was intended to join this to the French arc which began in the Balearic Isles and then to extend the whole arc to Shetland.

Mudge fully intended to go himself with Biot to Shetland and wrote

> I am overwhelmed with business, going again to turn myself to the stars. 26 years ago I commenced my career with a strong constitution, and with a good supply of bodily health, but I am now perhaps going to close my campaigning service with the performance of as arduous a task as can be given to the execution of any man.

However, although he sailed with Biot on board the survey ship, *Investigator*, he was 'obliged to return with much regret on account of illness' and Colby was appointed to travel in his place.

This was most unfortunate because Colby and Biot had developed a keen mutual dislike for each other which, because of perceived slights and subsequent misunderstandings, resulted in the British observations being made on the small island of Balta, and the French on Unst. The lack of co-operation between the two parties defeated one of the main objectives of the experiment which was to compare results obtained with the Ramsden zenith sector to those obtained with the French repeating circle; the Spanish scientist Don J Rodriguez had for some time claimed that the zenith sector results were of questionable accuracy.

Mudge wrote to Colby that 'I approve of everything you have done' but implied in the same letter that he had discussed at length with Biot the necessity of the English and French observations being made at the same place, and that he could not quite understand how it had failed to happen. Mudge could not hide his mortification and concluded, 'I do not wish to exhibit the folly of useless complaint; but as the Queen who gave up Calais said that "that word would be found written on her heart," I may say that Shetland will be written on mine, for I have never ceased to deplore, with the keenest recollection, the happiness that I thought before me nipped in the bud.'

Colby succeeds

In April 1820 Mudge died and Colby carried the responsibility for the survey while awaiting news of a successor. He was expecting the post to be made available to himself and was certainly the most capable person to take it, but for over two months, to Colby's increasing anxiety, no word was heard from the Board of Ordnance.

At length he could stand the suspense no longer and broke protocol by addressing a letter to the Master General of the Ordnance, reminding him of the vacancy, enquiring 'how far my conduct and character would render me deserving of confidence and enable me to conduct the survey with efficiency and credit to the country' and mentioning several eminent persons who would vouch for his ability. The chance paid off, and after a further month Colby was, after a long apprenticeship of eighteen years, promoted to Superintendent of the Ordnance Survey.

One of Colby's first actions on taking charge was to address the problem of slow-selling maps. He firmly believed that this was caused by 'want of sufficient publicity and the active opposition of some of the London mapsellers'. He went on to describe the cause of discontent in the trade as arising from 'the Ordnance Map being so accurate and so beautifully engraved that the taste and expectation of the public are not

Meridians and the unsquare map

The mounting is so inaccurately done that the bottom from Edge to Edge is 1¼ inch wider than the top and the left or Western side of the canvas is 1⅜ inch longer than the opposite side, consequently the Angles at the bottom are not right angles and it is impossible to hang it so as not to offend a moderately accurate eye.

This complaint to Faden illustrates one of the problems of attempting to place map detail on a flat piece of paper from what is, in effect, part of the surface of a sphere. The reply from Mudge to his customer explains:

When the idea of making maps from the Ordnance Trigonometrical operations first originated, it was proposed to publish the work in County Maps – Kent and Essex were the first engraved, and the Meridian of Greenwich was selected as the most proper to project them from. In course of time however the intention of continuing the publication merely as County Maps was laid aside, and it was determined to lay down what should follow, on the principle of one uniform map of the whole Island. To accommodate the meridian of Greenwich to the meridian of the center of the Island

being a matter of impossibility, in order to introduce as little error as possible on account of convergence, three meridians were established, one for the center of the Kingdom, the other two for the East and West parts of it. Thus, the south edges of the sheets being made at right angles with the respective meridians, and the East and West edges Parallel to the same, they cannot of course in all cases be rectangular, and the same particulars which you noticed to Mr. Faden are accounted for on the same principle.

Major General Thomas Colby. The scar from his accident can be clearly seen on his forehead.

Too much sketching

The legacy of the inaccurate 1-inch maps continued to haunt Colby for his first few years as head of the Ordnance Survey. In August 1820 he wrote to Captain Richard Mudge who was responsible for supervision of the surveyors' work, that 'You must not be backward in directing resurveys when errors appear' and that 'I shall be much obliged by your making them correct their work at their own expense whenever you find it erroneous. Experience will soon teach them that the cheapest way is to do their work well at first.'

In September he took with him on a journey to the north of England the unpublished Kings Lynn plans to cast a look over as he travelled through the region. He found that one plan was

> with the exception of the main roads, done in a most slovenly inaccurate manner; one wood was fully double its real size and more than twice its breadth out of its place. In short there was too much sketching and that of very bad quality.'

Colby's investigations revealed that, although expressly forbidden, surveyors employed their own unauthorised assistants in order to cover the ground more quickly. They found this profitable because part of the surveyors' pay was determined by the number of square miles surveyed. Colby was of the opinion that 'it would be better to have less dependence on quantity, and a higher salary', but he did not achieve this change for some years.

He set in train an extensive review of both work in hand and published maps. All work found to be inaccurate was gone over again. Colby also took the opportunity to have the maps revised to include new detail. Meanwhile, he prevented further abuses by relentlessly rejecting substandard work and any work found to be done by the unauthorised and untrained assistants. In all cases he insisted that the work had to be done again by the guilty surveyor. Although initially a severe approach, the close attention Colby paid to the standard of surveying began to pay dividends within a couple of years. Many more checks were introduced into the system and complaints from map users decreased.

By 1834 three-quarters of the imperfect work had been corrected and revised. Colby's perfectionist attitude was the main driving force which improved the Ordnance Survey maps to a standard of accuracy not previously seen in map-making. His insistence on correctness is illustrated by the fact that he would not even allow surveyors to compare and match detail on the edges of sheets, his attitude being that if the work was done correctly, then the edges would always match and comparison was unnecessary.

so easily satisfied with their imperfect productions'. This was an understandable statement of pride but perhaps closer to the heart of the trade was the fact that 'the allowances granted to persons selling the maps, being much less than the ordinary percentage of the Trade, affords a rate of profit too small to make their sale an object to them.'

Colby obtained permission from the Board to advertise the availability of the published maps, and also gave copies of maps to his surveyors with an instruction to show the maps to 'any Gentlemen who may appear interested in the progress of the survey'.

The problems with the trade were not easily solved. For instance, a strange situation existed that, by tradition, personal callers at the Tower, whether trade or public, could purchase the maps at trade price. Customers at Fadens always had to pay full price. As a first step Colby obtained permission to grant Faden the right to sell at an allowance of 10 per cent to the rest of the trade and sales began to improve.

On Faden's retirement in 1823, Colby, perhaps feeling that Faden had not always applied his best efforts to the sale of Ordnance maps above more profitable lines, took the opportunity to install a friendly face into the map trade. The Board's permission was gained to grant the agency to James Gardner, a long-serving surveyor on the Ordnance Survey, who was at that time retiring from the field. He purchased premises in Regent Street and held the agency until 1840.

3 THE IRISH SURVEY

The Irish priority

The assumption was made that both the Trigonometrical Survey and 1-inch mapping would be extended to Ireland in due course, but the need for an accurate map of the country was brought to the fore in the 1800s by problems with a local tax, known as the county cess. This tax was levied on land ownership and used in a similar way to the English rating system. The apportionment of the tax was grossly unfair, often being based on information from either the Stafford (1636–40) or the 'Down' (1654–9) surveys of Ireland. These laid out the boundaries of what were generally called 'townlands', averaging 300 acres each, which were subdivisions of the counties. The land was simply classified as either profitable or unprofitable, but the passage of time had eroded the distinction so that taxation injustice had become common in every district. An example was quoted of a farm in County Mayo which 'by some strange jumble the whole tax of a great part of the district is thrown upon it; and there is a large surface of fine land adjoining it which pays nothing'. These 17th-century surveys also contained considerable, and unacceptable, measuring errors.

For revaluation a new survey was needed to redefine the boundaries and to calculate the acreages of each townland. Each county could have directed its own survey, but in 1819 the Admiralty recommended that the Ordnance Survey should direct the Irish survey, pressing its own need for a triangulation of Ireland to be made that could provide a framework for a hydrographic survey. In February of that year the Duke of Wellington, as Master General of the Ordnance, agreed to take on the responsibility for the survey, prompted into action by his brother, Lord Wellesley, who was Lord Lieutenant of Ireland. Lord Wellesley declared that 'neither science, nor skill, nor diligence, nor discipline, nor integrity for such a work can be found in Ireland'. This prejudiced outburst was only correct in the sense that, for any cadastral (boundary and ownership) survey used for valuation, a more fair and accurate result would be likely if it was carried out under the supervision of a disinterested party.

A select committee was set up to 'consider the best mode of apportioning more equally the local burthens collected in Ireland and to provide for a more general survey and valuation.' Thomas Spring Rice was appointed chairman and the Irish members of Parliament, who mostly made up the committee, recommended that the Ordnance Survey should undertake the work, from triangulation to topographical survey, at a scale of 6 inches to 1 mile. In 1824, Colby received orders from the Master General to proceed with the survey 'without a moment's delay'. Wellington reiterated that 'the map must be drawn and filled up on the scale of six inches to a mile' and 'the record must be complete at that scale', but beyond this Colby was free to make maps at reductions to any scales that 'may be thought expedient'.

Colby's first task was to build up a competent body of men to proceed with this vast undertaking, estimated to cost £300 000 and to take seven or eight years to complete. At the same time he was expected to press on with the British survey. Some existing Ordnance Survey officers were transferred to Irish duties, supplemented with freshly commissioned officers and supported by men from the Corps of Royal Sappers and Miners. The military were chosen partly because they were cheaper to employ than civilians, but also because they were easier to control and were largely, in this time of peace, underemployed. The first detachment was sent to Ireland in 1825 and were unarmed, a decision made by Colby who insisted that the Engineers 'were there to survey the land and not for any military purpose'. A headquarters was established at Mountjoy House, Phoenix Park, Dublin where the Ordnance Survey of Ireland headquarters remain to this day.

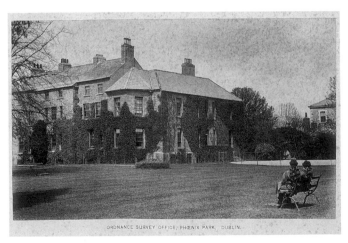

ORDNANCE SURVEY OFFICE, PHŒNIX PARK, DUBLIN.

'Sketch shewing the mode of proceeding in measuring the Lough Foyle Base'.

The triangulation was, as usual, the first priority and as a number of hilltops had already been observed from stations in Scotland this could proceed immediately. Ramsden's second (Board of Ordnance) theodolite was carried to the summit of Divis mountain near Belfast from where over 200 objects were observed. Progress was initially slow because new officers were under training and the notorious 'soft' weather of Ireland gave many days when visibility was too poor, but the observations from this one mountain provided the trigonometrical network for one-seventh of the island. Triangulation continued the next season on Slieve Donard, after which Colby entrusted the responsibility for the network to Lieutenant Joseph Portlock who completed the arduous task in 1832. A secondary triangulation (splitting each of the large triangles into a network of smaller triangles) was completed in 1841.

Reaction to the Engineers by the local people was mixed but generally they were regarded with suspicion. A particular nuisance was the removal by local people of the poles, set up as targets on mountains, before the surveyors had a chance to observe them and, in one case, the observers were attacked. However, by contrast, in Glenomara, County Clare, the people climbed the mountain with them in a great crowd, with flutes, pipes and fiddles, treating the building of the trigo-nometrical station as a festive occasion.

Initially Portlock was Colby's 'chosen assistant' but the relationship between the two men failed to flourish as it had between Mudge and Colby and in later years Colby completely lost confidence in Portlock, becoming embarras-sed by his over-zealous approach to geological work. He was

removed from the department in 1843 at Colby's instigation but, somewhat surprisingly, Portlock went on to forgive him and to eventually write a lengthy memoir of Colby's life.

In his memoir Portlock described Colby as 'rather short, and possessed of a singularly nervous and elastic frame, . . . his personal deportment was not perhaps dignified' but 'he would lend his own hand to the raising of stones and building objects for observations, or to make houses to shelter the soldiers in camp'. Colby responded to criticism defensively and could and did remove officers who tried to oppose him, even after perhaps years of working in harmony. This reaction meant that a number of talented men, capable of succeeding him as Superintendent, left the Survey because Colby could not tolerate their natural progress from pupil to challenger. Portlock, however, claimed that he could be 'as gentle and kind as a father or brother when personally communicating with his officers and men.'

Lough Foyle Base

To maintain the standards of scientific accuracy of the triangulation a base of verification needed to be measured, and Colby selected a line of nearly 8 miles on the plain of Magilligan near Lough Foyle in Londonderry. He was unhappy with the potential for error in previous equipment used for base-line measurements and during the winter season used several officers to investigate possible improve-ments. Colby himself came up with the solution of compensa-tion, a method using two different metals which expanded at different rates from each other, and already used in the

Plan showing position of the base line on the shores of Lough Foyle.

manufacture of balances and pendulums. The principle was to use two metal bars, one of brass and one of iron which were placed $1\frac{1}{8}$ inches apart but joined rigidly to each other at their centres. The bars were allowed to expand or contract freely, with pivoted steel tongues fixed to both bars at their ends. As the rate of expansion and contraction due to temperature change was different for each type of metal, points which did not move in relation to each other could be calculated and marked on the end of each tongue. These points were marked by silver pins, and, although the length of the bars changed with temperature, the distance between the two pins remained constant. Six sets of bars, each just over 10 feet long, were made.

The base was measured over the two years 1827–8 with any difficult ground, such as the crossing of the River Roe, repeated. At each end of the base line, permanent marks were set up on land purchased for the purpose by the Government. The base was remeasured in 1960 using electronic distance measuring equipment, with a difference found to Colby's original measurement of only 1 inch.

Colby's system

While the triangulation and base measurements were in progress, Colby left the management of the interior survey to

Drummond's light

Ireland is blessed, for trigonometrical purposes, with a particularly convenient spread of mountains. From these, trigonometrical observations were made by day to poles erected as targets, or at night to a target light. When neither were visible due to bad weather, nothing could be done except to camp out on the mountains and wait until the weather cleared.

An idea for improving the observing lights to allow observing to take place in poorer weather conditions came to Thomas Drummond, a young officer, while listening to a scientific lecture on the brilliant luminosity of incandescent lime. A trial was organised at the Tower of London, using a darkened room, 300 feet in length, where the standard light used by British lighthouses was first displayed, followed by a superior 'Fresnel' lamp and then the limelight which 'being brought now to its full ignition . . . shone forth overpowering, and as it were annihilating both its predecessors'.

Drummond also invented an improved heliostat to reflect sunshine to observers on distant hills. These two inventions were used in Ireland late in 1825 to make a connection between Divis mountain near Belfast and Slieve Snaght, Inishowen, in County Donegal, a distance of over 66 miles.

This talented officer also worked closely with Colby on the invention of the 'compensation bars' used for the Lough Foyle base measurement; so closely that in later years Drummond's family was to claim that he was the actual inventor of the bars. Drummond became a critic of Colby's blue book 'system' and later left the Ordnance Survey to become head of the Boundary Commission in Ireland. By 1835 he was Under-Secretary for Ireland, a situation that Colby found uncomfortable as Drummond became, in effect, governor of the country being surveyed.

As Under-Secretary, Drummond is remembered for the founding of the Royal Irish Constabulary and for his sympathy towards the Irish people, being 'pained by the evidence of misrule which everywhere met his eye.'

Captain Thomas Drummond as Under-Secretary to the Lord Lieutenant of Ireland.
National Gallery of Ireland

John O'Donovan

Colby recognised that the spelling of place-names on the Irish maps was a problem and devised a system of 'name books' into which his surveyors wrote down all variations in spelling of proper names, noting the authority for each. At first Colby accepted the most generally used spelling, but this perpetuated the corruption of names made by English-speaking settlers.

In his efforts to solve this problem Larcom engaged John O'Donovan, from County Kilkenny, to teach him the Irish language, but soon realised that the study of place names required a full-time scholar. After the first appointee died, Larcom offered the position to O'Donovan who joined the Ordnance Survey in 1830. To the spellings noted in the name books, O'Donovan added spellings gleaned from historical documents. From these the presumed original Irish name was decided and used as a basis for a recommended spelling for the published maps. This compromise allowed the Irish names to be retained in a form acceptable to the mainly English-speaking purchasers of the map.

Prefixes and suffixes were standardised where they occurred, so that Dirry or Derry (an oakwood) became Derry, and Drim, Drom or Drum (a ridge) generally became Drum. Although a logical and scholarly approach, this system naturally angered local people and the 'new' Ordnance names were widely ignored, even by other Government Departments. Two groups of names were not controlled by the Ordnance Survey – the names of townlands, supplied by Richard Griffith's department, and those of private property where the landowner's chosen spelling was always accepted.

Initially O'Donovan worked from academic sources, but he also considered it essential to hear the Irish name being pronounced by local

John O'Donovan, who made an 'invaluable contribution to our knowledge of the topography and local history of his country' (quoted from his tombstone). Royal Irish Academy

'aborigines'. These were often elderly people living in remote areas who O'Donovan asked to pronounce the local place names and tell him about their origin. As he wrote to Larcom:

> I travelled yesterday through the parish of Donaghmore and discovered one of the aborigines, 100 year old and on the point of death. He is blind and though in a most feeble state, he retains his reasoning powers in a most surprising manner. He is intimately acquainted with every field in the parish of Donaghmore, where he was employed for half a century as a bailiff. He was able to give me the ancient name of every townland in the parish in the most

satisfactory manner . . . I discovered him in a little cabin . . . I certainly felt very shy in disturbing him . . . Several persons of whom I enquired the way to his house told me that he was dead this 'many and many a year'.

O'Donovan's enthusiasm for the work meant that he was prepared to work for pay that was tight-fisted even for those days. His travel costs were paid, but not the cost of lodgings, and no money was allowed for any absence due to sickness or indeed for any overtime. He worked 'from dark to dark' in good weather and even on Sundays, finding that the old people were happy to sit and talk on this day. However in Elphin:

> I visited the church of Kilmore near which I read a long proclamation from the Queen, from which I have learned that I must work on Sunday no more. Hitherto it has been my principle day of business, and as I cannot pray all day, I intend still to work on the same day, but so privately in a garret room that it will be very difficult for anyone to know whether I am making holes in the floor with my knees or working at natural magic.

The distinguished antiquarian, George Petrie, in charge of the topographical department, urged O'Donovan to 'try to get as much of everything as you can, manners, customs, traditions, legends, songs, etc. The opportunities at present afforded may never occur again.'

O'Donovan's work for the Ordnance Survey continued until 1842, when the topographical department was closed. O'Donovan died, aged fifty-five, from rheumatic fever, leaving a widow and six sons.

his deputy, Major William Reid, but kept the methods used under close scrutiny; for, although Reid was an experienced military officer, he had limited knowledge of surveying. The larger scale of 6 inches being used in Ireland demanded greater accuracy than the methods used for the 1-inch mapping of England, and Colby came to develop what he called his 'system'. This relied on measurement with a chain in preference to traversing with a theodolite, and on division of labour so that, for example, no surveyor plotted his own work. Splitting the work into several separate operations gave the advantage of the men being able to become proficient very quickly and maintained a high degree of accuracy.

Traversing was permitted where it was impracticable to chain a line, for instance, across rivers or in wooded areas, but Colby never liked it to be used unnecessarily, believing it to be a method prone to error. This was an increasingly unfashionable view as traversing was much quicker and was in general use at the time by private surveyors. His system, which was issued as an instruction in what became known as 'the Colonel's blue book', relied on detailed 'booking' which allowed each part of the survey to be traced back to the individual man and the instrument he used. Opponents of the system, including Reid and Drummond, criticised particularly his prescribed method of measuring townland areas by

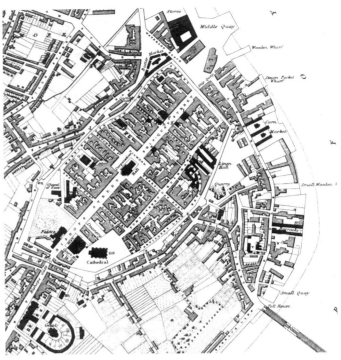

Part of the 1835 6-inch map of Londonderry.

Major General Joseph Portlock LLD, FRS, FGS.
Geological Society of London

chaining and calculation and claimed that his books were so laborious to keep that they resulted in more errors being made than they were designed to prevent.

At first, progress in Ireland was painfully slow and, although Colby's confidence in his system remained firm, critics began to gather against him. His orders for a completely military organisation were undermined by Reid who took it into his own hands, while Colby was away on business in England, to employ civilian surveyors in order to speed up the survey. Colby was clearly displeased, his prejudice against civilians dating from the inaccurate work he had seen them produce in Mudge's day, but he accepted the *fait accompli* on the condition that the work was strictly supervised. This peculiar mix of civilian surveyors and military personnel came to be the normal Ordnance Survey complement for many years, and in Ireland civilians soon outnumbered the sappers by more than four to one.

By 1828 still only 1 per cent of the country had been mapped and Reid's impatience with Colby's excessively slow and cautious survey methods made him approach the Irish government over Colby's head. At length Wellington, by now Prime Minister, was hearing tales of the survey's failure. This

time Colby was less forgiving and, after defending himself and his survey methods, informed the Master General that, as all preparatory work for the Irish Survey was complete, he could now supervise it himself and that Reid's services would no longer be required. Reid returned to the general duties of the Corps, having been effectively removed from the Ordnance Survey by this ploy. Reid's successor was Lieutenant Thomas Larcom whose duties were at first much confined by Colby who was reluctant to trust another deputy.

Rumours about the slow progress persisted and the Board of Ordnance twice arranged for formal inquiries to be made into the workings of the Irish Survey, one resulting in a direct order to Colby that he should spend at least nine months of each year in Ireland until the survey was completed. This was not such a disagreeable sentence to Colby who in 1828, aged 44, had married Elizabeth Boyd, daughter of the one time Treasurer of the county of Londonderry. They settled at Knockmaroon Lodge at the gates of Phoenix Park and raised a family of four sons and three daughters.

By 1830, 6 million acres had been surveyed with one whole county, Londonderry, engraved and the valuation of the land could now begin. The position of the townland boundaries was supplied to the Ordnance Survey by the Irish Government in the form of a team of men under Richard Griffith. A member of this team and a respected local resident, who acted as meresman, accompanied the surveyors along the boundaries, pointing out the correct position. In some areas, especially uncultivated parts of the country, no clear boundaries existed and had to be not only surveyed but created and defined. Once the maps were available, Griffith's men began to assess the value of the land by analysis of collected soil samples. The soil regions identified were to be sketched on to the Ordnance maps but embarrassing inaccuracies were exposed and the matter referred to Colby. Investigation showed that although the townland boundaries and acreages appeared to be comparatively accurate, buildings, roads and rivers were often misplaced or missing from the maps. Colby immediately recalled a large field force to the region to bring the maps up to standard before publication. The Irish Survey was inefficient, inaccurate and ill-defined and entering its ninth year, vastly exceeding its budget with still not a single finished map to show for it.

Yet another inquiry was held which, surprisingly, did not lay the blame on Colby, acknowledging the unexpected intricacies of the work and noting that most of these seemed now to have been overcome. Griffith's requirements were redefined in full and the survey allowed to continue. This confidence was repaid by Londonderry being published in 1833 followed by a further four counties in the next two years, all of which passed scrutiny by the valuators.

The detail collected increased as the survey progressed. At first, field boundaries were expressly omitted but later they were felt to be of value and were included on the maps.

Altitude was shown initially by spot height but later by numbered contours, particularly designed as an engineering aid for railway construction. Contours were by this time in use on the maps of other European countries.

Advances in engraving techniques

Larcom extended the principle of division of labour to the drawing office and, at one time he had almost sixty engravers separated into the three branches of Outline, Writing and Ornament. The superintendent of the office was James Duncan who deserves much credit for balancing the work of the three branches to achieve an exceptional and uniform standard of engraving, which aroused envy and a healthy sense of rivalry with the engraving branch of the English Survey.

New mechanical devices were invented to speed up the laborious process of engraving, including a spring-punch for hedgerow trees and another for altitude figures, a waterlining device and, most usefully, a ruling machine for fine dots and solid lines. The results obtained with these devices were agreed to be very beautiful whilst saving on the employment of individual and highly paid artists. The designer of most of these devices, William Dalgleish, went on to perfect an important new method for duplicating copper plates. Traditionally this was only possible by re-engraving, but his method involved the deposition of a layer of copper electrolytically on to the engraved plate, making in effect a positive image

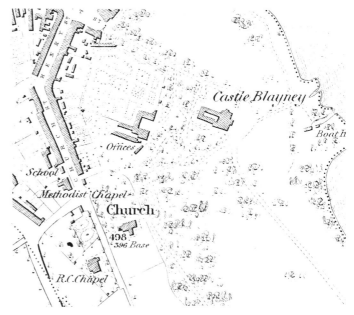

Extract from the 6-inch map of Monaghan.

Part of the Castle Blayney area of Monaghan, enlarged to show the fine quality engraving.

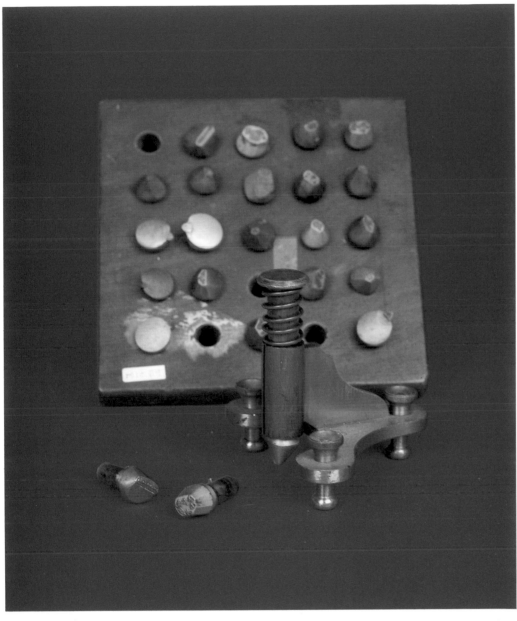

Engraver's spring-punch with a selection of tree and vegetation stamps.

(remembering that engraving was always cut in reverse on to the plate). This matrix, as it was known, could then itself receive a copper layer by the same means resulting in the duplicate plate. Not only was it much cheaper to duplicate plates by this 'electrotyping' process, but it was soon found to be a convenient way of making alterations and corrections. Detail could be completely removed from part of the matrix, presenting a clean blank space on the electrotyped plate for the engraver to insert new information.

Printing the maps was initially very expensive, with a single printer being paid a set sum for each impression he made of a map. Pleased with the success that division of labour had achieved in the drawing office, Larcom could see no reason why the same technique could not be applied to the printing process. He selected promising sappers and trained each in one aspect of the printing process (cleaning and inking the plate, dampening the paper, passing it through the press, etc.).

These innovations resulted in an increase in the number of impressions possible each day from a maximum of thirty to, literally, hundreds, reducing the cost of each impression by 8*d*.

The Londonderry memoir

From the very beginning of the Irish survey Colby set out to collect more information than could possibly be displayed on the maps themselves. The 'Colonel's blue book' directed that each officer should keep a journal of 'all the local information he can obtain relative to communications by land and water, manufactories, geology, antiquity or other matters connected with the survey.'

Larcom extended these aims and asked the officers to record detailed information under four main headings, Geography, Topography, People, and Divisions and Townlands. The following is an extract from Larcom's instructions:

Habits of the people. Note the general style of the cottages, as stone, mud, slated, glass windows, one story or two, number of rooms, comfort and cleanliness. Food; fuel; dress; longevity; usual number in a family; early marriages; any remarkable instances on either of these heads? What are their amusements and recreations? Patrons and patrons' days; and traditions respecting them? What local customs prevail . . . any legendary tales or poems recited around the fireside? Any ancient music, as clan marches or funeral cries? They differ in different districts, collect them if you can.

POPULATION.

Habits. The phrase *habits of the people*, taken in its most general sense, is applicable to the highest as well as to the lowest classes. It is abundantly manifest from the preceding parts of this memoir, that the tastes of the upper orders of the inhabitants of Derry, and its neighbourhood, are decidedly utilitarian. There is no place of public amusement, except the theatre, which is seldom open. The concerts also have been discontinued, which were formerly given at the King's Arms Hotel. Even the *coerie* has fallen into disuse, a name given to the assemblies of the nobility and gentry, which were under the control of a *king* and *queen* of the night.

In the general recreations of the community at large there is nothing remarkable or peculiar. There is, however, one observance which claims peculiar consideration. The *shutting of the gates* of Derry by the apprentice boys, on the 7th of December, 1688, O. S., and the *opening of the gates* on the 12th of August following, have led to the observance of a curious ceremony, and to the establishment of various clubs.

So early as 3 in the morning parties of youths marched through the streets, preceded by military bands, playing, among other airs, that of " No Surrender," an air connected with the siege, and to which words have been adapted by Mr. Henry Morrison, a descendant of one of the Morrisons who fought at it. The motto also of " No SURRENDER" was displayed on a flag over the four principal gates before day-break. The effigy of Governor Lundy was likewise suspended from a gibbet, erected in the Diamond. The commencement of the ceremony was announced by the firing of a large cannon, while the bells of the cathedral also chimed some popular airs, connected with the siege. The red flag of the virgin city was hoisted, the vessels at the quays were gaily decorated, and a royal standard, with the date " 1688" wrought in its centre, was planted formerly on the eastern end of the cathedral, but latterly on Walker's testimonial.

During the forenoon, crowds continued to pour into the city, and at noon several Orange lodges, adorned with standards and trappings, marched in to unite with the *apprentice boys* (a society so called,) in commemorating the day. After mustering at 1, they marched to the four gates in succession, and discharged volleys over them from the inside, according to the system of street-firing. After this they proceeded to the Diamond, discharged three volleys more, and gave three cheers for the king and constitution. The houses here were lined with people, and, amid shouts, music, and execrations, the effigy of Lundy was burned. The ceremony was concluded by an assembly of the gentry and apprentice boys in the corporation hall. Hither every man brought a glass, and a bottle filled with such beverage as he preferred ; and this conviviality, which was hence termed the *bottle and glass*, was celebrated with music, singing, and public speaking. On several successive anniversaries, divine service was performed in different places of worship throughout the city.

Extract from the Ordnance Survey Memoir of the County of Londonderry.

These were clearly not natural fields of inquiry for military officers and collection was therefore never made compulsory. As the rate of survey speeded up, the officers could spare less and less time for the memoirs, some contributing nothing at all, and gradually the task was taken over by a team of civilian assistants, employed primarily to hill-sketch in preparation for the 1-inch map of Ireland, and into whose pattern of work the memoirs fitted more easily.

Geological research was not entrusted to the men in the field, being deemed too important to leave to amateur analysis, and a special geological office was set up under Joseph Portlock. Historical research was the responsibility of the Topographical Department, who also employed artists to make sketches of antiquities.

The initial volume encompassed only the city of Londonderry in its parish of Templemore and was published in 1837. It ran to 350 pages at a cost of £1700, more than three times the original estimate for the whole country. Colby himself seemed to lose confidence in the project and somewhat reluctantly forwarded the published volume to the Chancellor, whose reaction was predictable and swift. He reiterated that he agreed to the original principle of the memoirs but 'that we should undertake to compile regular county and city histories of all Ireland, I cannot assent to.'

The collection of material for the memoirs continued in the hope of future publication, but eventually it was noticed that expenses had been incurred in areas where the survey was supposed to be complete. An inquiry accused the Department of 'indefinite research of curiosity' and Colby was ordered that it should 'revert immediately to its original object under the valuation acts', marking the end of the general memoir of Ireland.

In an attempt in 1842 to revive the project, Lord Adare, a friend of Thomas Larcom, amassed the support of an impressive body of Irish noblemen and gentlemen and had the sympathetic support of the press, who described the cost as 'less than the Queen's dog kennels at Windsor'. However, support melted away in the face of agreement to the memoirs continuing, if the gentlemen would contribute to their funding.

In later years the Ordnance Survey presented the unpublished memoirs and historical collection to the Royal Irish Academy and the geological and natural history papers to the National Museum.

Larcom alone

In 1838, with the Irish survey on a firm footing, Colby returned to England and turned his full attention once more to the survey of Great Britain and in particular to the completion of the Scottish triangulation which had been left unfinished in 1825. The remaining work in Ireland was entrusted to Larcom who, as well as being a man of great technical ability, also had an immense interest in all things Irish, making Ireland his adopted homeland. The language, history, literature and people fascinated him and he gradually acquired a deep knowledge which was to serve him well in later years. He sought as much autonomy as possible from the main Ordnance Survey office in Southampton, creating conflict between himself and Colby, who broadly hinted that Larcom would do better to make his career outside the Survey.

The year 1846 marked both the completion of the survey of Ireland at 6 inches to 1 mile and the departure of Larcom, who obtained a position as Commissioner of Public Works in Ireland. After a period as chief director of relief works during the Great Famine of 1845–50, Larcom rose by 1853 to become Under Secretary for Ireland in which post he remained until 1868, the second officer from the Ordnance Survey to hold the position. Like Drummond, Larcom 'undertook to govern all parties with even-handed justice to remove abuses and prevent disorder'.

In all of Larcom's offices after leaving the Survey he sought to apply the use of Ordnance Survey maps wherever appropriate to the task. Sales of the maps were much greater than originally envisaged partly through Larcom's enthusiastic use and partly due to the effort of the Dublin booksellers John Hodges and George Smith who were publisher and agents for the sale of the work. Their travelling representative claimed to have personally visited every potential customer in the whole of Ireland over fifteen years.

What had started out purely as a valuation exercise with scanty detail, had evolved into what Larcom called 'a full-face portrait of the land'. The maps were used for planning railways, roads, drainage, as a base for geology, on a national scale to aid social and economic planning, and even for individual owners of private estates to hang on their walls. Today they also provide an important historical record of pre-famine Ireland. Even this use was foreseen by Colby who described them as 'a record for generations to come'. His insistence on accuracy and completeness of detail, despite pressure to hurry out an inferior product, repaid his confidence and the final cost of £820 000 many times over.

Sir Thomas Larcom KCB, Under-Secretary for Ireland 1853–68.

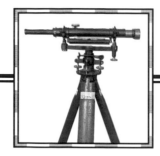

4 BACK IN BRITAIN

While the bulk of Ordnance Survey's men were deployed in Ireland, the 1-inch survey in England and Wales continued under Richard Mudge. Colby suggested that Mudge should be placed in independent command of the English work but this was not adopted and Colby retained overall responsibility, a sensible arrangement as many of the innovations of the Irish survey had applications in England and Wales.

The English survey work continued slowly between 1825 and 1830 as 'there were hardly any assistants qualified, and the work lingered very heavily'. However, progress was made and by the time Colby returned to England in 1838 the survey of Wales was almost complete as well as English counties south of the Wash.

On his return to England Colby made arrangements for the completion of the triangulation of Scotland which had ceased at the start of the Irish survey. He grumbled to his wife that, 'There is nobody that I could trust to put in charge of the Scotch Survey, and I suppose I must make it part of my business.' The completion of the triangulation of these remote areas took four 'hill seasons', the men being 'selected on account of their physical strength' because of the difficulties presented by the terrain. The triangulation of Great Britain and Ireland was completed in 1841, fifty years after the founding of the Trigonometrical Survey.

================== Tithes and railways ==================

In 1836 Parliament passed the Tithe Commutation Act. This provided for the payment of tithes in goods, such as crops, to be converted into the payment of a tithe rent, to be paid in money. Under the Act, accurate maps were needed to show the apportionment of rent to land and the circumstances were similar enough to those which gave rise to the Irish survey, to raise hopes that a large-scale survey of England and Wales would therefore be authorised. However, the important difference was that this time funds were being raised locally, with individual parishes bearing a charge based on acreage.

Lieutenant Robert Kearsley Dawson was seconded from the Ordnance Survey to the Tithe Commission to advise on the mapping needed to put the Act into effect. He pointed out that it would be just as easy to make a complete survey of

Robert Kearsley Dawson, a tireless campaigner for a national large-scale survey. G A Dawson

the country rather than a piecemeal survey, and that the resulting maps 'instead of being wasted for all other public purposes, shall be so expended as to be the means . . . of supplying all the wants of the Nation as connected with survey'. Private estates, at this time, were commonly mapped at 1 inch to 3 chains (26¾ inches to 1 mile, or 1 : 2376) and the Tithe Commissioners agreed that this was 'the smallest which can faithfully show all the detail required'.

THE SURVEYOR'S RETURN.

FAINT and wearily the way-worn Surveyor returns to the bosom of his family. He has finished his railroad labours, and they have nearly finished him. Six months ago he went forth, erect, elate, plump, rubicund; even as a boxer trained for the fight. Elastic was his step; his air was jaunty. Tight was the fit of his shooting-jacket; and sprucely did he look in it—for it was new. Unworn were the highlows which he marched along in, shouldering his theodolite, or brandishing his trusty level. Behold him now! His head droops, his form is angular, his cheek is sallow; he is like unto a pauper newly emancipated from the workhouse. Six months —six calendar months—at Brixton could not have brought him thus low. Loose are his garments; patched also, and shabby; and low as his condition are the heels of his boots. His level peeps timidly from his hinder pocket, and he trails his theodolite on the ground.

Will he be recognised by that family to whose bosom he is creeping! Will his wife and children hail the altered man! Or rather will not his domestic shut the door in his face, and tell him there is nothing for him! Surveyor, let thy knock be loud and double, lest thou be repulsed as a mendicant. And, Surveyor, a word in thine ear: Thou hast accomplished thy work; and the labourer is worthy of his hire. We would advise thee as a friend—a familiar friend—to look sharp after thine. Make out thy account speedily; send in thy bill with all despatch, while yet the bubble is roseate, and the JEREMIES who blew it, whose surname is DIDDLER, yet linger in the land of the solvent; and ere, borne far away o'er the broad Atlantic, the rogues of the railways have sought the realm of the Repudiator.

Cartoon from Punch, *1845.* Punch Publications Ltd

Although Dawson convinced the Tithe Commissioners about the overwhelming merits of a national survey, he failed, to his bitter disappointment, to win over the Select Committee set up to consider the issue. They concluded that not only was a general survey not required, but that it would be unfair on the landowners to insist that they should pay for the survey of areas not affected by the Tithe Act. Colby referred to the incident as 'poor Dawson's complete failure.'

The tithe surveys went ahead and were carried out by contracted surveyors whose charges were levied on the parishes. This enabled them to pay higher wages than the Ordnance Survey who lost many experienced men to the tithe surveys and had to introduce a 'working pay' allowance to try and minimise losses of staff.

The passing of the Enclosure Act in 1845 also generated a need for maps and it was here that the false economy of the 'cheap' tithe survey was exposed. Only a small proportion of the tithe maps were found to be accurate enough for the enclosure survey and most areas had to be resurveyed. Again Ordnance Survey staff were attracted away by higher wages paid by contractors.

The year 1845 was also the 'great railway year' when demand for maps, for planning and laying out railway routes, was at its height. As before, the tithe maps were found to be inadequate and new surveys were needed. Constrained only by commercial gain, and being aware that surveyors were in short supply, the railway companies competed with each other to procure the expertise they needed. Pay of 3 or 4 guineas a day tempted surveyors from the Ordnance, tithe and enclosure surveys. During this boom the Ordnance Survey discharged, at their own request, approaching 300 employees. Some regretted their chase after easy money as many of the railway companies collapsed as quickly as they had sprung up, leaving creditors, and employees, unpaid.

To say that none of this would have happened had the Select Committee considering the Tithe Act been more

Reward for vigilance

A watch is always kept in the camp for distant heliostats. The first man that calls out 'heliostat', when one of these star-like points shows itself, receives a shilling for his vigilance. In order also to incite watchfulness in the man directing the heliostat to the observing station, and that he might miss no gleam of sunlight, a pecuniary reward was proposed in 1840 by Captain Robinson, R.E., . . . The amount varied with the distance, being 6 pence for each time the heliostat was observed for a distance less than 10 miles, one shilling for a distance between 10 and 20 miles, and so on; whilst . . . for a distance over 100 miles, a guinea. The propriety of this allowance will be readily admitted when it is remembered that as long a period as a month has very frequently occurred between consecutive observations of very distant points. The value of an observation under such circumstances becomes very great.

From A R Clarke, *Account of the Observations and Calculations of the Principle Triangulation.*

A heliostat.

forward thinking, is too simplistic. Even if approval for the general survey had been given, there is no knowing whether it would have been completed in time to meet the exceptional demand. However, the sequence of events demonstrated beyond doubt the need for accurate, large-scale maps of the country. Ireland with its Ordnance Survey 6-inch map suffered no similar mania for maps for railway planning.

══ Six-inch mapping for Great Britain ══

Envious eyes were cast at the detailed 6-inch maps of Ireland as they began to roll off the Mountjoy presses, and in March 1839 the Directors of the Highland and Agricultural Society of Scotland called for the Scottish 1-inch mapping to be enhanced in manufacturing and mining districts, with a 6-inch scale map. The Tithe Commutation Act had no relevance to Scotland and, as they were without the benefit of even the poor quality tithe surveys, the Scots were more vocal than the English in pressing for better Ordnance Survey maps.

Colby asked that 'alteration should be immediately considered and decided upon', suggesting that 6 inches to 1 mile should be substituted for all future surveys. In 1840 the Treasury agreed that the remaining English counties and the whole of Scotland should be surveyed at the larger scale, but also recommended that any reduction of 6-inch maps to the 1-inch scale should be left to commercial map makers. Colby disagreed and again used the lessons of Ireland in argument, reminding them that commercial reductions of the Irish maps had been badly executed. It was finally agreed that the Ordnance Survey should continue to publish 1-inch maps in England but no decision was made regarding derived mapping for Scotland.

Surveys at 6 inches to 1 mile were an improvement on the 1-inch but what was suitable for Ireland was not necessarily, in some opinions, adequate for Great Britain. First among the complainers (and put up to it by Dawson, although he kept a very low profile) were the Tithe Commissioners. Their support for the Ordnance Survey to make a map of the country at a large scale had been ignored in 1836 but they pointed out that in some northern parishes the tithe survey had not yet commenced. These parishes were aware that the Ordnance Survey was to survey their counties at the 6-inch scale and so had put off their own survey, thinking that it would not be needed. As, in fact, the 6-inch scale was unsuitable for tithe purposes, it now meant that two surveys would have to be carried out in those counties, one at each scale. Faced with this duplication, the Treasury obtained an

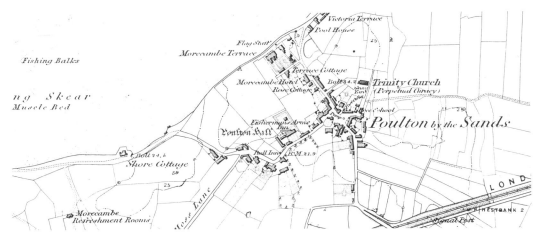

Poulton-by-the-Sands at 6 inches to 1 mile in 1845, later to be swallowed up by growth of the new resort of Morecambe.

estimate for Ordnance Survey to carry out the survey at the larger 26⅔ inches to 1 mile that the Tithe Commissioners wanted. Colby calculated the additional cost to be 2d per acre. Having only just come to terms with the 'heavy additional expense' of the 6-inch scale the Treasury asked for more detail and Colby, conscious that this was a rare second chance, made a full report containing 'very statesman-like reasons' for the larger scale. But the Treasury also consulted an eminent engineer, James Walker, who professed to be quite content with the 6-inch scale. He pointed out that any special survey at a larger scale could always be carried out by the Ordnance Survey and paid for by the landowner (or parish) who required it. The Treasury agreed that this proposal had considerable financial appeal, while apparently still satisfying the needs of the tithe survey. Some thirty-four tithe surveys were indeed carried out on this basis by the Ordnance Survey, in Lancashire and Yorkshire's West Riding. The Treasury had firmly decided in favour of the 6-inch scale, mainly on grounds of expense, but also because they believed a larger scale survey in northern counties would lead to similar requests for the whole country. 'Poor Dawson's complete failure' also became Colby's own.

The Survey Act, 1841

ANNO QUARTO & QUINTO

VICTORIÆ REGINÆ.

•••••••••••••••••••••••••••••••••••••

C A P. XXX.

An Act to authorize and facilitate the Completion of a Survey of *Great Britain, Berwick upon Tweed,* and the *Isle of Man.* [21st *June* 1841.]

WHEREAS several Counties in that Part of the United Kingdom called *England* have been surveyed by Officers appointed by the Master General and Board of Ordnance, and it is expedient that general Surveys and Maps of *England, Scotland, Berwick upon Tweed,* and of the *Isle of Man,* should be made and completed by Officers in like Manner appointed; and that the Boundaries of the several Counties in *England* and *Scotland,* and of *Berwick upon Tweed* and of the *Isle of Man,* should be ascertained and marked out: Be it therefore enacted by the Queen's most Excellent Majesty, by and with the Advice and Consent of the Lords Spiritual and Temporal, and Commons, in this present Parliament assembled, and by the Authority of the same, That from and after the passing of this Act, for the Purpose of enabling the Master General and Board of Ordnance to make and complete such Surveys and Maps of *England, Scotland, Berwick upon Tweed,* and the *Isle of Man,* in manner aforesaid, it shall and may be lawful for the Justices assembled at any Quarter Sessions, or Adjournment thereof, held in and for any County, Riding, or Division in *England, Scotland, Berwick upon Tweed,* and the *Isle of Man,* upon the Application

Justices at Quarter Sessions to appoint Persons to assist in ascertaining the Boundaries of Counties, Cities, Boroughs, &c.

4 C

With the change in surveying scale to 6 inches to the mile, legislation was needed to provide both for the collection of essential boundary information and to give surveyors the right of access to private property.

The Survey Act of 1841 (see extract), based on a similar Act made in 1825 for the Irish Survey, listed the boundaries which could be shown on each map. These were 'county, city, borough, town, parish, burghs royal, parliamentary burghs, burghs of regality and barony, extra-parochial and other places, districts and divisions, in England, Scotland, Berwick-upon-Tweed and the Isle of Man'. (Berwick-upon-Tweed was at that time still independent of England and Scotland, and Wales was lumped together with England.) Local justices were instructed 'to apoint one or more fit and proper persons' to point out the boundaries to the surveyors. Both were given the right to enter 'into and upon any land, ground or heritages of any person or persons whomsoever, for the purpose of making and carrying out any survey' and 'for the purpose of fixing any mark or object to be used in the survey or any post, stone or boundary mark whatsoever'.

The Act provided for penalties to be levied against the boundary man (meresman), if he failed to appear at the agreed time, and against any person who interfered with boundary marks or obstructed the survey operations. Importantly, the Act also made it clear that no legal claims to ownership of property could be made, based upon the sole evidence of the detail depicted on the Ordnance Survey map.

In later years the right of entry provisions became much more important as larger national mapping scales were introduced, and surveyors needed access to gardens of houses. The provisions of the Act were updated in later amendments and remain current to this day, although in 150 years the Ordnance Survey has never had to bring a prosecution under the Survey Act.

Fire!

At about 10.30 p.m. on the last day of October 1841, fire broke out at the Tower of London. Although alongside the Thames, the tide was out and it was difficult to obtain enough water to fight the fire, which spread rapidly. Within half an hour the Grand Storehouse was ablaze and the inhabitants of the Tower were forced to make a hurried escape as the fire raged out of control. Only an act of immense bravery by a police officer saved the crown jewels from their store in the Martin Tower. The Bowyer Towers and the Grand Storehouse were completely destroyed by the time the blaze was brought under control.

The Ordnance Map Office was at one stage threatened by the fire, and some damage was sustained, but troops and firemen together managed to avert the flames. The maps, records and instruments were all removed to safety except for the unique Ramsden zenith sector which was lost to the conflagration.

Colby had for some time been complaining that the accommodation at the Tower was too small for the additional men engaged to undertake the 6-inch survey. He calculated that he needed office accommodation 'not less than double its present amount' favouring location in a large building 'in London or its immediate vicinity'. The Master General disagreed, pointing out the expense of London accommodation and that much of the survey work could be carried out some distance away.

Meanwhile, in Southampton, the Duke of York's Royal Military Asylum in London Road had become vacant. This was a cavalry barracks converted to a school for soldiers' children. It

A great crowd gathered on Tower Hill to watch the flames as they engulfed the fortress. Painting by William Smith. Guildhall, London

had closed the previous year and the empty buildings were put up for sale. The War Office proposed that they should be converted to an Asylum for Insane Officers and Soldiers but the Master General of the Ordnance thought it objectionable to have such an asylum, not only in the middle of the town, 'but in the middle of the very best part of it'. He suggested that the Ordnance Survey might find the premises suitable.

In September 1841 Colby examined these offices and agreed that they 'may be made a convenient Office for the Survey at a very small expense' and on 14 October 1841 the site was officially granted to the Ordnance Survey. Although the buildings were not immediately ready for occupation after the fire, alterations were urgently carried out and, by the end of the year, Ordnance Survey was fully established at London Road, Southampton.

The third dimension

Sea-level was thought by William Roy to be consistent the world over and so, for the Hounslow Heath base, in order that it would represent 'a portion of the mean circumference of the earth', Roy related his measurement to sea-level. He levelled 'from the lower end of the base to the surface of the Thames at Hampton, and found the descent to be 36.1 feet'. He then calculated the further descent to the mean surface of the sea. Mathematically, he then reduced the length of the base to arrive at its theoretical length based on sea-level. Roy had not only set about putting his survey results on a scientific foundation, he had also recognised the need for accurate measurements in the third dimension: the measurement of height.

Levelling is the means by which points, known as bench-marks, are given an altitude value based on a known datum. Sea-level is chosen as the datum because most land in the British Isles, though not all, is higher than sea-level. This allows the assumption to be made that all values are positive, above sea-level, unless otherwise stated.

Rivalry has always existed between trigonometrical observers and levellers as to the relative importance of each job. The trig. observers rightly think their job important, as the framework and ensuing accuracy of the final map depends on the precision of their observations. 'True,' the levellers

Geological maps

By the time Colby took over as Superintendent of the Ordnance Survey in 1820, geologists had identified most rock types to be found within the United Kingdom. Colby, who fully intended that the Ordnance maps should serve as a base for geological survey, appointed Captain J Pringle to establish a geological branch of the Survey, in Ireland, in 1827. This early venture into formal geological survey lapsed after an inquiry concluded that the division officers who supplied geological information to Pringle were inadequately qualified.

In 1831, Sir Roderick Murchinson, Head of the Geological Society, suggested that a geologist should be attached to the Ordnance Survey in England. Colby agreed and accepted the proposal that the Secretary of the Society, Henry De la Beche, should add geological colouring to the 1-inch maps of Devon. Practical advantages of the work became evident for 'agriculture, mining, road-making, the formation of canals and railroads, and other branches of national industry', and in 1835 the Geological Ordnance Survey was formally founded under De la Beche's control. His first geological memoir of the *Geology of Cornwall, Devon and West Somerset* was published in 1839.

Illustration of rock outcrop, Ballynascreen parish.

Meanwhile, responsibility for geological mapping in Ireland had passed to Richard Griffith who was already working with the Ordnance Survey providing townland boundary and land valuation information for the Irish Survey. Griffith was a member of the Geological Society and thus had the unique opportunity of bringing geology and mapping together. He drew up a complete geological map of Ireland which was engraved by the Board of Ordnance at 4 inches to the mile and published, to wide acclaim, in 1839.

Colby appointed Joseph Portlock to take charge of a geological survey department of the Ordnance Survey in Ireland. Portlock was a gifted geologist who became completely absorbed in the new sciences of stratigraphy and palaeontology, eventually producing, in 1843, a detailed *Report on the Geology of Londonderry and of parts of Tyrone and Fermanagh.*

In 1845 it was decided that the geological survey should be a separate expert organisation and Sir Henry De la Beche (he was knighted in 1842) was made Director General of the new Geological Survey of Great Britain and Ireland which was placed under the control of the Office of Woods and Forests. However, Ordnance Survey continued to engrave and to print the maps on their behalf. One immediate advantage of the transfer of control away from the Ordnance Survey was that officers of the Geological Survey no longer had to wear the military uniform of a dark blue, tightfitting, well-buttoned frock coat and top hat, neither item of which was well designed for scrambling over rocks and traversing rough country. The brass buttons of this extraordinary uniform displayed a nice touch of humour with their device of crossed hammers.

Until 1990 the British Geological Survey's colourful maps were still printed by Ordnance Survey at Southampton.

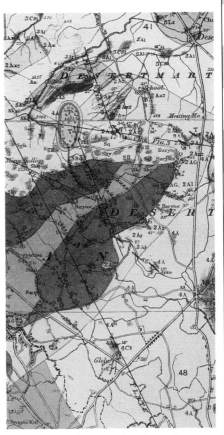

Extract from the ½-inch geological map of Londonderry, Tyrone and Fermanagh, from Portlock's 1843 report of the area.

may say, 'but where would your accuracy be without us?' And the levellers have a good and valid point.

If the triangulation was observed with all the stations at exactly the same height, there would be no need for the leveller, because the calculations to establish the true position of each station would be done on one flat, horizontal surface or plane. Triangulation stations are, however, not on one plane, they vary in height as much as the landscape on which they are placed. Therefore, to establish the accurate horizontal distance between each triangulation station, their heights, relative to each other must be established, leading to the leveller's final say in the dispute: 'It's possible to have good accurate levelling without trig., but you can't have good trig.

without levelling.'

The early Ordnance Survey method used to determine difference in height relied upon use of a theodolite telescope, pointed at the target and measuring the angle of declination (or inclination) on the telescope's vertical protractor. But experiments found that refraction, a distortion or deflection of the line of sight when looking through the atmosphere, affected the results. Refraction was worse over longer distances and the nearer that observations were taken to the horizon. It also varied according to how much moisture was present in the air. The problem could not be overcome, forcing the theodolite heighting observations to be restricted to distances of less than 10 miles.

WARMINSTER, SALISBURY, SOUTHAMPTON, WINCHESTER, AND BASINGSTOKE—*continued.*　　55

Numbers and Descriptions of Bench Marks, &c.	Approximate Distances between consecutive Bench Marks in Links.	Altitudes in feet above Mean Level of the Sea at Liverpool.	County and Sheet of Ordnance Map.
SALISBURY TO SOUTHAMPTON—*continued.*			
No. 363. Bolt in front of the Nelson Inn at junction of roads to Millbrook and Shirley ; 4˙66 ft. above centre of road, and level with mark - - - - - - -	1,455	45˙311	Hampshire 11
No. 364. ,, in small conduit-house at junction of Water-house-lane and Commercial-road ; 3˙46 ft. above centre of road - - - - - - - - -	2,226	40˙243	,, ,,
No. 365. ,, in brick wall in front of Doctor Simpson's house at junction of Commercial-road and High-street ; 4˙18 ft. above centre of road - - - - - -	1,780	60˙322	,, ,,
No. 366. ,, in pier of wall at junction of High-street and Brunswick-place, Southampton ; 3˙24 ft. above centre of road - - - - - - - -	1,084	65˙321	,, ,,
No. 367. ,, in pier of brick wall at angle of Guard Room at entrance to the Ordnance Map Office ; 3˙32 ft. above centre of road - - - - - - - - -	1,772	75˙285	,, ,,
ZERO OF TIDE GAUGE AT VICTORIA PIER, SOUTHAMPTON (*August* 1859) - -	-	—11˙577	,, ,,
SOUTHAMPTON TO WINCHESTER.			
No. 368. Mark on Peter Goater's Public House at West side of the Avenue, on Southampton Common ; 2˙33 ft. above surface - - - - - - - - -	6,066	105˙243	,, ,,
No. 369. ,, on West post of common gate at junction of road to Swathling ; 2˙45 ft. above centre			

Descriptions of Initial Levelling marks in Southampton.

One of the main preoccupations of early levellers was the question of where zero altitude should be. Although it is easy to talk about sea-level, it is no more level than land and, worse, it varies minute by minute with the tides.

From 8 April 1837, when it was selected and recorded, zero altitude in Ireland was taken as being the low-water of spring tide at Poolbeg Lighthouse, Dublin Bay (Irish datum). In 1842, as a result of scientific interest in tidal phenomena, Colby, in collaboration with George Airy, the Astronomer Royal, observed over a three-month period twenty-two points around the Irish coast. From this, it was discovered that low spring tide levels varied around the coast by as much as 9 feet but that mean sea-level only varied by 2½ feet. It was therefore decided that mean sea-level was a more logical datum but as many maps already showed height relating to Poolbeg this was kept as the height datum for Ireland.

Spirit levelling

Spirit levelling, and the accuracy that this method could bring to height surveys, had come to Colby's notice when he became involved in a committee 'for the purpose of determining the circumstances of the relative level of land and water'. In 1837 and 1838, the committee organised the levelling of a route from the English Channel, at Axmouth, to the Bristol Channel, at Portishead, under the supervision of Revd Dr W Wherwell. It was levelled in both directions, which allowed the work to be double-checked, a procedure which became standard practice. The information from this levelling was to have been used in the planning of a canal (which was never built) linking the English and Bristol Channels, the height information being essential for the correct placing of canal locks.

Colby seems to have needed little convincing of the advantages of spirit levelling and, in the period 1838 to 1843,

2000 miles of forward and back levelling took place along the main Irish roads. The results of the levelling were then added in the form of the bench-mark symbol and height, straight on to the 6-inch maps.

The progress of levelling was recorded on the ground by establishing marks along the route at intervals. The bench-marks placed in the 1830s and 1840s were usually cut into a vertical brick or stone surface with a hammer and chisel, although some were also cut on wooden posts. The mark took the shape of a horizontal bar or bench, which acted as the point of reference, with an identifying arrow below it. On more permanent structures, such as churches and bridges, the horizontal cut-mark was augmented by a brass bolt. Marks were also placed on horizontal surfaces, with either a bolt or spike driven into the surface, or an indentation into which a regulation size (⅝ inch) ball-bearing would be placed when reference was required. Levelling also took place to establish the height of the numerous trigonometrical stations.

The levellers themselves were non-commissioned officers and sappers although some civil assistants were employed as well. 'Each leveller had three labourers under him; two acted as staff holders and chainman, and the third carried the instrument from station to station, and sheltered it from the wind with a large umbrella, while the leveller made his observations.' They used Gravatt levels and 'ordinary 10 inch Y levels' for the main levelling lines. The levelling staves were in three pieces; put together they reached 17 feet in height. Pasted to the face of the stave were slips of paper which had graduations of feet, tenths and hundredths of feet printed on them. These were aligned to points marked on the wood with a beam compass.

In a typical levelling operation the leveller had one stave (the back) placed on a point of known altitude (a bench-mark) and the other stave (the forward) placed some distance away, but within horizontal sight of the levelling instrument. The instrument was placed at a measured point midway between the staves. The leveller first checked that the telescope on his instrument was exactly horizontal, with the aid of the long spirit-bubble fixed to the instrument, and observed to the back stave, and then swung the telescope around to face the forward stave, taking care not to alter the position of the main body of the instrument. After checking once again that the instrument was level, he made the forward observation. The difference in height, one stave to the other, could be abstracted from the observations.

The back stave and the level were moved past the forward stave (which then became the back stave) and the leveller repeated the operation. In this way, progress was made over the ground in a leap-frog fashion, with benchmarks newly placed along the route at half-mile intervals. The line of levels was always started and finished on a point of known height. Any discrepancies were adjusted along the line of bench-marks, but, where a difference of more than $1/10$ foot was found, the levelling was repeated.

Many Initial Levelling cut-marks still survive to this day, this one on a bridge in Christchurch.

The initial levelling

The drift back of the sappers from Ireland to England in late 1841 saw the start of a systematic network of levels. The first line ran from Gloucester to West Angle Bay in Milford Haven. Eventually, 10 000 miles of forward and back levelling was done, following the roads of England, Wales and Scotland. It took over twenty years, ending in 1860, at Ballinluig near Pitlochry. The datum, or zero level, chosen in 1841 was an arbitrary point, 100 feet below a bench-mark bolt in the face of St John's Church tower, Old Haymarket, Liverpool. This was superseded in 1844 by another Liverpool datum, 47 feet above the first to take into account Colby's and Sir George Airy's investigations into mean sea-level. The datum was based on nine days' observations in March 1844, of high and low water on to a tide pole at the entrance to Liverpool's Victoria Dock.

As the levelling extended across the country, it was linked to thirty-two tidal observatories, where readings were taken for one month in 1859 and early 1860. As a result of these observations, it was found that the Liverpool Victoria Dock datum was actually 0.65 feet below mean sea-level. The Liverpool datum continued to be used, but a statement had to be included on each large-scale plan, that all bench-marks were shown in relation to Liverpool datum and, to achieve heights relative to mean sea-level, users should add the stated amount to each height shown.

Computation of the results was carried out by a staff of men using pencils, paper and ten-figure logarithmic tables.

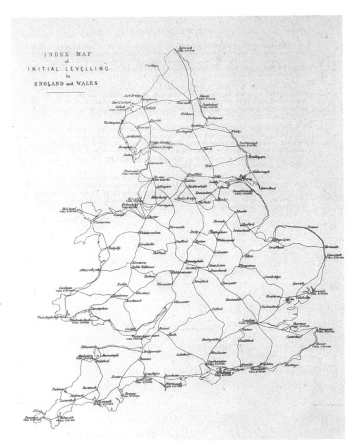

Initial Levelling lines in England and Wales.

They used a mathematical method known as 'least squares' which enabled them to determine the best values of unknown quantities. For the levelling it was used to find ninety-one unknowns in one adjustment block (England and Wales) and seventy-seven in the other (Scotland). The results of the initial levelling were finally published in a weighty *Abstract* in 1861 and the bench-marks listed within this have ever since been known as PA (published abstract) marks.

Colby's successor

In November 1846, Colby was promoted to Major General and in accordance with military custom had then to retire the following year. His pleasure on gaining his promotion was marred by the refusal of the Board of Ordnance to accept his recommended successor. As with all things relating to the Ordnance Survey, Colby had very definite views and he believed that only one man was capable of successfully taking over from him. His nominee was Captain William Yolland, an able, talented and unusually popular officer. Colby knew his appointment would not be straightforward, writing that:

> An objection may arise to the appointment of so young an officer as Captain Yolland; the continuance of peace has made promotion slow, but he is about the same age (37 years), and has about the same length of service (19 years), which I had, when I succeeded the late Major General Mudge in charge of the survey in 1820.

Unfortunately, this was not a powerful enough argument to sway the Board of Ordnance, who took the view that the small operation Colby had taken charge of in 1820 was somewhat different from the mature organisation that he had built up before his retirement. An officer as junior as Yolland, in both age and rank, could not be placed in command of it, even if he was the best person for the job. No other nominations were made from within the Ordnance Survey and the Board of Ordnance appointed a complete outsider to the post.

Lieutenant Colonel Lewis Hall RE was aged fifty-three at the time of his appointment and had no knowledge of survey matters, having served mainly overseas for much of his career. Colby was furious and his passage into retirement was marked by sustained but unsuccessful lobbying against the appointment of Hall.

Colby was head of the Ordnance Survey for twenty-

Brevet Colonel L A Hall.

seven years, longer than any other superintendent. It was directly due to his energetic leadership that the Survey progressed from being a small piecemeal operation to that of a large, well organised and efficient mapping organisation. He always held the long-term objectives for the Survey to be above those of the immediate task in hand, being aware of the work in terms of scientific achievement and as a base for planning national improvements. His common-sense approach and infectious enthusiasm endeared him to the men, but he expected the same high standards from them as he set himself.

In retirement Colby took his family to the continent to live but, on finding the political climate unsteady, they returned and settled at New Brighton near Liverpool. Here Colby died in 1852, aged sixty-nine. An obelisk erected to his memory can be found in the precincts of Liverpool's Anglican Cathedral.

5 THE BATTLE OF THE SCALES

When the announcement of Hall's appointment was made public, Yolland received a sympathetic letter from a friend which shows the extent to which his succession to Colby had been taken for granted.

> The high and deserved praise of the present state of the Survey makes me the more regret that the new Superintendent has been appointed . . . everyone who knew anything about the Survey knew that all improvements of late years had been introduced at your suggestion, and that although it is quite fair that General Colby should have praise due to those improvements, because he placed you in that situation, yet it is not fair that on his retirement a fresh person knowing nothing of the subject should be brought in to gain credit from your brains.

However, Hall was already fifty-three and Yolland would therefore only have to wait patiently for a few years to gain the age and rank that the Board of Ordnance thought necessary. Unfortunately, he found it difficult to accept the situation and tended to act as if he was already in command of the Ordnance Survey, making Hall uncomfortably aware that he was head of an organisation that was clearly waiting for him to leave. Hall had to depend on Yolland while learning about the Ordnance Survey, but once he had found his feet, he then found Yolland continually under them. He reacted by enforcing strict military etiquette and discipline, to keep Yolland firmly in his place.

The situation was always potentially explosive and in 1852 a dispute arose between the two men which, although in itself of little importance, became symbolic of the power struggle between them. Yolland, who had previously written two weighty scientific accounts of survey operations, had completed a third book, *Astronomical Observations with Airy's Zenith Sector 1842–50*. Hall noticed that the title page omitted any mention of himself as head of the Ordnance Survey, and that the preface contained reference to future action on which he had not been consulted. He objected that the book had been printed without him seeing a proof copy for approval and reprimanded Yolland, insisting that the bound copies should be unbound and the offending pages reprinted. Yolland defended himself in a long letter of explanation, citing previous publications as examples he had followed and stating that 'had any instructions been given by you for my guidance . . . it would have been my duty to have adhered to them.' He also expressed his displeasure at being addressed 'in a style in which it had never previously been my misfortune to be addressed by any of my Commanding Officers'. In return Hall accused Yolland of acting in 'an unmilitary and dictatorial manner', and lacking the 'proper feeling, which should have prompted Capt. Yolland to submit a copy to me.' A further frank exchange of correspondence only served to deepen the rift between them until, unable to agree, they appealed to the Inspector General to give his opinion. Naturally, he supported Hall's right to organise the Survey in whatever way he chose, but made it plain that no censure upon Captain Yolland was implied and hoped for a more cordial relationship to be resumed.

This neutral approach did not satisfy Hall, whose dislike of Yolland had intensified to the point where he was determined to have him removed. He dug up a further complaint against Yolland, accusing him of 'interfering with official correspondence', and asked directly for his removal from the Survey. Yolland, with a sense of shock, now realised the seriousness of his situation and his denial of this charge was couched in far more humble terms than the spirited and clever replies with which he had incensed Hall before, insisting that he 'had determined to perform my duties cordially', and regretting 'that anything has in your opinion, since accrued to cause you to think any further steps, necessary'. The Inspector General asked Hall to reconsider and, faced with a flat refusal by his own superiors to remove Yolland, Hall agreed to retain him – but posted him first to Dublin, and then to the remotest office in the Ordnance Survey, Enniskillen in Ireland. Yolland evidently decided to make no further move, perhaps waiting until Hall had gone, to return as rightful head of the Ordnance Survey. Hall, though, ensured that this didn't happen, and his successor in 1854 was announced as Major Henry James RE. On hearing this news, Yolland immediately resigned. He became an Inspector of Railways and eventually Chief Inspector, achieving, at last, recognition of his talents. But not by the Ordnance Survey.

Maps for public health

In 1844 a report on fifty towns found that 'in scarcely one place can the drainage or sewerage be pronounced to be complete and good, while in seven it is indifferent, and in 42 decidedly bad as regards the districts inhabited by the poorer classes.' This was nothing new, but advances in medicine had proved beyond doubt that diseases such as cholera and typhoid were spread by contaminated drinking water and bad sanitation. The 1844 report exposed to public view the appalling living conditions of the working classes, and disease, being no respecter of class, lent urgency to the improvement of sanitary conditions in general.

Town plans were already being prepared by the Ordnance Survey for northern counties where mapping was proceeding at 6 inches to a mile. Each town with a population of more than four thousand people was mapped at 5 feet to a mile (1:1056), a procedure imported from the Irish Survey. This satisfied the demands for large-scale plans which could then be reduced to form part of the 6-inch map. Progress was limited to the rate of the 6-inch survey and, although individual towns in other parts of the country could apply to have town plans made by the Ordnance Survey, the cost was prohibitive. In 1848 Hall admitted that only two towns had been surveyed specially for sanitary purposes. These were Windsor, at the request of Prince Albert, and Southampton which as the headquarters town of the Ordnance Survey was surveyed as a training exercise for new recruits. Hall's attitude to the town plans was one delaying factor. He had only a limited number of surveyors and was reluctant to undertake

special surveys which caused the programme of 6-inch mapping to fall behind. His military mind preferred a systematic county by county approach to the task, rather than having surveyors dotted randomly around the country in whichever town happened to be shouting the loudest for maps.

In 1849 Hall and Yolland had appeared together before a Select Committee on Army and Ordnance expenditure. They were closely questioned on the progress of town plans and how the increasing demand could be met. Yolland pointed out the relative cheapness of employing Ordnance Survey staff whose costs were reduced by the system of division of labour. Private surveyors, he pointed out, were skilled in all aspects of map making and so commanded a higher fee, but actually produced less accurate plans. The decision of the Committee was not to Hall's liking:

> It appears advisable that the survey of the large towns should be preferred before the general survey of the counties . . . and moreover, it will hasten the adoption of sanitary measures throughout densely populated districts, where such improvements are most needed.

Hall liked even less the suggestion that the 5 feet to 1 mile plans were at too small a scale and that this should be doubled to 10 feet to 1 mile. He called this scale 'preposterous'. The suggestion for the larger scale was made by the General Board of Health who employed the tireless Robert K Dawson as advisor. Aware of Hall's reluctance to commit staff to the town plans, Dawson suggested, by way of compromise,

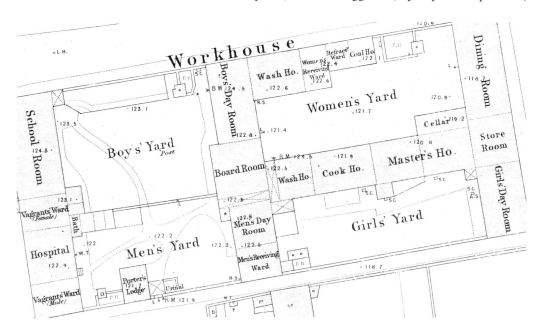

Extract from the 10 feet to 1 mile (1:528) plan of Berwick-upon-Tweed, sheet 2, showing the interior arrangements of the workhouse in 1852.

The survey of London

Between 1800 and 1841 the population of London more than doubled to 1 874 000. The living conditions of the poorer classes were squalid and overcrowded, water closets were almost unknown to them and drinking water was supplied by private water companies using mainly unfiltered Thames water, into which ran London's open drains.

The Metropolitan Sanitary Commissioners were set up to tackle the problems of water supply and waste disposal in the capital, but to plan their improvements needed an accurate map. In 1847 they approached the Ordnance Survey asking that the 'largest practical force' be made available for a survey of the city. The survey proposed was to accurately show only roads and frontages, to keep the expense to a minimum.

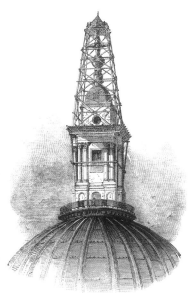

The observatory was perched on top of the golden cross of St Pauls Cathedral.
Illustrated London News

SURVEY OF LONDON.

CONSIDERABLE alarm has been excited in the minds of some of the Londoners by the appearance of soldiers in sundry high and elevated positions commanding the metropolis, or at least some of the most important parts of it. One of the towers of Westminster Abbey, which immediately overhangs the Houses of Parliament, is at this moment mysteriously manned by a military party, who, it turns out upon inquiry, are engaged in a plan for levelling the Metropolis at the request of the Sanitary Commissioners. Directly this fact was made known, the consternation, particularly that of the lower classes about Tothill Street and its vicinity, increased in a painful degree, for their only idea of the levelling of the Metropolis suggests to them its being levelled with the dust in the ordinary manner. They exclaim that it is the act of an Insanitary rather than a Sanitary Commission to give orders for the levelling of London; and though they have been told that the process includes its triangulation, or reduction to triangles, it has been found impossible to drum into them a just appreciation of what is going forward. Some old women belonging to the party of the DUKE OF WELLINGTON believe that London is already in the hands of the French, and that they are on the top of the Abbey, holding in abey-ance the formidable power they are about to exercise.

It is satisfactory to know from LORD JOHN RUSSELL, that our foreign relations are in an amicable state; though it will be difficult to make the nervous portion of the population believe this, while military men are walking about the streets with a machine that seems like a cross between a telescope and a howitzer.

Engineer. "DON'T BE ALARMED, MA'AM, IT'S ONLY A DUMPY LEVELLER."
Old Lady. "LAW! DEAR NOW! WELL, I'M SURE I THOUGHT IT WAS A BLUNDERBUST. BUT DON'T FIRE IT OFF, YOUNG MAN, TILL I'M GOT BY, FOR I WAS ALWAYS TERRIBLE FEARED OF GUNS."

From an 1848 edition of Punch. Punch Publications Ltd

Ordnance Survey work began in 1848 and the surveying, at 5 feet to the mile (1:1056), took two years. The appearance of soldiers on the streets of London caused some excitement amongst the public. With soldiers manning observation stations on high buildings and rumours of 'levelling', speculation ranged between impending invasion and demolition, both far from the truth.

The London survey taxed both the ingenuity and the nerve of the sappers who manned the observation stations, the best and highest of which was on top of St Paul's Cathedral. Here the sappers designed and erected a scaffold to raise the observing station to sit upon the very top of the cross, 92 feet above the highest point of the dome. To this dizzy perch they took the Ramsden 18-inch theodolite and made thousands of observations over four months, suspending this activity whenever Divine service took place in the Cathedral below them.

that they could be made by private surveyors using Ordnance Survey triangulation and under Ordnance Survey control. In practice, towns were generally surveyed either wholly by the Ordnance Survey or by commercial surveyors and the co-operation advocated by Dawson rarely occurred.

Thirty-five towns were surveyed by the Ordnance Survey at the large 10 feet to 1 mile (1:528) scale, mainly on a repayment basis by which the local authority paid for the maps. From about 1855, a further 440 town plans were made, at the equivalent natural scale of 1:500 (10.56 feet to 1 mile), including revisions of town plans at smaller scales. The 1:500 surveys were mostly made at national expense and were often engraved and issued as Ordnance Survey maps. The early plans showed sanitary features in great detail including the position of drains, privvies and cesspits.

The town plans are remarkable for their fascinating detail. As well as the buildings and roads that are expected on a map of this scale, a wealth of other information is depicted, such as fire plugs, lamp posts, garden paths, fountains and even a note of the number of seats in public buildings such as churches. Perhaps most impressively, the *inside* of important public buildings was surveyed as well as the outside, showing the layout of the rooms, each labelled with their purpose.

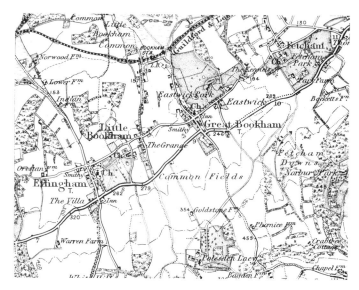

Part of an 1896 1-inch map of Effingham, Surrey.

The majority of the town plans were 'one-offs', produced for the laying out of town improvements to drainage and water supplies, and were never revised at this scale.

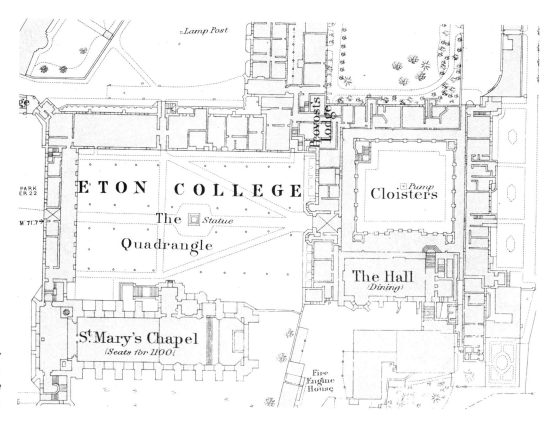

Part of the 5 feet to 1 mile (1:1056) plan of Windsor, published in revised form in 1871.

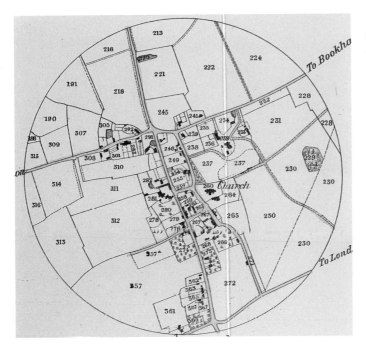

Effingham, Surrey shown at 6 inches to 1 mile, from evidence given by the Copyhold and Tithe Commission in 1853.

The 'Battle of the Scales'

As well as the difficulties Hall had with Yolland, he also bore the brunt of what became known as the 'Battle of the Scales': a period of bureaucratic indecision extending over some eight years. During this time heated debates took place over the scales of mapping that would be most generally useful to the country. In 1840 the Treasury had decided to allow the northern counties of England and the whole of Scotland to be surveyed at 6 inches to 1 mile, like the survey of Ireland, but in 1851 a Select Committee was appointed under Francis Charteris (later Lord Elcho) to enquire into the state of Ordnance Survey in Scotland. They recommended that the 6-inch scale should be abandoned in favour of the familiar

1-inch scale because, in their opinion, 'the six-inch map alone was not of sufficient public utility to justify the large expenditure of public money that was required.' These findings came as a sharp reminder to the Ordnance Survey that many people remained unconvinced of the merits of large-scale national map coverage.

The Charteris Committee were, in fact, correct to advocate the abandonment of the 6-inch scale, if it is remembered that they were only considering the scale for Scotland. Two-thirds of that country was described by the Committee as 'barren waste and rugged mountains' for which 6-inch mapping offered little advantage. The Treasury though, observing the cost savings involved in reverting to 1-inch mapping, decided to interpret their recommendations as applicable to the whole of Great Britain and felt 'disposed to concur' with the abandonment of the 6-inch scale.

The Treasury asked the Board of Ordnance for comment. Hall pointed out that the recommendations were totally against those reached after much consideration and representation in the 1840s, and brought to the Treasury's notice the inexperience of the committee in relation to maps. He reinforced his opinion with letters from civil engineers and scientists who regarded the abandonment of the 6-inch scale as 'an intense absurdity'.

This achieved a stay of execution and the Treasury permitted work to continue on the 6-inch scale in counties where it had already been started, but forbade new work at that scale, until the matter 'shall have received more full consideration'. During 1852 protests from Fife, Haddington and Durham forced the Treasury to allow 6-inch work in those counties, and the following year Lord Elcho upheld the decision of the Charteris Committee in favour of the 1-inch scale but agreed that cultivated districts would benefit from the larger 6-inch scale. Indeed it was suggested that there was a case for an even larger scale for such areas, and further investigation was recommended. By this time Lord Elcho was a junior Lord of the Treasury and in charge of the Ordnance Survey scale question, becoming effectively 'poacher turned gamekeeper'. He consulted Dawson who, as a leading map-

Effingham, Surrey shown at 26²/₃ inches to 1 mile (1:2376), from evidence given by the Copyhold and Tithe Commission in 1853.

Contours versus hachures

As well as disputing the scale of Ordnance Survey maps, the Charteris Committee also recommended that depiction of relief by contours should be abandoned as being 'of no real practical use'.

First introduced to the Ordnance Survey Irish maps by Thomas Larcom, the process had been continued on the 6-inch maps of northern England, with every intention of making the practice nationwide. Contours were already in general use in European countries and were considered superior to hachuring for engineering purposes. Both of these facts made the recommendation of the Charteris Committee seem completely out of step with international usage.

Hachuring was indeed an art. It allowed the map user a birds-eye view of the terrain and a far more immediate feel of the countryside than contours. The field task was done by individual hill sketchers who submitted their drawings to hill engravers at Southampton. These skilled men commanded the highest wages of their respective trades. Contouring used levelling methods and although slower to survey in the field the results were easier to apply to maps in the office.

Hall could not 'understand that doubts should exist as to the superiority of contouring over any other system' and argued that in mountainous areas hachures became overpowering at the expense of other map detail. He also preferred contours as a more truthful depiction than hachuring which was an artistic interpretation. In 1853, a committee set up to discuss the design of the 1-inch map of Ireland kept a foot in both camps by deciding that relief should be shown by contours 'supplemented by hillshading [hachuring] of a character as transparent as possible'.

Inevitably the controversy led to the appointment of a Select Committee to discuss contouring as a separate issue. They agreed with the Irish approach. For 6-inch maps, contour depiction alone was recommended with selected contours, to be reduced and applied to the 1-inch map as well as hachures. The new 1-inch maps published after 1855 had the hills engraved on a separate plate. This allowed the map to be produced in two forms: outline with contours and a hachured hill version.

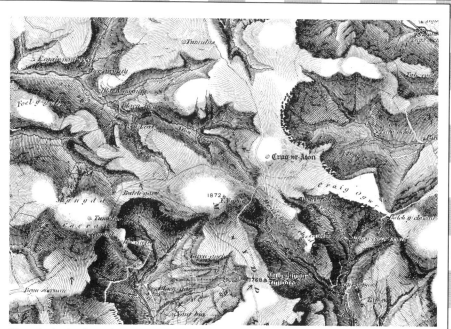

Heavy hachuring depicted ground relief at the expense of clarity of other map information. Extract from sheet 36 of a 1-inch map published in 1833.

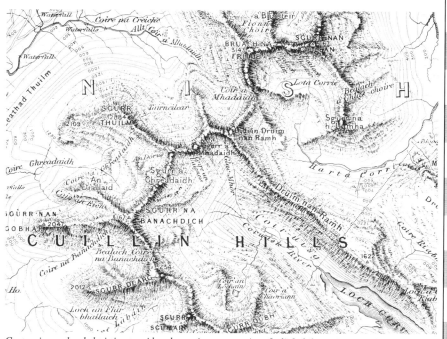

Contouring and rock depiction provide a dramatic representation of relief whilst maintaining legibility on this 1-inch map published in 1885.

ping expert, and no friend of Hall's, reiterated once again his favour for the 26⅔ scale, that he had once advocated for the tithe surveys.

While discussions continued, the surveyors ran out of work and by April 1853 Hall wrote that 'officers and men are at the present moment awaiting the allocation of new districts and . . . a continuance of delay in receiving orders will cause considerable loss to the public service both of time and money.' Still unwilling to make a decision, the Treasury decreed that survey work should continue with a degree of accuracy which would allow plans to be 'drawn to the scale of 24 inches to a mile, if desired'. This allowed surveying to continue but left the scale of the final published map completely open.

The Treasury then conducted a remarkable piece of market research, the first ever in the history of the Ordnance Survey. They gathered together all the relevant papers supporting different scales of mapping and sent them out with a simple Treasury circular asking what increase, if any, ought to be made in the present scales. The question was put to a full cross-section of map users, including government departments, estate and land agents, academics and private individuals, particularly civil engineers. The Ordnance Survey was also invited to comment. Of 152 replies only thirty-two wanted to retain the present scales, the rest asked for larger scales. Most wanted to see 24–26 inches to 1 mile for the scale of survey with publication at 6–12 inches to a mile. For towns, survey at 10 feet was requested with publication at 5 feet. It was also suggested by W S Farr, a leading statistician representing the Registrar General, that a 'natural' scale, such as 1:2500, rather than a scale expressed in inches should be used to fall in line with European mapping.

Hall agreed that 12 inches to 1 mile was best for publication, but he could not see the point of surveying to a larger scale when most people could only access the published maps, not the unpublished tracings at a larger scale. For town plans, Hall maintained that they should vary 'according to the nature of the place'.

As a result of the answers received, the Treasury drew up a second questionnaire listing three combinations of scales and asking map users to vote for the scales they thought would be best. The three options were:

1 24 inches to 1 mile for rural areas and 10 feet to 1 mile for towns;

2 26¾ inches to 1 mile for rural areas and 10 feet to 1 mile for towns;

3 1:2500 for rural areas and 1:500 for towns.

They also asked if the use of a 'natural' scale would prove to be a problem to any of the map users. The replies were considered by a committee set up for the purpose, and in July 1854 it was reported that 191 replies had been received. Option 1 received 39 votes, option 2, 62 votes and 79 votes were given to the 'natural' scale third option.

As a result of these findings the Treasury authorised work to begin at 1:2500, but requested from the Ordnance Survey that the cost of survey at this scale should be investigated before final agreement was given. They also insisted that the Ordnance Survey should begin trials to assess both the possibility of letting some of the work out to private contractors and organising its own work on a piece-work basis.

In August 1854, Hall was promoted and posted to Corfu for his last years of military service. His term as Head of the Department had consisted mainly of defending existing practices rather than making any significant advance in national mapping techniques. The technical detail of the mapping he left to others. Hall was a capable administrator but the prospect of him 'lending his own hand' to the work, as had been Colby's habit, was unimaginable. It was also impracticable and Hall made no attempt to seek popularity in this way.

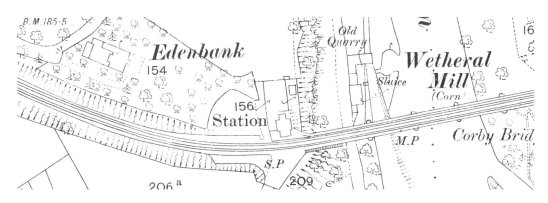

Extract from the 25 inches to 1 mile (1:2500) plan of Wetheral, Cumberland, First Edition, 1861.

The military

For most of its history the Ordnance Survey has been a hybrid military and civilian organisation. Officers were drawn from the Corps of Royal Engineers, and a spell at the Ordnance Survey was considered to be almost part of their training. Typically an officer would sandwich his Survey years between an overseas posting and 'the general duties of the corps', although there were always exceptions, the most notable being Colby who remained at the Ordnance Survey for his entire career. Before the mid 1830s, Royal Artillery Officers also served with the Ordnance Survey and the first two Superintendents, Williams and Mudge, were both from the Royal Artillery.

In 1800, the Corps of Royal Military Draftsmen was set up (later the name included surveyors), but was disbanded in 1817 after the Napoleonic War. This brief span of seventeen years was the only time that the Ordnance Survey ever approached being a wholly military operation, the engravers being the only civilians.

In 1786, companies comprising of skilled artificers and labourers had been formed in England, at the instigation of the Duke of Richmond, for the construction of fortifications. In 1813 these became known as the Royal Sappers and Miners and at Colby's suggestion three new companies were formed, expressly for the purpose of carrying out the Survey of Ireland. In the Ordnance Survey, 'sappers' and non-commissioned officers were outnumbered about four to one by the civilian assistants they supervised. In this way a relatively small number of Royal Engineer officers kept control of the survey operation.

In 1856, the separation of officers into 'Engineers' and men into 'Sappers and Miners' was felt to be an anomaly and the latter were amalgamated into the Corps of the Royal Engineers. Indeed the title of 'Sappers and Miners' with its labour-like connotations had been proving a bar to attracting men to the Corps. The term 'sapper' was, however, retained and used instead of private in the Corps of Royal Engineers.

After the First World War, the survey com-

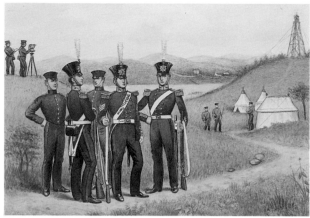

Royal Sappers and Miners, 1837.

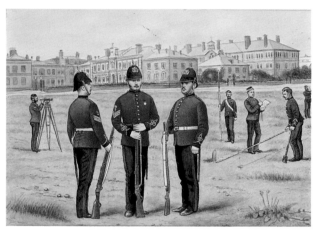

Royal Engineers, 1887.

panies became the 'Survey Battalion RE' funded by Ordnance Survey, except for the 19th (Field Survey) Company a training unit for war, which was funded by the War Office. On mobilisation for the Second World War the Battalion was disbanded and two war establishments created, one for the small body of officers for key posts in the Department, and the other, 522nd (Ordnance Survey) Company RE, for the men. This was an independent military unit, complete with its own administrative staff, but was under the command of the Director General of the Ordnance Survey.

In 1946 the 522nd Company was disbanded, leaving only Royal Engineer officers at Ordnance Survey. However, substantial num-

bers of regular sappers, on completing their army service, were re-employed as civilian staff and their military background continued to influence the Department for many years.

In 1948 a committee examined the extent to which the Royal Engineer connection should continue, if at all, and recommended that the number of officers retained in the Department should not exceed thirty-five. In fact it never exceeded twenty-seven, gradually reducing to six by 1982. In 1983 the remaining military posts were phased out and the Band of the Royal Engineers performed the ceremony of Beating Retreat at Southampton in October. The last military officer to serve at Ordnance Survey was Colonel Hugh Woodrow.

6 THE IMPORTANCE OF BEING JAMES

In contrast to his predecessor, Major Henry James had many years of solid Ordnance Survey experience behind him by the time he took over as Superintendent. James had previously been employed on the Ordnance Survey in Ireland for fifteen years under Colby and a short spell on general military duties ended in 1850, when he returned to the Survey to take charge of the Edinburgh office. He was aged fifty-one on appointment to Superintendent in 1854 and, although his experience was not gained at headquarters, he had kept such a close eye on events that within two weeks of taking office he was already suggesting changes and improvements. He entered into the scales dispute with enthusiasm, presenting a clear and consistent case for standardisation of the map scales.

James had his first success in 1856 when he gave evidence at a Select Committee on the Ordnance Survey of Scotland and successfully dealt with opposition from some of the expert witnesses. The Ordnance Survey had always maintained that the larger scale of mapping was practically indispensable, to engineers and for laying out railways. But the engineer George Stephenson denied that he would find either Ordnance Survey large-scale maps or contours useful in his work and Isambard Kingdom Brunel unhelpfully declared that 'I really do not care whether you have a 20 or a 25 inch, or anything else, for I feel it would be of no use to me'. Despite this, James managed to convince the Committee that the 1:2500 scale should be adopted for cultivated areas, with a general map at 6 inches to the mile.

James concluded his evidence with a measured attack on the system of decision by committee, which had continually held up the Ordnance Survey's work. Without laying the blame on any one committee he pointed out that £25 000 of public money had already been lost by years of indecision. He gave details of areas of mapping that had been surveyed, and then the work thrown away because one committee decision had been overturned by another. He drew attention to his current orders which were for survey teams to continue to work 'in sufficient detail to allow for reduction to whatever scale was decided' but confirmed that no committee had decided what the scale should be. James said that 867 000 acres were now surveyed but the draughtsmen sat idle for want of instructions on the scale they should be drawn to.

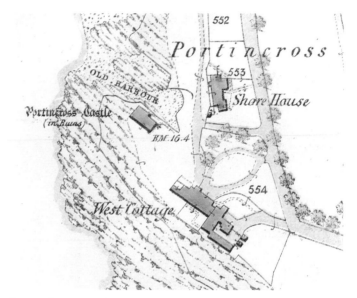

Extract of a specimen 1:2500 map from the first Report on the Ordnance Survey *for 1855–56. Except for the following year and the interruption caused by the Second World War, reports have been published annually ever since.*

Perhaps shamed by this, the Committee made the recommendations that James wanted and these were sanctioned by Parliament in June 1856. However, almost a year to the day after this, a motion was tabled in the House of Commons by Sir Denham Norreys which called for the abolition of the 1:2500 scale mapping. Norreys, who had given evidence against the adoption of the 1:2500 to the Select Committees, now used his position in Parliament to overturn their recommendation. He argued that 6-inch mapping had proved adequate for almost all purposes in Ireland and, touching on the nerve that to sanction anything larger would be a waste of public money, he asked for its return for Great Britain. The motion was carried by a small majority of ten votes.

This was a bitter blow to James who wryly noted that 'after a seven years' discussion, we revert to precisely the same position we were in when the Treasury minute of 1st October 1840 was issued.' For James it was a personal disappointment but to many Ordnance Survey staff it was personal disaster. As a result both of the move back to 6-inch

In 1857 evidence was given to a Royal Commission on Title Registration which suggested that a public authorised map, at a scale large enough to show properties and their boundaries, would provide the best means of describing and identifying the land. Although the Commission in the end made no specific recommendation regarding maps, the seed had been sown. James's case was also aided by the fact that the introduction of photographic techniques had reduced the estimated cost of making the map on the larger scale. The Commission became convinced that the 1:2500 scale was not only the most desirable but also, in the long term, the most cost effective, as it would obviate the need for costly *ad hoc* surveys in the future, and in September 1858 they recommended that the Parliamentary ruling of 1857 should be overturned and that all *new* surveys of cultivated districts should be made at this scale. In addition the Commission decreed that the whole country was to be mapped at 6 inches and at 1-inch to the mile. For town plans, a scale of 1:500 was agreed. This ruling laid down the scales of survey to be used, and gave, for the first time in over eight years, firm and irrevocable direction to the Ordnance Survey. James's dogged determination had finally paid off and the Battle of the Scales was over.

However, one more important issue remained unresolved. No decision had been made about the southern counties which had already been surveyed at 1-inch scale. The Commission calculated that with the new surveys authorised for northern counties and Scotland, the Ordnance Survey had about seven or eight years work ahead of it before the southern counties could be considered for resurvey. They believed that the decision on scale for the resurvey of southern counties would be better left until it might be more obvious which was the correct course of action to follow.

In 1859 James made the forecast that the survey work for northern England would be completed within one year and began to lobby for the extension of the 1:2500 scale to cover southern counties. That same year Lord Palmerston, in his second term as Prime Minister, came to the conclusion that war with France and an invasion attempt by them was once more a possibility. He ordered the fortification of coastal ports and arsenals as a priority. The Ordnance Survey was press-ganged into providing extensive military surveys of the southern coasts and James turned obstacle to advantage by deliberately surveying them at 1:2500 scale, strengthening the case for its extension across the country.

James had also latched on to the happy coincidence that, at 1:2500 scale, a square inch on the map was very nearly equal to an acre on the ground. This, he said, would be very acceptable to all landowners and farmers who would find it an easy scale to work with.

Major General Henry James, Superintendent of the Ordnance Survey for over twenty-one years.

survey and because of post-Crimean war economies James was forced to discharge 850 civilians, almost half the civilian workforce, with a further loss of eighty men transferred from the survey companies to other duties.

James immediately set about trying to have the decision reversed and six months later his perseverance paid off in the form of a Royal Commission being set up to inquire into the Ordnance Survey and to report on its purpose, progress, scales of maps and cost. James dominated the proceedings and swung opinion back in favour of the 1:2500. He was helped by the emergence of a new use for mapping at this scale.

Principal Triangulation

Infilling the completed primary triangulation with smaller 'secondary' triangles and then by 'parish triangulation' was initially done in a manner expediential to the mapping that was taking place at the time. This satisfied the needs of the maps that it fell on, but fell short of providing good overall national accuracy.

Captain William Yolland began to improve observing techniques and methods of computing to give better consistency to the internal triangulation. Additional observations were made where original work had been skimped, and most of the observations taken before 1824 were repeated.

Yolland was guided in his work by the new Astronomer Royal, George Airy, who, for the forty-six years he held the position, took on 'as it were, the position of official scientific advisor to Colby and his successors'. Airy designed and had constructed a new zenith sector with which observations were made to provide true geographical coordinates for the trigonometric stations.

In 1844, the triangulation was extended to reach the westernmost tip of southern Ireland, and Airy took the opportunity to measure the difference in longitude between Greenwich Observatory and Valentia Island, Ireland. This was done by setting thirty chronometers, packed fifteen to a padded box, to Greenwich time, and transporting them to Valentia Island. Local time, calculated from star positions, was then compared to the chronometers and the difference in longitude deduced.

Another officer of outstanding mathematical ability, Captain Alexander Clarke, took on Yolland's work, after his banishment to Ireland, establishing and perfecting his methods and directing the computation of what became known as the Principal Triangulation. This involved a recalculation of the whole framework from available triangulation data, without recourse to making any new observations. Some of the observations accepted dated from as early as 1792, but the majority came from the 1840s and early 1850s.

The Principal Triangulation established a consistent framework but it was more of a

Colonel Alexander Ross Clarke CB, RE, FRS.

Figure of the Earth

In 1830 Airy deduced his Figure of the Earth which he calculated from arcs measured in France, Peru, Denmark, India, Russia, Prussia, Hanover and England. This spheroid was used as a base for mapping Great Britain.

Clarke used the results of the Principal Triangulation to deduce his own spheroid in 1858, which was immediately used in an international venture to measure an arc along the 52° parallel (latitude), for a distance of 75 degrees of longitude, representing a measurement of about one-fifth of the circumference of the earth. Obviously the greater the proportion of the earth measured, the more accurately its shape could be deduced.

Clarke calculated a revised spheroid in 1865 from which he deduced that the Equator was not truly circular. This spheroid was used in the survey of the United States, Canada and Mexico. His final spheroid figures were published in 1880, and the Clarke 1880 spheroid is used as the basis for mapping in several coun-

scientific achievement than a practical one; it was decided that existing maps would not be altered in consequence and would continue to be based on local triangulation networks.

tries. His book, *Geodesy*, remained the most authoritative work on the subject for many years.

However, for mapping Britain, the spheroid calculated by Airy in 1830 is still used, because it is the mathematical figure best fitting the mean sea-level surface in Great Britain.

Clarke served with the Ordnance Survey for twenty-seven years, during which time he considerably raised the scientific profile of the department. It came as an enormous shock to him to receive in 1881, at the age of 52, a posting to Mauritius. He at once 'sent in his papers' and his retirement was approved. Despite a storm of protest the War Office stood by its decision, and consequently Ordnance Survey lost touch with the international scientific world, isolated for the lack of an officer of sufficient ability to continue his mathematical work.

The Bar Room

To define an arc measurement in any one single unit of measurement each participating country's own standard, metre (France), toise (Russia, Prussia and Belgium) or foot (Great Britain), had to be accurately compared. Standard metal bars were therefore sent to Ordnance Survey where they were placed in the Bar Room. Built within another building, it had double doors, double glazing, thick walls and a concrete roof, to prevent sudden changes in temperature, and the floor was mounted on rubber blocks to prevent vibration. Independent foundations were provided for the bars under comparison and for the micrometers and their microscopes. Each bar was compared against a series of standards, including the Ordnance Survey 10-foot standard bar O_1, 'O' indicating an Ordnance bar. As well as comparing standards of length for arc measurement the room was also used, in 1861, to provide the Government of South Australia with a standard 10-foot bar marked with a fathom, a yard, a foot and a half foot. The work done in the bar room served as an early form of calibration, which was to become a regular activity for all surveyors within Ordnance Survey in later years.

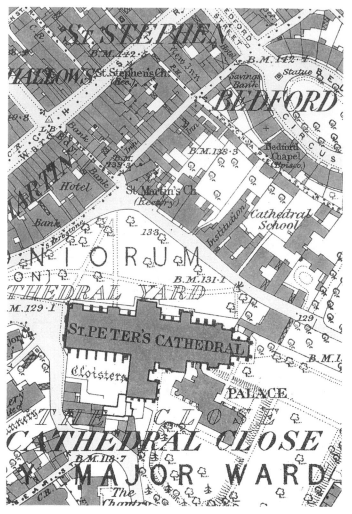

Part of the First Edition 1:2500 plan of Exeter. This was one of the later surveys at this scale and was published in 1890.

Yet another Select Committee met in 1861/2, to discuss formally the extension of the 1:2500 scale and they agreed that it should be extended into southern Britain. By this time the need for maps for land registration was becoming pressing and the usefulness of the scale was proved by demand for the northern maps already published.

In March 1863, the Committee's recommendations were sanctioned by the Cabinet and the Treasury issued formal instructions to proceed with the 1:2500 for the southern counties, bringing them into line with the scales authorised for the rest of the country.

The 1:2500 maps were initially termed 'parish maps' and mapping was only filled out to the parish boundary with areas outside of this left blank. During the 1870s this practice was abandoned and maps were filled out to the sheet edges to

give complete rectangles. However, blank areas still appeared where maps fell against county boundaries as mapping remained county based.

Like all other map series, the 1:2500 evolved in appearance as the country was covered. Improved methods of production brought economies but also called into question the need for certain items depicted on the maps. The general effect was that less detail was shown on the later 1:2500 maps than on earlier ones. The first casualty was the practice of naming fields; this was abandoned after 1888, and from 1892 surveyors stopped recording individual trees within hedges.

The Ordnance Survey under James

After seven years of Hall's meticulous and military correct behaviour, James must have seemed a revelation. His respect for authority was unquestionable but he abided by the rules when it suited him, tempering his actions with diplomacy and humour. The end, in James's view, justified the means and he rode roughshod over the needs of the staff – for the greater good of the Survey.

He began by reviewing working practices at Southampton and, following the instructions of the Treasury to his predecessor, he started to experiment both with contracting out work to private surveyors and the introduction of piecework to Ordnance Survey. Despite the contractors being given every assistance, their maps were substandard and the scheme was abandoned. By contrast the piecework system was most successful (from James's point of view), the work being 'more expeditiously and more economically performed, and without any falling off in its quality'.

The piecework rates were applied to all aspects of work done by the civilian staff. The map areas were classed according to how much detail, and therefore work, was contained in each. The classes ranged from 'waste' through to 'very close' in six stages. A different rate of pay was awarded for each category and according to the shortage or otherwise of the different skills necessary to do the job, hill engravers being the most highly remunerated. The men were paid by results and pay was generally low, much lower than that in other government departments, the hours were longer, and the civilians only received fourteen days leave against the usual month for government employees. Prospects for promotion were severely limited by the fact that all senior posts were held by the military.

In 1855 the Board of Ordnance was abolished during a military reorganisation. It signalled the end of an institution which had existed since Tudor times for the defence of the realm. The War Office absorbed the Ordnance Survey and gave James responsibility for two other small departments, the

Topographical Department and the Depot of Military Knowledge. These were merged to become the Topographical Depot and James had his own ideas on what his new department should do.

He saw it as a depository for the military archives of the country, primarily as a library of 'the most perfect set of maps and charts of every part of the world' but also as a source of drawings of military equipment, plans of barracks, atlases, maps of battles and other sundry military information. He expressed surprise that such a collection had not been amassed before, continuing:

> We know the cost of War by experience, and we also know the mistakes which we made for want of such information as I have adverted to; and when we consider that the hourly cost of such a war as we have recently been engaged in [the Crimean War] would more than suffice to purchase all the maps and books required, we ought not to hesitate a moment in providing ourselves with them.

The Topographical Depot was, for ease of access by the War Office, Admiralty, Foreign and Colonial Offices, situated off Whitehall in London and employed civil assistants on broadly similar duties to those employed at the Ordnance Survey. These civilians retained a rate of pay at nearly double the Ordnance Survey level. Understandably, complaints from the Ordnance assistants intensified until in 1859 their case was taken up by Mr Digby Seymour, Liberal MP for Southampton. No improvements were won. The Secretary of State for War, in an argument that has echoed again through the Civil Service in recent times, claimed that the adequacy of pay and conditions of service were proved by the ease of recruiting new staff. Low rates of resignation were also cited as evidence of contentment, but the reality was that the system of division of labour meant that the staff were highly skilled at just one part of a job. Only in times of exceptional demand, such as the railway boom, was there anywhere else they could take their specialist abilities.

Photography and printing

Shortly after taking over as Superintendent of the Survey, James, while in Paris, took the opportunity to find out more about the new science of photography. He satisfied himself that it would be practical to use photography to make reductions of maps and immediately had two sappers trained in the art. Although photography hadn't been applied to map making before, James immediately saw the potential for producing maps at different scales at far greater speed and much more cheaply than was possible by existing means.

The traditional method of reducing a map to a smaller scale was by use of a device called a 'pantagraph'. One end of this was used to trace over a map producing a movement, via a number of pivoted arms, at the other end which replicated the map, but at a smaller scale. The process was tedious, laborious, expensive and potentially inaccurate. The device contained so many joints and wheels that it introduced error without even taking into account any mistakes by the draughtsmen.

With photography there was some concern that the image of the map would be distorted by the camera, but

The following is the scale of prices per acre now in force for rural surveying, the surveyor paying his labourer and making all necessary corrections :—

Waste.	Very Open.	Open.	Medium.	Close.	Very Close.
$\frac{1}{2}$d.	$\frac{3}{4}$d.	$1\frac{1}{4}$d.	$2\frac{1}{2}$d.	4d.	6d.

A form of weekly progress report and balance sheet combined is forwarded regularly by each superintendent, accompanied by a diagram on thin paper showing the state of progress and the triangle in which each surveyor is working. On this diagram he enters the lengths of the main lines as they are chained; if correct when compared in the office with the trigonometrical distances, the lines are ticked off, if not passable according to the customary allowance of 2 links in 1000, the pen is drawn through them, and the superintendent in receiving back his diagram knows which lines require to be remeasured.

The surveyor, in common with every other person employed on the Ordnance Survey, keeps a journal according to a prescribed form accounting for the time and detail of employment. The journals of men in the field are required in addition to show the distances walked to and from work.

Piecework rates for rural surveying, 1875.

The stone store at Southampton in the 1930s.

Negatives were made on glass plates and then placed in contact with a piece of light-sensitive paper in a printing frame, so designed that it could be attached to the top rail of the balcony that ran round the whole of the first floor. The frames, strung like washing round the balcony, could be tilted to catch maximum sunlight and moved around to follow the sun's course. The exposure time for the 'sun-print' varied according to the weather, and on dark winter days 'less effect was produced by exposure to light during an entire day than would be produced in one minute on a fine bright morning.' The glasshouse was demolished at the turn of the century to make room for more printing works, by which time this architectural oddity had, in any case, outlived its usefulness.

Maps were never supplied to the public as photographs. The main use of photography was to make reductions of 1:500 plans to 1:2500 scale and from 1:2500 to 6-inch mapping. For the former, a tracing was made from the photograph or drawing in a greasy ink which was then transferred to a lithographic stone or zinc plate for printing. For 6-inch maps, the photograph was used as a basis for engraving.

Zincography began to replace lithography (the use of stone) in 1855 at the Ordnance Survey. The processes were basically similar, but the zinc plate was cheaper and lighter than the stones which required four men to lift each one. The stones were also brittle and occasionally they fractured during use. Stones remained at Southampton until the 1950s when they were sold off, probably to a local builder. Tradition has it that, being just the right size, they ended their days, face down, as doorsteps in Southampton houses. In one known instance, they were used as paving slabs in a garden path!

Up to a thousand impressions could be pulled from a zinc plate before the detail began to lose quality. Enough impressions were usually made to satisfy demand for the map, so there was only occasionally a cause for preserving the image on the zinc plate. Usually this image was removed each time until the plates became too thin or uneven. Most of the 1:2500 maps were produced by zincography, a fact that James proudly announced in the legend of each map, and in the 1880s zincography was also extended to 6-inch map production.

On average two men could print 80–100 copies of large maps in a day. After printing, any colouring was carried out by boys, and the maps were then placed in a hydraulic press for approximately eighteen hours to improve their appearance, giving them 'the smoothness of the glazed boards with which they are in contact'. Great care was taken at every stage to ensure that the paper was kept to a uniform dampness so that accuracy of the map would not be affected or distorted by uneven drying of the paper.

experiment found this to be so minute that it could be safely ignored. James's excitement and pride comes bubbling out of his 1855 report.

> I may mention, that during last week one man, with the assistance of a printer and labourer, reduced 32 000 acres from the 25-inch to the 6-inch scales, and that he produced . . . 135 impressions in six days, besides some other work. One hundred draftsmen could not have produced so much work.

Reduction of large-scale maps to 1-inch could not, however, be made by photography as the result would have been unreadable and 1-inch maps continued to be produced using pantagraphs for the time being.

James was granted the funds to erect a purpose-built photographic workshop. The 'glasshouse', as it became known, was, according to James, designed by himself and looked rather like an overgrown conservatory, with the top floor entirely of glass.

Photozincography

This was the process for which James is best remembered. In later years he claimed to have invented it himself but this must have been a slip of his memory because the credit for it was clearly given in his 1859 Annual Report to Captain A de C Scott and Lance-Corporal Rider. The name, however, was his own idea.

Photozincography was a process of transferring a photograph on to zinc or stone, which could then be used directly for printing, or on to the waxed surface of a copper plate where the image formed a guide for engraving. Previously, although reductions could be made by photography, they had to be manually traced back on to copper for engraving.

The process had applications, not just for maps but for any document, and James immediately suggested that it would be ideal for making cheap facsimile copies of the Domesday Book. By 1863 the Ordnance Survey had photozincographed this in its entirety, publishing it in thirty-two county volumes. Fired by success, James turned his attention to the first folio (1623) of Shakespeare, but two sappers who had become experts in photozincography bought their discharges and defected to a private publisher, where they immediately put this in hand.

Undaunted, James's next publication was a collection of National Manuscripts, an apparently random selection of important historical documents which included the Magna Carta, an account of the Battle of Flodden, and the 'confession' of Guy Fawkes to the Gunpowder Plot. A number of books were also produced for the Church of England, including the Black Letter Prayer Book of 1636.

The full list of photozincographed publications is staggering in its variety and although the cost of many was met by the organisation requesting the work, these projects inevitably delayed map production and in later years the Department was criticised for this.

Photozincography was of course successfully applied to maps and was used when the

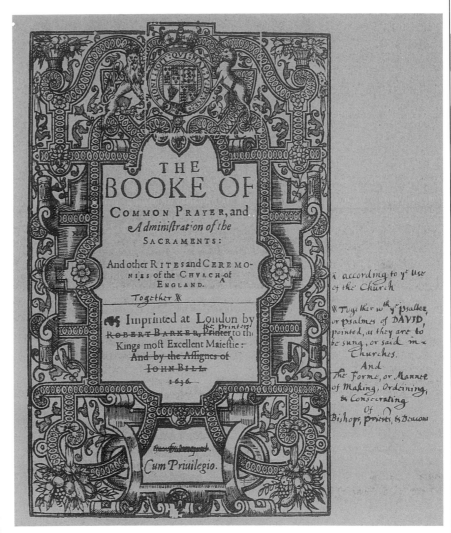

Extract from the Black Letter Prayer Book, *reproduced by photozincography.*

original was not too large to be photographed in a single picture. However, as the size of the negative that could be produced at that time was limited to 18 by 12 inches, the only way to reproduce large maps was to take a series of overlapping pictures. It was a fiddly and time-consuming job as the sun-prints varied in tone and, patched together, the inconsistencies showed. Because of these limitations, zincography was still preferred to photozincography for standard map production until the 1880s when larger negatives could be produced.

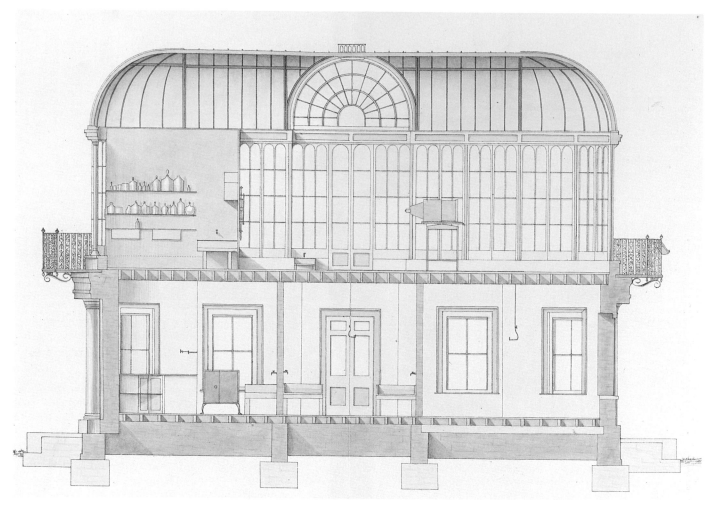

Section through the photographic building at Southampton.

James and the One-inch

One-inch maps continued to be printed from copper plate, as it was felt that their delicacy of linework benefited from the sharper results gained by printing from an engraving. In the 1860s these maps began to attract criticism from customers with complaints that they were out of date and of poor quality, with the hill hachures disintegrating and the impressions becoming faint. The cause of the problem was that the copper plates, which mainly dated from before electrotyping was introduced, were wearing out. New engravings were needed which could then be preserved by electrotyping. Meanwhile Parliament had decreed that the price of the printed maps should fall and this had created extra demand for the maps and additional wear on the plates.

Some of the maps were out of date, but not as badly as might be imagined from the date on the map. This remained unchanged throughout the life of the copper plate, even though it may have been revised – a poor piece of salesmanship. James claimed that all railways were surveyed and engraved as soon as they were opened but, apart from this and other limited updating in urban areas, revision was not tackled systematically. Meanwhile some areas of the country were still waiting for their first edition 1-inch map. The last for England and Wales was published in 1870 with Scotland completed in 1887. Part of the reason for the delay of the Scottish maps was said to be that James, as a sportsman, was 'particular to clear the survey men out of the deer forests'

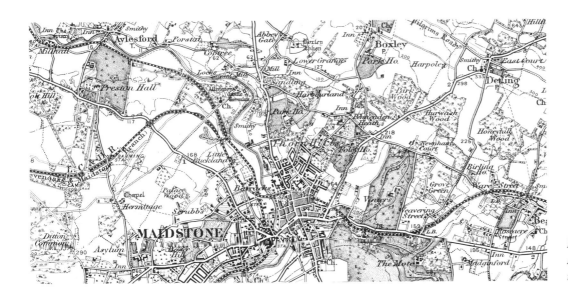

Part of the 1-inch New Series of Kent showing Maidstone c.1870 with railways inserted to 1892.

before the beginning of July. As deer stalking continued until October, and the weather in the Highlands made surveying difficult and dangerous in winter, little time each year was left to make the survey. Once the surveying was completed the Scottish maps were further held up by a shortage of skilled engravers, particularly hill engravers, so that the published maps for Scotland with hill-engraving included were not completed until 1895.

As soon as the 1-inch map for England and Wales was complete, James began planning a 'New Series' of maps. The existing maps had been partly based on drawings at 2 inches to a mile in southern counties and at 6 inches to a mile in northern counties; the latter were therefore more accurate than the old southern sheets. As the 1:2500 mapping was extended across the country in the wake of the Battle of the Scales the New Series of the 1-inch followed, using the larger scale mapping as a base. However, in the northern counties the existing sheets were merely renumbered to match the rest of the New Series.

International status

James was one of the great image builders of the Ordnance Survey. He saw it as an important task to promote the Ordnance Survey, and to an extent therefore, himself, throughout the Empire and the world. In 1867 a committee of officers was appointed by the French to examine the maps, plans and publications of the topographical departments of all nations represented at the Paris exhibition. They reported of the Ordnance Survey that it was 'a work without precedent, and should be taken as a model by all civilised nations'. This was the height to which James had brought his department.

James welcomed visitors from all countries to Southampton for instruction in the methods and techniques used. He impressed them, not only with the photographic and photozincographic techniques but also with the latest in equipment and purpose-designed buildings. As well as the photographic glasshouse James also had a fireproof store built which featured iron doors, window sashes, pillars and girders. In this he had placed all the most valuable engraved copper plates and manuscripts, which were priceless in terms of the information they contained. By this time facilities also included an astronomical observatory which was used for training surveyors prior to them undertaking surveys in the colonies.

James ensured that the Ordnance Survey's inventions, mathematical tables and scientific data were published and made available to governments who might require them. A general work was also produced as a result of 'numerous applications from Foreign and Colonial Governments'. This book, *Methods and Processes adopted for publication of the maps of the Ordnance Survey*, endured for more than a quarter of a century as a standard reference work. Clearly written in layman's terms, with illustrations and examples, it described every process from triangulation to printing in just over 200 pages. James was considerate enough to include information which could be adapted by foreign countries. Thus, he gave the name of the supplier of lithographic ink to the Ordnance Survey, but in case there was difficulty in obtaining the ink the following method was suggested:

The tallow and wax are heated in an iron saucepan till they take fire, the soap cut up in small pieces is gradually stirred in, then the shellac, and the flame is extinguished with the lid of the saucepan. When the substances are thoroughly incorporated a portion is taken out, allowed to cool, and examined; if it appears satisfactory and will rub up into a somewhat viscid liquid with water in a saucer, the Paris black is added and stirred into the contents of the saucepan at a low heat; the composition may then be cast in mould in sticks of a convenient size for use.

The book was reprinted in 1902 with few material changes, an indication that the system of working practices introduced by James remained little changed until the First World War.

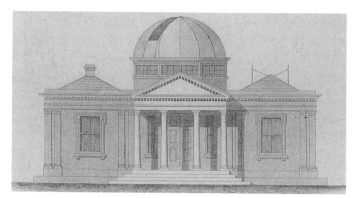

Ordnance Survey's observatory.

James as archaeologist

James's interest in history seems to have come upon him in his later years. Certainly when he worked on the Irish survey he was one of the officers who made no contribution at all to the historical memoir project. Once Director of the Ordnance Survey, however, he channelled large amounts of energy and resources into historical projects. As well as the photozinco-graphed copies of the Domesday and National Manuscripts, he took an increasing interest in the depiction of antiquities on the maps themselves.

Photograph of Stonehenge from the southwest, taken in 1867 to illustrate Henry James's study of the monument.

Survey of Jerusalem

In Victorian Britain opposing theories about the geography of the Bible and the true location of places mentioned in it were the subject of lively public debate. The survey of Jerusalem, however, apparently originated with the wish of a wealthy philanthropist, Miss Burdett-Coutts, to provide the city with a better water supply, an accurate survey being necessary before any improvements could be made.

James calculated that the cost of the survey would be about £500, which Miss Burdett-Coutts provided in full. However, the pay and expenses for the officer in charge were not included in this figure and the War Office thought that 'there may be an engineer officer who would like to undertake this interesting work without remuneration'; a vain hope for a survey scheduled to take five months. Eventually Charles Wilson RE (later Director General) accepted the appointment and observed that 'I was generally considered to be going on a fool's errand'.

The objectives were to produce a plan of Jerusalem at 1:500 scale, surveying principal buildings inside and out, as well as completing surveys at smaller scales of the city environs. In addition, all principal buildings and other places of interest were to be photographed and the comparative heights of the Mediterranean and the Dead Sea established.

In October 1864 Wilson began the survey with a party of five men. They found the physical effort very hard, suffering from the extreme heat and also from attacks by mosquitoes, fleas and other vermin. There was no sanitation, but interestingly the survey showed that in ancient times the city had been well supplied with pure water. Wilson's team were 'struck with admiration' on seeing the remains of the works whose 'boldness in design and skill in execution, rival even the most approved system of modern engineers'.

It was soon clear that the funds were insufficient to complete the survey and, in typical style, James placed a letter in *The Times* purporting to be a progress report, for the 'information of those who have contributed to the fund' (one person) in which he mentioned the need for an additional £200. The Royal Geographical Society and the Royal Society paid the additional cost between them.

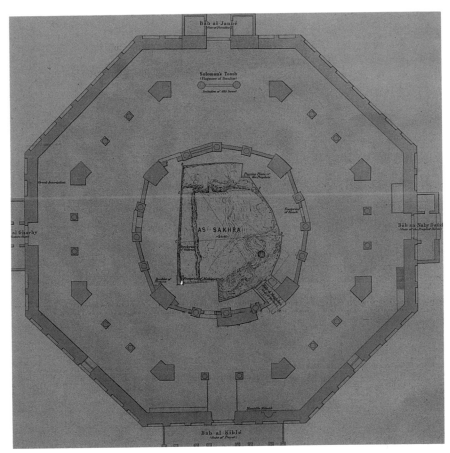

The Dome of the Rock, surveyed in 1864 by Charles Wilson.

The surveyors found themselves in a race against time to complete the survey before the full onslaught of the summer heat. Wilson writes of his regret that a more thorough approach could not be taken, but acknowledges that: 'I do not think the men would have stood [any longer]. The cholera is now at Alexandria.'

The survey was a complete success and Wilson, by correlating all the geographical evidence in the Bible to the survey of the ground, was able to confirm beyond doubt that many sites which claimed authenticity were correctly placed. It was also established that the Dead Sea was some 1289 feet lower than the level of the Mediterranean. James declared that he was 'convinced that the traditional sites are the true sites of Mount Zion and the Holy Sepulchre,

and of Mount Monah and the Temple [of Herod]'.

The success of the survey of Jerusalem led directly to the founding of the Palestine Exploration Fund whose purpose was to carry out further scientific exploration of the area. Wilson, having proved himself ideally qualified for the work, was given command of two of its expeditions including one to the Sinaitic Peninsula. No less than three mountains had at various times been credited with the distinction of being the Mount Sinai of the Bible, but Wilson's survey concluded that a mountain called Jebel Musa was the true Mount Sinai. Wilson remained one of the mainstays of the committee of the Palestine Exploration Fund until his death in 1905.

In 1816, William Mudge had sent a memorandum to surveyors which included the instruction: 'That all remains of ancient Fortifications, druidical monuments, vitrified Forts, and all Tumuli or Barrows shall be noticed in the Plans wherever they occur.' The standard of work, however, varied as much as the interest, or otherwise, of the surveyor making the map and the availability of published books about the area. However, the keenness of local historians to see their work included on an Ordnance Survey map, thus giving credibility to their theories, sometimes led to the inclusion of completely unfounded information.

From the 1840s local history became an increasingly popular leisure pursuit and many archaeological societies began to lobby the Ordnance Survey for more historical information on the maps. James was sympathetic to their requests and encouraged his men in 'the necessity of officers making themselves acquainted with the local history of . . . the districts they are surveying'. A couple of years later he had again to exhort them to 'read up the histories of counties in which the survey is in progress'. James was unlikely to meet with any more success than Colby in trying to turn soldiers into historians but he dared not re-enact Colby's mistake and set up a branch devoted to history, as memories of the bitter and premature end of the Irish memoir project still lingered.

Instead he set out to prove, by example and for his own amusement, how it should be done. He made a short study of Stonehenge and other ancient sites including Turuscachan in the Island of Lewis, and of some Irish cromlechs. Having travelled the whole length of the country to obtain the information, he had it compiled

for the information of the Officers on the Ordnance Survey in the hope that it may stimulate them to make Plans and Sketches, and to give Descriptive Remarks of such Objects of Antiquity as they may meet with during the progress of the Survey of the Kingdom.

Later James had the studies published and put on sale at 12 shillings a copy.

James's new-found enthusiasm for history led to one of the most enduring archaeological blunders on Ordnance Survey maps. Without sufficient evidence, he named a footpath along the North Downs as 'The Pilgrims' Way'. Later this was discovered not to be the route the pilgrims took but the name stuck, despite efforts to correct it on later maps.

In 1844 instructions were more clearly laid down with the onus on the Southampton office to use literary sources to prepare briefs about antiquities of an area. These were used by the field revisers who visited the sites and noted any new sites or changes to descriptions of old information. As with place names, new antiquities required written authority before they could be included on the map.

These workshop staff, pictured c.1870, were known as 'the five beauties'. The man on the right was chain-maker to the department.

The latest acceptable date for a site to be deemed an antiquity was set at 1688, the end of James II's reign. Anything newer was not included. Many employees became skilled at searching out the archaeological detail and liaising with historians, but no professional archaeologist was appointed to oversee the work until after the First World War.

The Office of Works

Traditionally, during peace time, defence spending becomes a target for cost cutting, and in 1868 the War Office searchlight fell squarely on the Ordnance Survey. Although a high proportion of mapping was carried out for the military, a larger amount was for civilian use and, in seeking to reduce its expenditure, the War Office concluded that the Ordnance Survey should no longer be its responsibility. The only Ministry that seemed to be a suitable home for the Ordnance Survey was the Office of Works, and the transfer to their control caused James some anxious moments as the whole structure of his empire hung in the balance. He immediately lost control of the Topographical Department which, with its by now magnificent collection of world mapping, remained the responsibility of the War Office.

A Committee of Inquiry was set up by the First Commissioner of Works to examine the Ordnance Survey, firstly, turning its attention to the military structure of the department. It had been made plain to the Office of Works that the Royal Engineers were there to stay but, noting the popularity of a posting to the Ordnance Survey among officers, they examined the possibility of lowering their pay, on the grounds that high calibre officers would still be attracted by the interesting nature of the work. At length they settled instead for a restriction on promotion opportunities for officers, by enforcing a maximum number of each rank that could be employed. In general, and on grounds of cost savings, they agreed that the military system should remain, realising that numbers could be easily reduced, if the demand for maps fell off, by returning officers and sappers to general duties.

The civilians' hopes that their situation might be improved were dashed by the Commission's opinion that it was unfortunate that civilians had been allowed to assume that the Ordnance Survey was a permanent institution. Pension rights should not, in their view, have been granted to staff and though they could not be removed from existing employees, any new recruits were to be accepted only on the understanding that their service was not pensionable. No increase in pay was recommended.

It was the 'erroneous' granting of pension rights to civilian staff that kept the Ordnance Survey intact. The Commission would have swept away the entire engraving and printing departments and placed these operations under the control of Her Majesty's Stationery Office, except that the cost of pensions, which would then be payable to the engraving staff, did not make it cost-effective to do so.

The Ordnance Survey emerged shaken from the transfer to the Office of Works but, apart from the loss of the Topographical Department, remained more or less intact. James's status was reduced and his authority undermined in staffing and other organisational matters. A lesser man of his age, (sixty-eight) would have decided that this was a convenient point at which to retire. James, however, carried on much as before, ignoring the recommendations of the Commission where he thought he could get away with it.

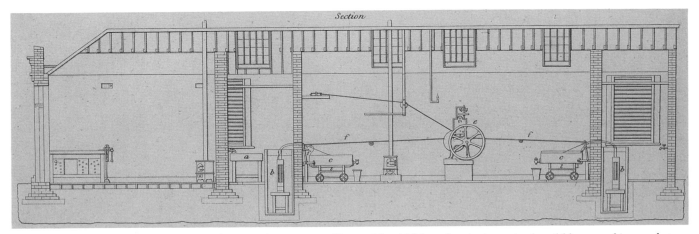

Section through the electrotyping room. The rocking troughs were powered by a weight which 'completes its descent in about 14 hours, and is wound up again by one man in about an hour.'

66 ORDNANCE SURVEY

When James eventually retired in August 1875 he was seventy-two years old and had served as Director General for twenty-one years. Even then he only resigned because he was forced to do so by increasing ill-health. At that time army officers were allowed to continue to serve until they died, and many must have despaired of his ever retiring before that event. This was especially the case for the civil assistants who considered that they had been particularly downtrodden under James. They, through the pen of the anonymously named 'Civilian', had the last word and less than a month after his departure James must have found it particularly galling to read, in the *Hampshire Independent*, a tirade against himself, thinly disguised as a welcome to the new Director General. The article related that the new Director General's predecessor

with the most consummate tact and diplomatic skill increased the renown of his Department and persistently drew public attention to its manifold merits on the judicious principle, we suppose, of one of the characters in Tristram Shandy that this is not a world to hide your virtues in.

The offending article concluded that

it is hoped that the time of vaunting and trumpet blowing respecting the Ordnance Survey is over and that General Cameron will initiate a policy of internal reform which may obviate the necessity of a searching Governmental enquiry.

A distinct silence followed James's departure. For a man whose greatest pleasure was to be held in high regard and who did everything in his power to enhance his own importance, this may have been the most effective insult. In any case no valediction followed his retirement and when he died in 1877 only a bald announcement was made in *The Times*, with no list of the glorious achievements of which he was so proud.

James, though, had quite literally left his mark on the Ordnance Survey. His initials were incorporated, carved in ornate letters above the doors of the buildings he had erected at London Road during his term as Director General. Carved plaques on each building told that he had designed them and how much they cost. James even had a bas-relief portrait of himself cast in bronze, although in at least one office it was not 'treated with the respect it deserves'.

James's early years as Director General were marked by a spate of important inventions, innovation and progress.

Plan of the Ordnance Survey office in Southampton, from the 1855–56 Annual Report.

Despite his enormous egotism and the fact that he clearly outstayed his welcome, his achievements far outweighed his faults.

James had married Anne Matson, the daughter of the Brigade Major of the Royal Engineers, and was survived by two sons and a daughter. Even his marriage was fortunate, as his father-in-law was a very influential man who, when James was under consideration for appointment to Director General, neatly elbowed aside a potential rival by pointing out that the man (Tucker) was extremely deaf and therefore was not a good candidate for the position. James was knighted for his services to science in 1860, one of only two Director Generals to receive this honour for Ordnance Survey service.

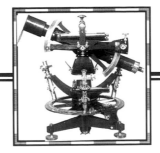

7 FULL STEAM AHEAD

Three directors

Major General John Cameron waited a long time before being made Director General. Prior to his promotion he had spent six years in charge of Mountjoy House in Dublin and twenty years as Executive Officer at Southampton (second in command of the Ordnance Survey). After this long apprenticeship it was a pity that his appointment lasted for such a short time. Cameron died suddenly in June 1878 from pneumonia, less than three years after taking office.

Cameron was not able to leave much of a personal impression on the Ordnance Survey but it is known that he was welcomed by the civil assistants who praised him as a man with 'kindliness of disposition and uprightness of character'. But whether they retained this opinion after he was forced to reduce staff numbers by ninety Civil Assistants and fifty-four labourers is a matter for conjecture. In 1875 Cameron kindly lent several of the Ordnance Survey's most remarkable scientific instruments, by then no longer in use, to the Science Museum in London. Colby's compensation bars, the Board of Ordnance Ramsden 3-foot theodolite, a 2-foot Troughton and Simms theodolite and Airy's zenith sector still remain on loan to the museum.

The tradition of long directorships was thus broken and, from this time, no Director General has stayed more than eleven years, with the average length of service being only five and a half years.

Cameron was succeeded by Colonel A C Cooke who was immediately caught up in Select Committee investigations into land title transfer. Their findings recommended the use of the 1:2500 map for land registry and considered that it left 'little or nothing to be desired', except that mapping of this scale was not scheduled for completion in England and Wales until 1900.

The Committee recommended that the staff of the Ordnance Survey should be 'about doubled' so that the work would be completed ten years earlier by 1890. Numbers had only recently been reduced and yet now the department was told to double in size. The problem with this dramatic increase was that enough trained men could not be instantly found to supervise and train the new recruits whilst continuing with the survey work.

In order to spread the 1:2500 mapping as quickly as possible, and in the most useful manner across the country, nine towns – Bedford, Bristol, Chester, Derby, Hereford, Ipswich, Norwich, Plymouth, and Reading – were chosen as convenient centres of operation. From each of these towns, survey at 1:2500 scale was spread in ever-increasing circles until the whole country was covered.

In 1882 Cooke was promoted to Major General and under War Office rules should have retired. However, the expansion was causing such an organisational headache that he was allowed to stay on for an extra year to see through the worst of the changes. Colonel Stotherd was made Director General in 1883, but was unexpectedly retired, in 1886, with only two months notice. This was due to a new rule which fixed the retirement date for colonels at fifty-seven years of age.

The last year of Stotherd's directorship was also the year that electricity came to the Ordnance Survey. Until this time photography was dependent on sunlight for making prints, but in 1885 a 'dynamo-electrical machine and steam engine' was installed to power a light of 'about 10,000 candles', from which excellent photographic results were obtained.

Hero at the helm

Sir Charles Wilson was appointed Director General in what must be the most popular appointment in the history of the Ordnance Survey. After returning from Sinai in 1869 Wilson had been made Executive Officer and then Director of the Topographical Department of the War Office. In 1876 he was placed in charge of the Ordnance Survey of Ireland, a position which he held for ten years until his promotion to the post of Director General. However, within these ten years he was often detached overseas for special military duties, including a period in Egypt working on the 'Reorganisation in Egypt', an ambitious plan for the provision of a new constitution for the country. Wilson's tasks included responsibility for lighthouses in the Red Sea, sanitary improvements, quarantine regulations and the abolition of the slave trade. He gained a reputation for fairness and justice and for trying to relieve the problems of the native people.

Major General Sir Charles Wilson. Director General 1886–94.

At this time, 1877, Egypt was controlled by the British, and Sudan, which had previously been conquered by Egypt, was under the charge of Colonel Gordon. A disagreement between Gordon and the Cairo Government arose over payments to be made to Egypt which Gordon could not see how to fund except by unreasonable oppression of the Sudanese. Gordon resigned over the issue and within a year Sudan was in a state of civil disorder, with Egypt (whose army has been disbanded by the British) unable to restore peace. The British Government at first refused to take responsibility for Sudan but then offered Wilson the post of Governor General. Wilson was tempted to accept but considered that it would be 'utter banishment' from his wife and children and so turned it down, returning to Ireland. Eventually Gordon (by now a General) was persuaded to return to Sudan, and began to restore order. The revolt, led by a religious fanatic who called himself the Mahdi, gained impetus and Khartoum, where Gordon was stationed, was besieged. Mahdi let the people of Khartoum starve for as long as possible and then, on hearing that British troops were on their way, attacked and took the town, killing Gordon. The British Government were aware of the siege and had over-estimated the amount of time that Khartoum could hold out. Wilson, arriving up the Nile with an advance relief party in three steamers, ran the gauntlet of fierce attack and had to retreat back through the gunfire, it being clear that Khartoum had fallen. Wilson's adventures were not over, as two of the three ships were holed and Wilson was forced to give the order to abandon ship. The men took refuge on an island until rescued, stuck midway between the enemy who controlled both banks.

The death of Gordon and the loss of Khartoum became a national scandal and an attempt was made to pin the blame for the disaster on Wilson, as it was said he should have reached Khartoum more quickly. Wilson, however, had kept a complete journal of the whole episode and was persuaded to publish this in his own defence. The book, which vindicated Wilson, became an immediate bestseller making him a national hero. Wilson was knighted and expressly invited by the Queen to recount his adventures to her in person.

His return to Ireland was triumphant. The staff had avidly followed news of Wilson's exploits overseas and welcomed him home with triumphal arches erected at Mountjoy and a firework display in his honour. On his appointment to Director General the staff had very high expectations of their hero and held out hopes that he would now turn his attention to the long-held grievances within the Ordnance Survey.

Wilson did not ignore the complaints of the civilian staff but had limited room for manoeuvre. In 1888 he set up a Departmental Committee to look into the rates of pay of the civilians but this inquiry did not attempt to question the quasi-military structure of the Ordnance Survey, merely to ensure that fairness existed within it. Once the rates of pay were approved by Wilson, he circulated the information to Division Officers so that undue anomalies of pay did not occur between men with equal experience and length of service. This memo was obviously confidential but the staff came to know of its existence and called it the 'secret circular'.

A more in-depth study of the situation was carried out in 1891 but this came to the same conclusion as all previous inquiries into the structure of the Ordnance Survey. The military system was found to be efficient and cheap and as there was no shortage of people wanting to join the Ordnance Survey and very few resignations, the pay and conditions were deemed to be adequate.

Pay increases were only given on merit and length of service after a recommendation by the officer in charge. The civil assistants wanted fixed annual pay increases like other civil servants but once again the differences between the Ordnance Survey and the Civil Service in general were underlined. The Ordnance Survey was considered to be a great manufactory and the Committee was of the opinion that 'No private manufacturer would listen for a moment to such a

Cover of the 1887 Jubilee Book.

Plan of Windsor Castle, from the Jubilee Book.

The Jubilee Book

After the honour of a knighthood and an interview with Queen Victoria, Wilson was keen to present a special gift to commemorate her Jubilee. The result was the Jubilee Book, an illustration of the changes and inventions that had marked the progress of the Ordnance Survey during the fifty years of Queen Victoria's reign. The design for the title page, by Mr H Constable, was selected from twenty-seven entries to a competition amongst the staff and two more of these designs were used for the

front and back covers. These were modified to include a picture of the Tower of London within one and a photograph of the Southampton Office within the other, reproduced on copper plate with the pictures plated in silver.

The sumptuous gold-tooled and leather-bound book contained the signature of every member of staff employed at the time, as well as original paintings, drawings, photographs and engravings, and of course maps. These were chosen to be of special interest to Her Majesty and included a plan of the Tower of London,

Buckingham Palace and other Royal residences. Queen Victoria was presented with the volume at Osborne House on the Isle of Wight in 1887 by Sir Charles Wilson and some of the non-commissioned officers and civilian assistants.

Two exact copies were made of the book. The Ordnance Survey copy was destroyed in the blitz but Ordnance Survey of Ireland generously presented their copy to Southampton in 1969 when the new Ordnance Survey building was opened at Maybush.

---

proposal if put forward by his employees, as his expenditure must be governed by due regard to the cost of production of the article manufactured'. Rather than improving pay this inquiry had the opposite effect, as Wilson concluded that during the years of staff expansion pay rises had been given too freely. Now that numbers had to be reduced, he reasoned that the civil assistants, as a body, would rather that the maximum number of them were kept in employment than a fewer number be given higher pay. Therefore he reduced the number of pay rises granted.

The civil assistants did win some improvements in allowances and sick pay but were, on the whole, disappointed, although it should perhaps have been obvious that no inquiry staffed by military men would advocate a radical change from

a system that had worked so well for so long – from the military point of view.

The principal of revision

When Wilson took over as Director General of the Ordnance Survey in 1886, its future role was quite uncertain. Although hopes had been expressed that a regular map revision programme would be set up, no decision had yet been taken by the Treasury. The completion target of 1890 for the 1:2500 scale mapping was now within sight. With nearly 3000 civil assistants employed, compared to only 1400 in 1871, Wilson could see that a vast reduction in staff numbers was inevitable unless a revision programme could be agreed.

In 1886, the Treasury did agree to the principle of revision and that it should at once commence but tempered this with the proviso that they did not 'bind themselves . . . to the annual provision of any fixed sum for carrying it out'. In other words, for some years there might be money available but for others there might not. As the progress of the revision and the continued retention of men skilled to undertake the work depended on a regular supply of funds, the uncertainty cast a shadow over the whole revision programme.

The cost of the 1:2500 revision had been estimated by the selection and revision of sample maps and, once begun, the Treasury kept a close eye on the cost of the revision programme. The oldest maps, and those which had to be revised first were the maps of northern counties that had been surveyed at 6 inches to the mile on Colby's return from Ireland. They needed to be resurveyed at 1:2500 but Wilson was hindered by evidence that James had given during the Battle of the Scales. James had said that these counties could be redrawn to 1:2500 by replotting the work from the original manuscripts and the redrawn maps could then be revised in the normal way. Not wishing to prejudice the Treasury against the whole revision programme, Wilson chose to accept the opinion of his Executive Officer that 'the work looks good and I can see no reason to doubt its general accuracy'. This

was totally the opposite of the opinion of the officers out in the field who reported inaccuracies of as much as 25 and 30 links (17–20 feet). The decision not to resurvey was a disaster in terms of accuracy and was to leave a long legacy of problems for future surveyors.

Forty-five years later, in 1934, the then Director General, Brigadier H St J L Winterbotham, was still having to cope with the problems of the 'replotted counties'. He thought that in Wilson's time the Ordnance Survey 'did a thoroughly unsound thing. We surveyed at a scale less than a quarter that of publication.' He described how

> Since then periodical revisions have struggled with a growing evil. Skilled revisers, finding serious errors, have pushed them into unimportant parcels; anywhere, in fact, where property lines and areas were not important. Then these same areas have fallen to the builder.

The surveyors coped with the situation as best they could and following the logic that no one was likely to build on a river they 'pushed' inaccuracies into the River Ouse where practicable. The replotted counties were not resurveyed until after the Second World War, showing just how long it can take for the effects of a single bad decision to work its way out of the Ordnance Survey.

Employees of the Ordnance Survey Boundary Division, 1888.

In 1890, the Ordnance Survey was moved from the control of the Office of Works to the newly constituted Board of Agriculture, an arrangement that was to continue for seventy years. Wilson welcomed the change knowing that he had an ally in the First Secretary of the new Board, Sir George Leach. As a Royal Engineer who had for many years been employed on the Ordnance Survey, Leach fully understood the nature of the work and supported proposals for change made by Wilson. Perhaps for the first time since the 3rd Duke of Richmond was Master General of the Board of Ordnance, the Ordnance Survey had a truly knowledgeable and sympathetic master.

As they are and as they ought to be

In 1891 Henry Tipping Crook, a civil engineer from Manchester, made a critical address to the British Association in Cardiff on the subject of Ordnance Survey maps which sparked off a debate leading to a complete reorganisation of the Survey. A Captain in the 1st Lancashire Engineer Volunteers and author of a pamphlet about maps for war games, Crook was deeply interested in Ordnance Survey and its maps and disappointed by their shortcomings. With his blunt speaking, common-sense approach and detailed knowledge of the subject, he systematically dismantled the myth of perfection that Sir Henry James, as a talented public relations man, had woven around the Ordnance Survey.

The very week that Wilson was using the occasion of the fiftieth anniversary of Ordnance Survey in Southampton to extol the virtues of the Department, Crook was saying something very different indeed.

He claimed that the number of people who had a thorough knowledge of the Ordnance Survey was so small that the faults of the Department were concealed by a process of 'continuous self-laudation' and that this 'engendered in the public mind an idea that the work was beyond criticism'.

Crook exposed the scandal of the true state of the national mapping which was generally, he claimed, so out of date as to be of little practical use. He said that the new 1-inch map was so long in production that it was often obsolete before it had even been published and asked 'Does any other nation in the world exhibit such a spectacle as a Government cartographical institution engaged in the production of obsolete maps?' He approved of the 1:2500 scale mapping but noted that many of these also required urgent revision. For slow revision progress, Crook laid the blame firmly on the Government who, he pointed out, had been told by successive Director Generals that revision must be done and had even themselves agreed that it was an urgent necessity. He pounced on the absurdity that, having agreed in principle, the Treasury would not then 'bind themselves to . . . the provision of any fixed sum for carrying it out', a statement 'fatal to the proper conduct of . . . the Ordnance Survey'.

Crook went on to ridicule the attitude that 'the beauty and accuracy of the Ordnance Survey work is the admiration and envy of the civilised world' and suggested that this was of little consolation to a tourist trying to find his way by a map representing the country as it had been a generation before. Attempts to update the map had sometimes, he thought, been worse than useless. New railways were shown laid across old maps, that showed what had now become towns as the villages they were half a century before. This served only to highlight the agedness of the rest of the map. All in all, Crook concluded that the work was one of 'phenomenal slowness'.

He was well informed, not just on the age of the mapping but also on the processes of map-making, distribution methods, sales policy and pricing considerations.

Colonel Henry T Crook, the most influential private individual in the department's history.

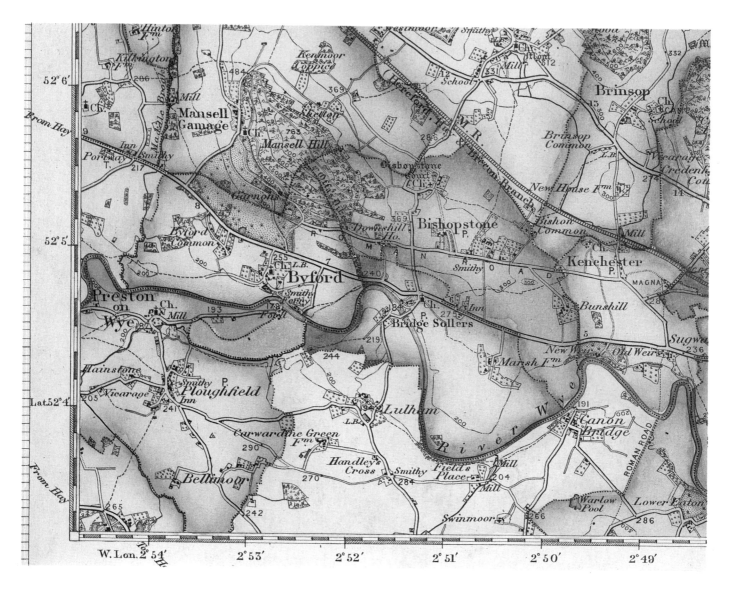

Part of a hand-coloured 1-inch map of Herefordshire c.1898, showing parish boundaries.

Crook concluded that, as well as being out of date, the maps were inaccessible, largely unknown to the public and, more importantly, the information shown did not meet public requirements. Bad impressions gave unreadable names and 'woolly' hill-shading, the price was too high, the official catalogue was a 'bewildering maze' and indices to county maps he called 'a series of Chinese puzzles'. Crook expressed admiration for the maps produced by the French Government and thought that the British maps were inferior in appearance. He was also unsurprised by the general public preference for the cartographically inferior but infinitely more useful maps made by other British publishers.

Undoubtedly much of what Crook said found a sympathetic ear within the Ordnance Survey. Some of the points he made had been argued without success to Ministers for many years. It is suspected, though never proved, that Crook was actively supported in his campaign by Ordnance Survey employees who found in him an apparently independent mouthpiece through which to bring the plight of the department to public notice.

Crook's timing was perfect and he struck a chord with many when he said that 'By a thorough revision most of the defects in the maps might be remedied, and a great national work saved from ruin for want of the proverbial ha'p'orth of

Stanford's – map agents for 140 years

Stanford's premises at Cockspur Street, London. From the 1902 history of the firm. V Orford

Stanford's (then Saunders and Stanford) were first appointed as an Ordnance Survey map agent in 1851 and gradually built up their trade so that by 1873 about one-quarter of all Ordnance Survey maps were sold through their shop at Charing Cross.

Stanford's went to great lengths to promote Ordnance Survey maps, compiling their own catalogue, monthly list of new publications, circulars and placing advertisements in newspapers. They also employed a clerk full time on 'advices'. Here each new map was studied as it arrived, the addresses of places of importance listed, and 'advice' sent to the householder that the new map was available. Stanford termed this early form of direct mailing 'intelligent advertising'. Success was rewarded when in 1885 the firm was appointed sole Ordnance Survey agent for England and Wales. In 1888 the firm moved to new premises, specially designed for storage, examination and sale of maps, in Cockspur Street, and in 1900 to their present site at Long Acre.

Sir Charles Wilson did not approve of this sole agency and relations with the Department reached an all-time low when he read a paper, in February 1891, before the Society of Arts, in which he placed the blame for 'small use' of the maps on the sales system. Wilson had little experience of commercial practices and described the 'reward' to Stanford's to be 33⅓ per cent, simply 'for handing the maps over the counter'.

Edward Stanford junior, by then head of the firm, considered these comments, which were widely published, to be extremely injurious to him. In reply he published a pamphlet, *The Ordnance Survey from a Business Point of View*, in October that same year, in which he pointed out that from the 33⅓ per cent, which Wilson had implied went straight into his pocket, he had to supply the rest of the trade at a discount of 25 per cent which left only 8⅓ per cent. From this

he had to pay the expenses of his building, staff salaries, insurance, racks for storage *and* pay the Ordnance Survey £600 each year for the privilege of selling their maps.

A change in policy in 1897 resulted in provincial agencies being set up with Stanford's remaining as the main London agent, holding a complete set of maps for England. This arrangement continued until 1941 when Stanford's premises were bomb damaged and most of their stock destroyed. During the War, the number of maps available to the public was severely restricted, not only for security reasons but because resources at Ordnance Survey could not be spared to replenish commercial mapping. This so badly affected Stanford's business that he could not meet the expenses of running the agency. As a temporary measure Ordnance Survey arranged for Stanford's to take over the supply of maps for government departments, the Services and all retail outlets, except Ordnance Survey agents. This freed staff at Southampton to concentrate on production of maps for the war.

Stanford's continued to supply maps on this basis until 1971 when Ordnance Survey, having moved into purpose-built accommodation, could once again cope with distribution of its maps across the nation.

In 1971 the main agency for England and Wales was moved to Cook, Hammond and Kell of Caxton Street, but Stanford's have continued to be a valued Ordnance Survey agent in London. Visitors to their emporium of world mapping at Long Acre will find that courtesy and detailed knowledge about the maps they sell are still considered important traditions.

tar.' A supporting resolution was passed by the British Association and the debate widened and gathered momentum.

Crook also lobbied the Ordnance Survey directly, writing at length to Wilson and on some small points, such as the inclusion of a legend on each map instead of the customer having to purchase a separate sheet of 'characteristics', he claimed success. Wilson, though, did not concur with Crook on all points and disclosed that production of maps more suited to popular requirements had been purposely left to private enterprise. Ordnance Survey maps, he said, were made for purposes where accuracy was essential, but all publishers might, with permission, base a map on the Ordnance map, and the public in this way devolved great, though indirect, benefit from the national survey.

Crook published his theories in a pamphlet entitled *Ordnance Survey Maps – As they are and as they ought to be* in which he expanded his arguments making far ranging proposals for improvements. These included the setting up of a 'continuous revision' system where maps would never be allowed to become more than a specified number of years out of date.

Crook was thirty-six when he began his campaign for improved Ordnance Survey maps. He already had a successful engineering career but he devoted his life increasingly to public service on a wide range of subjects: town planning, preservation of the countryside, common rights, rights of way, national parks and ancient monuments. He was Vice Lord Lieutenant of Lancashire in 1917 and died, aged eighty-one in 1935.

The Dorington Committee

As a direct result of Crook's campaign the Board of Agriculture set up a committee in 1892, 'to inquire into and report upon the present condition of the Ordnance Survey.' The committee headed by Sir John Dorington called, as etiquette demanded, Sir Charles Wilson, Director General of the Ordnance Survey, to be the first witness, but then called Crook. The fact that he was requested to appear for examination before any other witnesses, who included Stanford and Bartholomew, showed the importance that the Committee attached to his evidence.

The Dorington Committee examined all the complaints raised by Crook, including the revision policy for all map scales and the suitability of the maps for the 'reasonable requirements of the public'. Their recommendations took on board many of Crook's ideas for improvements and most were in turn accepted by the Board of Agriculture. The Dorington Committee recommendations provided a framework for the Ordnance Survey which was to last for the next forty-five years.

It was agreed that the revision of the 1-inch map should be independently carried out by a team of dedicated surveyors with the aim that no map should ever become more than fifteen years out of date. Approval was also granted for the Ordnance Survey to venture into making new maps at the 1-inch scale, based around important areas of tourist interest and at a larger scale around important towns.

The revision of the 1:2500 and 6-inch maps was more of a problem and the department would not formally commit itself to a specified revision cycle. Privately, however, it was hoped that, after catching up with the backlog of revision, no map should ever be more than 20 years out of date. To emphasise the age of the maps, colour coded indexes were included in the Annual Reports, effectively highlighting the revision dates and keeping the general age of the mapping under public scrutiny.

The Committee also looked into twenty-seven complaints and suggestions relating to the usefulness of the maps to the public, ranging from the question of contour intervals to the origin of place names.

The use of Ordnance Survey maps as a source for other publishers was also closely examined by the Dorington Committee who considered that 'great freedom' should be allowed. This was clarified to mean that transfers of the maps at 1-inch scale and smaller should be supplied to publishers who required them at cost price, but that all other reproduction of Ordnance Survey maps should be prohibited. The intention was to prevent any direct copying of the maps but to allow publishers to produce maps of a type that Ordnance Survey did not themselves publish. No hard and fast rules were drawn up as the department felt it desirable to deal with each on its merits and the general principle of freedom was agreed.

The reforms proposed by the Dorington Committee absorbed much of Wilson's time in the year leading up to his retirement in 1894. As a colonel, he should have retired at the age of fifty-seven but exceptions are always possible and it was considered desirable that he should remain as Director General for an extra year, to begin the implementation of the Dorington Committee recommendations.

Wilson's term as Director General was considered to be a great success and the Board of Agriculture took care to express its appreciation of the admirable manner in which he had discharged his duties. Certainly the Ordnance Survey was on a much firmer footing than when he had taken over, but the credit for this must be shared with Henry Crook. Wilson gave many lectures about Ordnance Survey and also about his experiences in Asia Minor and Palestine. His standing as a respected public figure gave some reflected glory to the Ordnance Survey and inspired loyalty from the staff. Even if Wilson could not do much to improve the lot of the civilian staff, they could at least take comfort in his even-handed approach and his justifiable reputation as a fair man. Always keen to help the disadvantaged, Wilson set up a charitable school for boys in Southampton in memory of his friend General Gordon.

After retiring from the Ordnance Survey, Wilson became Director General of Military Education at the War Office and later took up his Palestine interests with renewed vigour.

An Englishman's home

In the Middle Ages land transfer was made openly, and often with public ceremony, but methods gradually became increasingly secretive, to the extent that later attempts to unravel legal complications made conveyancing of deeds expensive, difficult and time consuming. This was prevalent to such an extent that, in 1846, the House of Lords concluded that it was 'convinced that the marketable value of real property is seriously diminished by the tedious and expensive process attending its transfer'.

However, it was not until 1857 that the Royal Commission on Title Registration recognised that 'the use of a Government map, properly authenticated, for each individual property, together with the customary verbal description, would furnish the best means of describing and identifying the land and indexing it correctly.'

. . . by any other name

Under the 1841 Survey Act the Clerk of the Peace of each county had to deliver to the Ordnance Survey 'a list of all the cities, towns, boroughs, parishes and so on'. However, names for other features including hills, valleys, rivers, woods, buildings, roads and antiquities were collected by Ordnance Survey and recorded by surveyors using the Name Book system invented by Colby for the survey of Ireland.

The spelling of each name was, wherever possible, endorsed by written evidence as 'when taken down by word of mouth, errors are very liable to occur' and surveyors often pasted into the Name Books typed examples to support their recommendation. Almost anything seemed acceptable, from letter headings and local advertisements to extracts from Bradshaws' Railway Guides.

Printing of names on the maps followed a careful hierarchy with the most important names written in the largest and boldest type. The typestyle used for each name gave further information. For example, if a Borough returned a member of Parliament, then its name was printed the same size as other Borough names but in bold type. Market towns were distinguished from ordinary towns in the same way.

Names could be altered with the support of 'at least two good authorities' but important names tended to remain, even if they dropped out of general use and the maps tended to preserve some that would otherwise have faded from existence.

The Dorington Committee paid particular attention to the problems associated with Welsh place names. The Ordnance Survey used one authority, Mr Rowland, a Welsh scholar and author of a Welsh Grammar. On his death, his widow, a scholar in her own right, became the authority.

Some of the Welsh names had been 'incorrectly caught and written down by a person ignorant of the language' and to illustrate the problem to the Dorington Committee a list of names in Merioneth, Wales were submitted and discussed during the proceedings.

DUMBARTONSHIRE—ROSNEATH PARISH.				
List of Names as written on the Plan.	Various modes of spelling the same Names.	Authority for those modes of spelling.	Situation.	Descriptive Remarks, or other General Observations which may be considered of Interest.
Knockderry Castle on Site of **Fort**	Knockderry Castle on site of Fort.	Lorn Campbell, Esq. Mr. Marcus Alexander Weir	XVI. 2. Trace 5	An elegant mansion built on the summit of a projecting rocky headland, and commanding an extensive view of Loch Long and the opposite shore. This castle occupies the site of an ancient castle or fort the remains of which were removed when this was erected. "There are no ruins or monuments to throw any light on the more remote history of this Parish, with the exception of the debris of an old Danish or Norwegian fort at Knockderry, on the Loch Long shore. This must have been coeval at least with the battle of Largs (2nd October 1263) and is admirably situated for observation, commanding an extensive range of the Firth and its shores in all directions."—New Statistical Account.
Eilean Beag	Eilean Beag Eilean Beag Eilean Beag	Lorn Campbell, Esq. Mr. Marcus Alexander Weir	XVI. 2. Trace 5	A small rocky point on the low water line near Knockderry Castle. This rock is covered at high water.
	" *Eilean Beag*, Little Island "—Gælic.			
Tom an Dubh	Tom an Dubh Tom an Dubh Tom an Dubh	Lorn Campbell, Esq. John Mc Cunn Alexander Weir	XVI. 2. Trace 5	A black heathy eminence east of Barbour farmsteading.
" *Tom*, Hill; *an*, the; *Dubh*, Black; *Tom an Dubh*, The Black Hill "—Gælic.				
Creagan Breac	Creagan Breac Creagan Breac Creagan Breac	Lorn Campbell, Esq. John Mc Cunn Alexander Weir	XVI. 2. Trace 5	A small rocky hill about half a mile east from the above.
" *Creagan*, a rocky place; *Breac*, spotted; *Creagan Breac*, The Spotted Rocks "—Gælic.				

Extract from 'Methods and Processes', showing the ideal layout for a Name Book and type of detail to be recorded.

'Then with regard to the name Hendre-gwen-llyffaint. 'Hendre' means an old habitation. "Gwen" is a proper name; and "llyffaint" signifies frogs, so that the meaning of the name as now printed is "the old habitation of Gwen of the Frogs". But the real name is "Hendre of Gwenllian"; "Gwenllian" being a Welsh proper name.'

(Chairman) 'That is a fine instance of the person who corrected the names being a little too learned?'

'Yes I think so . . .'

(Chairman) 'In the next "Glan-Gwilym", which you say should be "Glan William", is not "Gwilym" the Welsh form of William?'

'Yes, but he was an Englishman. It is named after Mr William Oakley, a nephew of Sir Charles Oakley who built the house. It was not called by the name of "Glan Gwilym" at all; probably Mrs Rowland may have corrected that.'

(Chairman) 'But generally the names on this sheet are right?' 'Yes, I believe with these exceptions. I helped the Ordnance Men as far as I could. They used to come to me very often, because there was not a single Welshman on the group.'

The Dorington Committee recommended urgent improvement to the system of collecting names and, in fact, moves were already underway to revive the tradition of including Welsh and Gaelic speaking men in surveying parties where appropriate. For Scotland, a place names Committee was set up under the control of the Royal Scottish Geographical Society which advised Gaelic speaking revisers who should be consulted in each area. The Committee then examined the surveyor's findings and made recommendations to the Ordnance Survey. A similar system was used in Wales.

However, in making their recommendations, the Committee always abided by the long-stated principle that Ordnance Survey names should follow those in common use by the residents of an area, even if these were etymologically incorrect or suspect.

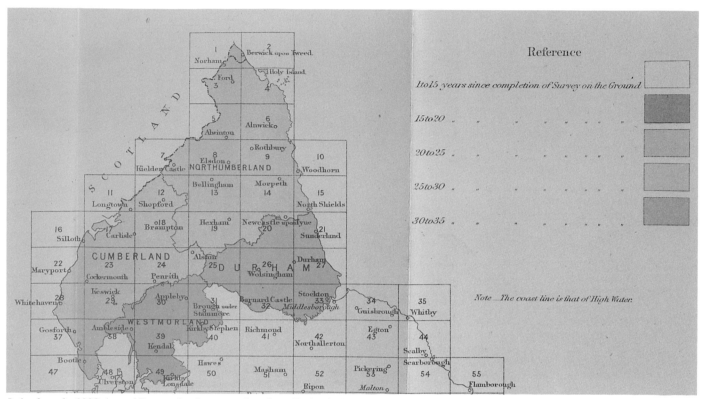

Index from the 1893 Annual Report, showing areas of northern England where mapping was more than twenty-five years out of date.

The Land Registration Act of 1862 introduced a system of registration of title for England and Wales and a new department, now called Her Majesty's Land Registry, was expressly formed for the purpose. At first the system of registration was unsuccessful partly because suitable maps were largely unavailable, and also because registration was purely voluntary. However, the potential need for large-scale mapping for land registration was timely for the Ordnance Survey and proved to be a prime factor in obtaining Treasury authorisation, in 1863, for the extension of the 1:2500 scale to the southern counties of Britain.

The 1:2500 Ordnance Survey maps were adopted as a public index showing land-registered property. Before a property was added to the index it was surveyed to establish the position of its boundaries and a copy of a plan of the property was held at the Land Registry together with details of ownership. Most of this survey work was at first done by surveyors from the Copyhold Inclosure and Tithe Office, as Ordnance Survey staff were fully occupied on the new 1:2500 mapping.

In fact, for the land registry system to work it was essential that the 1:2500 map coverage of the whole of

England and Wales be completed as soon as possible. The target of the year 1900 was brought forward ten years and Ordnance Survey was instructed to nearly double its staff to achieve this date.

As the 1:2500 mapping neared completion, Ordnance Survey set up a three-man branch within the Land Registry, whose task was to prepare and maintain the 1:2500 public index map. In 1897 selective compulsory registration was introduced which allowed a County Council to request that registration of title be made compulsory upon sale of a property. The first county to apply, at the turn of the century, was London, causing a sudden and substantial increase in Land Registry work.

With this increase, conflict between Ordnance Survey and the Land Registry arose over exactly who should do the work. In essence, the Land Registry, giving evidence to a Committee in 1898, argued that all Land Registry survey work should be done by Land Registry staff, whereas Ordnance Survey considered that all survey work, for whatever purpose, should be carried out by Ordnance Survey staff. By that time up to sixty registrations a day were being made, a substantial survey task. However, Ordnance Survey lost the

Office of Land Registry.

Land Certificate.

No. 40.

The Register of ESTATES with an INDEFEASIBLE TITLE.

Reference No. 40. vol. 1, p. 80. Record of Title.

No. 40.

Date of Entry.	Description.
Feb. 20th 1864	**All** those hereditaments called or known as WHITEACRES in the Parish of A in the County of B, containing by admeasurement 90a. 1r. 39p. or thereabout, and delineated on the Map No. 40, deposited in the Office of Land Registry as part of the description of the same hereditaments, and thereon edged with red. TOGETHER with the mines and minerals under the same.

The Record of **Title** to LANDS on the REGISTER.

Reference No. 40. vol. 1. p. 50. Register of Estates.
No. 40. vol. 1. p. 40. Register of Mortgages and Incumbrances.

No. 40.

Date of Entry.	Estates, Powers, Interests, &c.
Feb. 20th 1864	RICHARD ROE of Cheapside in the City of London, Esquire, is entitled for an Estate of Inheritance in fee simple in possession. THE said Richard Roe has by Deed declared that his Widow, if any, should not be entitled to Dower.

The Register of MORTGAGES and INCUMBRANCES.

Reference No. 40. vol. 1, p. 50. Register of Estates.
No. 40. vol. 1, p. 80. Record of Title.

No. 40.

Date of Entry.	Charges and Incumbrances.
Feb. 20th 1864	**By Deed** dated the 14th of March 1863 the hereditaments were granted to John Doe of Margate in the County of Kent, Esquire, in fee, to secure the sum of £3,000 and interest.

A Copy of the above-mentioned Map is attached hereto.

It is hereby Certified that the above-mentioned hereditaments are registered with an Indefeasible Title.

DELIVERED to the above-named RICHARD ROE, at his request, this Seventh day of March One thousand eight hundred and sixty-four.

(Signature of the Registrar.)   L. S.

(Certified Copy of Map annexed).

COX AND WYMAN, LAW AND GENERAL PRINTERS, GREAT QUEEN STREET, LONDON.

Specimen Land Certificate, 1864.

argument, and a survey and mapping branch was formed almost immediately within the Land Registry, with some of its own staff and sixteen civil assistants from Ordnance Survey. The following year another Committee endorsed this decision. Although unhappy with the situation, Col. D A Johnston, the new Director General, had to acknowledge that Ordnance Survey was unable to undertake the work because substantial numbers of officers and men had been withdrawn from the department for the Boer War.

Eventually, though, it became obvious that Land Registry and Ordnance Survey were duplicating effort. Land Registry were in some cases producing completely new surveys as well as revising plans, and even had the intention of putting the plans on sale to the public.

A compromise was reached where it was agreed that the Ordnance Survey should bring its maps up to date in advance of Land Registration becoming compulsory in an area. Any further revision made by Land Registry was then to be incorporated into the Ordnance Survey 1:1056 plans, and these plans, printed and published by Ordnance Survey would be marked 'Land Registry Series'. This arrangement continued until 1923. To safeguard the integrity of the surveys, it was agreed that any revision exceeding 20 acres would be surveyed by Ordnance Survey.

By these measures, the possibility of two separate mapping organisations doing the same job was avoided but an atmosphere of rivalry between the Ordnance Survey and the Land Registry continued for many years.

Over the counter

From 1823 until his retirement in 1840, the sole agent for supply of Ordnance Survey maps to the trade was James Gardner, previously a surveyor under Colby. Two agents, John Arrowsmith and Messrs Grattan and Gilbert, were appointed to replace him. Each received 33⅓ per cent discount on the price of the maps which they then resold to the trade at 25 per cent discount, and to the public at full price.

However, in 1845 the Treasury considered that the discount was too high and reasoned that if a larger number of agents were appointed, but given a smaller discount, then the result would be greater revenue. Accordingly the discount was reduced to 25 per cent and, by 1866, 150 agents were scattered across the country.

At the same time the Treasury also reiterated its rejection of a sale-or-return system and the agents had to pay, in full, for any stock of maps that they wished to keep. Any unsold maps could not be returned, even for another sheet of the same value. Stanford, who was the main agent for London, argued that the more active an agent was on behalf of the customer, then the more bad stock he accumulated. But the system worked well for the Ordnance Survey and as more agents were appointed, sales increased. Annual revenue from the sale of maps rose from £4599 in 1856 to £8213 in ten years.

In 1866, it was decided that it was too troublesome for the Ordnance Survey to supply this large number of agencies and, with the approval of the Treasury, they abolished all but six, who were then to supply the rest of the trade. Four were located in London (Letts, Longman, Stanford and Wyld), one (Johnston) was in Edinburgh and the last, (Hodges and Smith) served Ireland from Dublin.

At the same time the department undertook a complete review of the method of calculating the price of the maps. A principle was established that map prices only need cover the cost of printing, storage and distribution of the maps. All costs relating to the surveying, drawing, engraving and photography were held to be chargeable to the Exchequer. This policy, which remained in force for most of the next century, initially led to some strange price adjustments. The 1-inch map prices were increased by one-quarter to 2s 6d for a full sheet and the cost of a quarter sheet doubled to 1s. The 6-inch map prices were cut by half. In marketing terms these were not good decisions. The increase in the price of the 1-inch maps meant that people were encouraged to purchase cheaper maps produced by other publishers. However, the purchasers of 6-inch maps who generally needed Ordnance Survey accuracy were not persuaded to buy twice as many.

The immediate result of these changes was a dramatic decline in revenue and various efforts were made to improve the situation including the setting up of three Ordnance Survey 'depots'. These were open to the public and provided access to complete sets of maps in London, Edinburgh and Dublin. These depots also sold the maps in direct competition with the Ordnance Survey map agents close by, arousing a great deal of anger from those affected.

Although by these measures a slight improvement was seen in revenue, the level of sales remained disappointing,

and after a few years Sir Henry James, then Director General, asked his new masters at the Office of Works to abandon the system. By 1880 over a hundred Ordnance Survey agents were, once again, spread country-wide.

Still not content with the prospect of supplying all agents with map stocks from Southampton, the Office of Works decided, in 1885, to try a system of sole agency once again. This was very much against the advice of the Director General, by now Col. Stotherd. Stanford was chosen to be sole agent, on a trial basis at first, and all the other agency agreements in England and Wales were terminated. Initially sales did decrease but, once Stanford's were operating from the convenience of their purpose-built map shop, revenue soon increased and surpassed previous levels. Sole agents were again established for Scotland and Ireland and the Ordnance Survey sold the maps only to the three agents, who in turn supplied the trade.

The provincial agents, some of whom had by now twice taken on the Ordnance Survey business for their area and twice lost it to the sole agency system, must have wondered at Ordnance Survey's indecision, when in 1897, once again, it advertised for agents across the country.

The change of heart was prompted by the recommendation of the Hayes-Fisher Committee, which was appointed in 1896 to consider particularly the arrangements for sale of Ordnance Survey maps. Although they were happy with the way Stanford had conducted his agency, they thought that, by making sales only through sole agents, the department became out of touch with what the public wanted from the maps. Also they were worried that the current system gave the sole agents too much authority over the Ordnance Survey who had always to be wary of upsetting them. It was precisely this fear that had prevented the department from issuing a cheap 1-inch map at only 6d a sheet; although this would have satisfied a public demand, it was not done for fear of injuring the sole agent's position.

The Committee agreed that Stanford's and the Edinburgh and Dublin agencies should keep a complete stock of maps but decided that they should be agents only for their own cities, with others appointed for each of the larger towns. To ensure that the maps were widely available it was arranged that any bookseller or map seller could order directly from Southampton at 25 per cent discount, and in towns where no appointed agent existed, the public could order maps through their local head Post Office.

The Post Office scheme was never very successful, possibly because they held no stock so a map could not be viewed before purchase, or perhaps because the scheme was insufficiently advertised. After struggling along for a few years the Post Office ordering facility was abandoned, to the relief of all involved. The provincial agencies were more successful and gradually sales through these outlets increased to satisfying levels. In 1904 the total sales revenue of the Ordnance Survey was £22 891.

As before, Ordnance Survey in Southampton found it a burden to support the whole distribution operation, and in 1905 a new approach was tried. For the first time it was acknowledged that customers for large-scale maps tended to be different from those for small-scale maps. It had been noticed that the popular 1-inch editions were sold mainly through booksellers, whereas the large-scale map purchaser tended to go to a specialist map seller, who could give expert advice. The map distribution methods were then split accordingly and, although large-scale maps continued to be supplied to map agents from Southampton, the Ordnance Survey put the whole of the small-scale map distribution into the hands of a wholesaler (Fisher Unwin). They supplied both the bookselling trade and the Ordnance Survey map agents with the small-scale maps.

Proving section in the 1920s. Paper was placed on the hand-inked litho-stone and the 'Tinpan' cover lowered over it. The whole bed was rolled through a compression roller to transfer the image onto the paper and provide a proof copy.

8 GATHERING CLOUDS

The years between Wilson's retirement in 1894 and the beginning of the First World War were a period of continuous change at the Ordnance Survey, both in terms of leadership and methods of map production. Like many other businesses at the time, Ordnance Survey was caught up in a rush of advances in new technology, and new production methods were barely invented before they were replaced by better ideas.

An aura of mystery surrounds Wilson's successor, Brevet Colonel John Farquharson. He joined the Ordnance

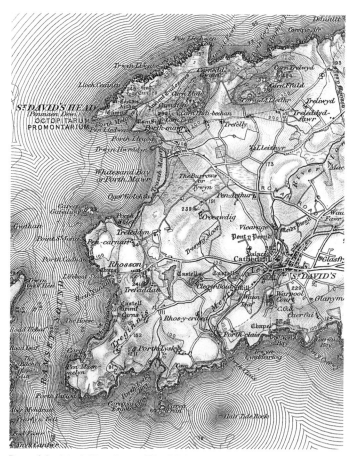

Part of the 1-inch New Series (Third Edition) map of St David's, originally published in 1894, revised to 1909.

Survey in 1872 and, apart from a brief four-year span spent on other duties, he worked continually for the department in various field divisions, rising to second in command by 1887. Whilst in this post of Executive Officer he changed his name to John Farquharson; previously he had been Iain Cosmo MacPherson. No reason for the name change is apparent. The second unusual aspect of Farquharson's career was the fact that he retired from the army in 1896, but continued as Director General of the Ordnance Survey for a further three years. This made him, technically, the first civilian head of the Ordnance Survey, a circumstance that must have caused a great deal of controversy within the department at the time.

Farquharson continued to build on the recommendations of the Dorington Committee, and during his term of office a complete revision of the 1-inch mapping was made by a team of surveyors, formed expressly for the purpose. Additionally a system was devised for annually updating the sheets with regard to railways, canals and other public works. To this end it was arranged that other departments, such as the Board of Works, should give notice to the Ordnance Survey of new constructions undertaken.

The detail shown on the revised 1-inch maps was also carefully reconsidered with a view to improving the usefulness of the series. The most major change was the introduction of symbology to distinguish metalled from unmetalled roads so that 'roads fit for wheeled traffic' were easily identifiable. Similarly it was decided that single line railway tracks should be depicted in a different manner from double tracks.

This second edition of the new series gave to the general public, for the first time, 1-inch maps of the whole country, uniform in style and up to date. As a result complaints about the maps were reduced and sales improved.

Further advances were made for production of the third edition of the 1-inch maps. The engraved hachured version of these maps, with the hills overprinted in brown, are considered to be, by some people, the most beautiful Ordnance Survey 1-inch maps ever produced. The hills were printed from a separate plate and the clarity of the outline map was not therefore dominated by the hill hachures as had tended to happen when hills were printed in black.

Keeping the hills on a separate plate also helped to

speed up production. A map could be engraved in outline and published, and later an edition could be produced with hills. The engraving of the hills was the most time-consuming and skilled part of the operation and although it lent much to the beauty of the maps, many customers preferred to have a more up-to-date plain outline map without hill hachures.

The first 'combined' 1-inch maps were also produced at this time for areas of popular interest. These maps were produced for towns where their conurbation spread over two or more maps. The first maps produced were for Brighton, Derby, Gloucester and Cheltenham, Plymouth, Nottingham, Chatham and Winchester.

The first colour 1-inch maps were trialed at this time for an area of mapping around London. These were published using blue for the depiction of water, red for the contours, brown for hills green for woods and burnt sienna (light brown) for metalled roads. These colours were already in established use on military manoeuvre maps but, although the colouring made the roads much more prominent, there were problems with making map detail, such as houses, woods and names as clear as they had been on the ordinary engraved black and white copies. The maps were produced by making a number of identical thin zinc 'set-offs', or copies,

from the original plate. The detail for one colour, say red, was inked in on one set-off and all the other, non-red, information removed from the plate. The process was repeated for each of the colours and the resulting set of plates could then be used to print a coloured map with excellent registration of detail.

However, the first sales of the first twenty coloured maps, available by March 1898, were disappointing and caution was expressed over 'whether their preparation should be continued over a great area'. Poor sales were blamed on lack of public knowledge of the maps and ultimately coloured mapping was produced for the whole country.

Printing at full-stretch

After Farquharson retired in 1899, his place was taken by Colonel Duncan A Johnston, whose background of field survey experience was enhanced by years in charge of the photography and printing areas. Naturally the needs of the zinc-printing department were on his mind when he came to be Director General and he devoted much space in his first annual report to their achievements and problems, perhaps feeling that their contribution to the Ordnance Survey had been undervalued in the past.

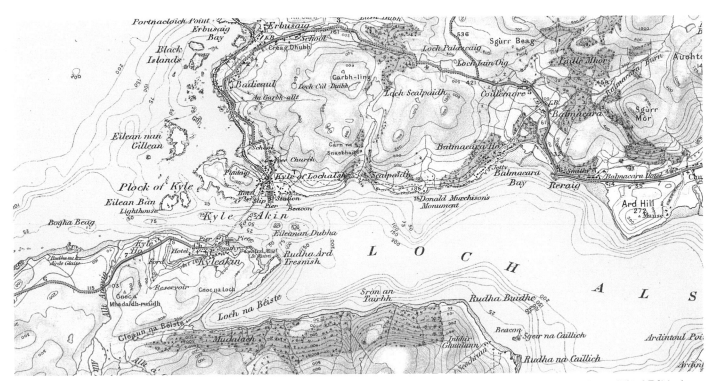

This extract shows one of the original colour schemes for Ordnance Survey 1-inch coloured maps. Part of sheet 71, Glenelg, New Series (Third Edition), published 1885 and revised to 1905.

Johnston declared that the 'temporary iron building' used for zinc-printing was 'quite worn out'. He also pointed out that if sufficient storage space could be found to house zinc plates, containing heavily detailed maps, then reprinting these maps would be at a minimal cost. Generally he described the work as 'severely hampered by want of space'.

The problem was partly relieved, at Johnston's own inconvenience, by the conversion of the Director General's residence into offices. From this time onwards the Director General was no longer given a house within the grounds of Ordnance Survey and although Johnston received compensation by way of an allowance, the Treasury drove a hard bargain, and would not extend this housing allowance to his successors.

In 1900 permission was granted for the construction of a new building for zinc printing, to be erected on the site of the old observatory and the photographic 'glasshouse', and by 1903 a complete purpose-designed workshop was in place.

Printing methods continued to be improved. Heliozincography was introduced for printing the 6-inch plans. As well as being quicker, this process gave sharper and clearer results than photozincography. The prefix 'helio' was used because it was found that the best results were obtained by using the sun to expose the negative, although electric light was later used. Heliozincography allowed a negative to be directly printed on to a thin, sensitised, zinc plate.

The 'Vandyke process' was a further advance which made it possible to transfer a manuscript drawing to a zinc plate sensitized by the application of a thin film of fish glue. The drawing to be copied was laid, face down, on the plate and exposed to light. The plate was then washed with water, and only glue which had been protected from the light by the lines of the map, was washed away. Ink could then be applied to the exposed metal. Finally the 'insoluble' exposed glue was removed with dilute sulphuric acid, and the plate was then ready for the printer. Perfect cleanliness at each stage was the key to achieving good results. The great saving was that no camera work was necessary. The inventor of the process was Conductor Vandyke of the Survey of India, who received £700 from the Government for the unlimited use of the process in any government department in the United Kingdom. The process was used for making copies at the same scale as original work.

During the Boer War (1899–1902) the Ordnance Survey was deprived of a significant number of its small complement of two dozen officers, who left to serve in South Africa. The remaining officers had, literally, twice as much ground to cover in supervising the survey in the field but were reported to be 'cheerfully doing their best to overcome these difficulties'.

Besides sending officers, the Ordnance Survey supplied a total of five survey sections to South Africa and lost a further number of civilians who were called up from the reserves or chose to enlist in the regular army. The loss of so many good men was 'much felt', especially on the surveying side, as it was felt necessary to pick the most talented men for the survey sections sent abroad.

Coupled with this drain on personnel, there was a huge increase in demand for maps from the War Office who tasked the Ordnance Survey with printing maps of South Africa. All soldiers proceeding to South Africa were provided with a map of that country which they found most useful, although not always in the way intended. Major Charles Close (who become Director General in 1911) recalled in later years that the high quality paper on which they were printed made them very suitable for lining uniforms to keep out the cold winds of the veld. The casualty amongst mapping work during this time was the Land Registry which the Ordnance Survey could not fully support during the war.

In 1902 conversion to electric lighting of the London Road office was completed and plans were drawn up for the new zinc-printing building to be fitted out for electrically driven machinery. This was early days for such extensive electrical plant. Previously the machinery was steam driven, and a great deal of careful research was done to ensure that the scheme would work. Captain Casgrain was sent to America and Canada to look at a number of electrical installations and Messrs Preece and Cardew, eminent electrical engineers, were commissioned to oversee setting up the machinery at the London Road offices.

It was calculated that electricity would be cheaper than steam power for running the printing process but more expensive than gas lighting. However, the benefit of electricity was that it not only gave a better light for the work but was also much cleaner.

Having committed itself thus far the department took a deep breath and determined that the whole Ordnance Survey office should be converted to electricity. It was a bold move and a successful one, the only problems encountered were with Southampton Corporation who found that they could not at first cope with the power demands made by the Ordnance Survey. Intermittently unsatisfactory levels of current remained a problem until a new generating station and special plant was installed in 1905. By then Johnston had been sufficiently convinced of the merits of electricity to arrange for the Ordnance Survey office at Mountjoy House in Dublin to be converted to electricity.

In 1905 Johnston was replaced by Colonel R Hellard in the tradition that the serving Executive Officer should take over as Director General on retirement of the postholder.

Revision section, Ramsgate 1907

During this period the work began to settle down and steady progress was made with the installation of new machinery. By 1907 fourteen printing presses were in operation to cope with the vast increase in colour printing. These were necessary because every extra colour on a map meant that the map had to make an additional pass through the press. Each colour also required a separate printing plate. Yet more space was needed and the Ordnance Survey annexed a house at 8 Carlton Crescent, Southampton, to house the bookbinding and map-mounting sections. This work was mainly done by women.

Greater automation led to a gradual decrease in staff both at headquarters and in the field survey divisions, and work for the 1:2500 was reported to be up to date to within the twenty-year age of map limit. The Ordnance Survey had finally caught up with itself and fewer staff were now needed to keep the maps to the correct level of revision. This time the problem had been foreseen and staff numbers were reduced through 'natural wastage' with only a few men having to be discharged. The reduction in civilian staff numbers was matched by a similar fall in military personnel to the extent that four survey companies were no longer needed. As a result the 16th Survey Company of the Royal Engineers ceased to exist as a survey company from 1907, leaving the 13th, 14th and 19th companies to continue.

In 1908 Colonel Samuel Charles Norton Grant took over from Colonel Hellard. It was one of the shortest appointments to the post lasting less than three years. But it may have been a deliberately temporary arrangement as Grant had not been Executive Officer under Hellard and his experience within the Ordnance Survey was limited. Although his previous eight years as Head of Reproduction were undoubtedly valuable, the reprographic area was settling down after its recent spate of automation and a Director General with a broader background was needed to give new direction to the Ordnance Survey, which in more ways than one seemed to have 'run out of steam'.

Preparing for war

In May 1911 French forces occupied Fez, the capital of Morocco, in order to suppress an uprising against the pro-French Sultan. They effectively took control of the country and in response, Germany sent a gunboat to Agadir. Britain became alarmed that the Germans were both threatening France and looking to establish a Mediterranean naval base. A period of intense and prolonged international tension followed and Germany, Britain and France made preparations for war.

The position of the Ordnance Survey at that time was that, for the first time in its history, most of the maps under its control were reasonably up to date and it was well placed to satisfy the country's normal mapping needs. Ordnance Survey had also proved itself capable, during the Boer War, of responding to the heavy War Office demand for maps.

However, the Ordnance Survey was no longer a world leader in cartographic innovation, and it was out of touch with the public generally and the scientific world in particular. It performed its allotted task well but needed a strong, politically aware leader, an experienced surveyor, who, in the run-up to a war, would be in sympathy with the thinking and needs of the War Office. It so happened that, in 1911, the very man for the job was on the War Office's own General Staff as Head of their Geographical Section.

Charles Close was born in 1865, one of thirteen children, and was commissioned in the Royal Engineers in 1884. After gaining experience in Gibraltar and the East he was attached to the Survey of India, for whom he undertook topographic work in Burma and triangulation at Mandalay. Wishing to be involved in more exploratory surveying he transferred to Africa in 1895 where he carried out boundary surveying through thick bush across uncharted territory.

When this survey was complete he was sent to Ordnance Survey in what must have seemed a very dull posting after Africa. He served under John Farquharson, in charge of the Trigonometrical Branch, and wrote of the Ordnance Survey:

> It was a regular machine; each man and officer had his appointed job, and the work of making and revising the large-scale plans of the United Kingdom went on with accuracy and despatch, and that after all, was the main purpose of the Survey. But the small-scale maps left something to be desired, and the Ordnance Survey was quite out of touch with the world of science, and decidedly at a loss when anything out of the normal routine was put before it.

In 1898 Close returned to Africa as British Commissioner to delimit the frontier between German East Africa and British Central Africa and Northern Rhodesia. A spell surveying for the Boer War ended when he contracted typhoid fever and was invalided home.

Luckily Close made a complete recovery and by 1902 was Chief Inspector in Surveying at the Chatham school of military engineering where he wrote a text book on surveying which became the topographical surveyors 'bible'. By 1905, at the age of forty, he was at the War Office, as Head of the Geographical Section where he built up close links with both the Foreign and Colonial Offices, and was involved in preparations for the future Great War.

In August 1911 Close accepted the post of Director General of the Ordnance Survey. Shortly afterwards the crisis in Agadir subsided after the Kaiser drew back from Morocco and the threat of war receded.

Sir Charles Close, Director General of the Ordnance Survey, 1911–22.

Close handling

Close modestly stated that he

> had a very easy task in obtaining the goodwill of the two thousand civil assistants, because there had recently been published the report of a committee which had been formed to discuss their grievances, and we were able, with Treasury approval, to adopt all the recommendations of the committee.

The measures he was empowered to take included an improvement in pay scales, allowances and promotion by which he believed that before long there would be 'no assistant classed below his deserts and no genuine grievance unredressed.'

Newlyn tide gauge

General dissatisfaction with Liverpool as the national bench-mark datum led to the construction of three new tide-gauges at Felixstowe, Newlyn and Dunbar, which began recording in 1913, 1915 and 1917 respectively. It had been intended to calculate mean sea-level from the results obtained from all three, but it was found that although there was only ½ inch difference between Newlyn and Felixstowe mean sea levels, there was nearly 10 inches between Newlyn and Dunbar.

As a result Ordnance Survey decided to continue using a single reference datum. Newlyn was preferred as it was situated in an area of stable granite rock and because the gauge, perched on the end of a stone pier at the harbour entrance, was exposed to the open Atlantic. It was not therefore liable to be influenced by silting-up or the undue effects of estuary or river tide delays, as had been the case at Liverpool.

During six years of continuous recording, abstracts were made of the hourly records, from which mean sea-level was deduced. The gauge was checked twice daily, by manually measuring the drop to the surface of the water and comparing this with the recording on the tide-gauge. Barometric readings were taken, and the temperature and density of the sea water were also recorded.

Ordnance Survey ceased to maintain its general scientific interest in sea-level changes,

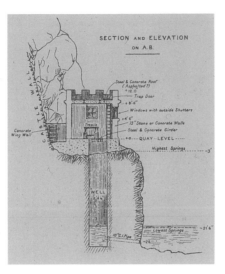

Section through the tide-gauge at Dunbar.

Roy Mitchelmore, successor to Mr Hutchens, with the Newlyn tide-gauge. The gauge is now preserved at Ordnance Survey's headquarters.

handing over the responsibility of Felixstowe observatory to the Harbour Board in 1930, and eventually abandoning Dunbar in 1950 when low tides failed to be registered because of silting-up. Responsibility for the Newlyn tide gauge continued to rest with Ordnance Survey, who provided a full-time observer at the station until 1983 when the station was handed over to the Institute of Oceanographic Sciences. It was one of the most unusual jobs on the Survey, demanding twice daily attendance to the exposed site, 365 days a year. The job demanded

a special sort of dedication personified by Mr W Hutchens who was tidal observer at Newlyn for twenty-three years. In 1965 he was congratulated that 'your gauge produces the most accurate record of mean sea-level in the world, with the exception of Genoa in Italy where the tidal range is less than 1 ft'.

All altitudes of bench-marks, apart from those on outer islands, are now related to Newlyn, and known as Ordnance Datum Newlyn (ODN).

Close began his term of office by taking stock of the reasons for the Ordnance Survey's existence. He observed that 'There is, indeed, no portion of this world's surface, of a similar area, which has been so minutely surveyed' and considered that there were four main reasons why the Ordnance Survey was still needed.

The most important task, Close believed, was to maintain the 'cadastral' survey, keeping the large-scale plans up to date, and the triangulation and levelling frameworks on which the plans were based. He pointed out how much the landscape had changed over the past hundred years and observed that the pace of change was quickening. In order to remain useful the maps had to reflect these changes. Close ranked the small-scale mapping, which required revision at least every fifteen years, as the second task.

The third reason he gave was that the Ordnance Survey was a training school for surveyors employed in the colonies. This was of special interest to Close. While at the War Office he had been instrumental in the formation of the Colonial Survey Committee. He thought it was essential that all colonies should be adequately mapped and was instrumental in arranging for men from the survey companies of the Royal Engineers to be seconded to the colonies. In return for their services the colonies paid their salaries and allowances. Close reported, in 1911, that as many as seventy-five men had, at any one time, been employed in the dominions and colonies that year. Governments could also send their own men to the Ordnance Survey at Southampton for training in 'practical surveying'. These measures benefited the department by enhancing its international reputation.

Stoke-on-Trent surveyors, 1911.

The last category of work undertaken by the Ordnance Survey was that for other government departments. Close gave some examples of how Ordnance Survey maps were used and listed some recent work, such as maps to show the geographical distribution of animal or human disease, and prevalence of crime, maps to show the location of canals and to depict the density of London traffic. All of these were Ordnance Survey maps overlaid with the additional information and printed at Southampton. The department's two largest customers were the Stationery and War Offices and, in 1912, impressions of maps printed on behalf of other government departments were well over double the quantity of maps printed for sale under the Ordnance Survey name.

Close found much that needed improvement and he immediately stated his intention of upgrading the scientific foundation of the Survey. He did not criticise his predecessors but warned that 'the Department which ignores its scientific duties tends to fall into routine and to adopt a habit of accepting methods which are supposed to be just good enough, but which as a fact, are never good enough in the long run.' He added that:

> It is no reflection on the labours of our predecessors to take
> advantage of the progress of science . . . They laid a good
> foundation. Their ideas were in advance of their time. They
> would have rejoiced to see the Survey doing its best to meet
> the wants of a new age.

Close's impact on the work of the Ordnance Survey was dramatic. He gave direction and purpose to the Survey, a series of stated aims and reasons for the employees to be proud of their work. He quickly won their respect and, importantly, was perceived as respecting them. Close married

late in life, at the age of forty-eight, in 1913, and the affection that the employees by then felt for their chief can be measured by the fact that they gave him a complimentary concert in honour of the occasion, attended by all ranks of staff. A large silver rose-bowl and an elaborately tooled autograph book were presented as gifts. In a speech replying to their congratulations, Close claimed that on more than one occasion he had been saved from making mistakes by talking to the staff, not just to the officers and superintendents, but particularly the representatives of the men's associations who were in close touch with the views of the staff they represented.

Close gave the staff two additional aims to bear in mind. Firstly, that all should try and work together with mutual confidence and with as little internal friction as possible. Secondly, that all should try and increase the prestige and enlarge the reputation of the Ordnance Survey, both at home and in foreign countries. With an admirable sense of timing that further cemented the staffs belief in their Director General's generosity and concern for their well-being, Close was able to finish his remarks with the announcement that the pension scheme which by now covered most, but not all, staff, was being extended to cover everyone. This ended one of the last major injustices in the conditions of service of the Ordnance Survey employees and was greeted with much applause.

A war to end all wars

The smouldering tensions of the years before the Great War finally exploded in the summer of 1914. On 28 June, the Austrian Emperor's heir, Archduke Franz Ferdinand, and his wife were murdered by a student member of the terrorist Black Hand society from Serbia. Within a few weeks the continent was at war. Britain entered the war on 4 August 1914 after Germany invaded neutral Belgium in their push towards France. Britain had, in any case, pledged to protect the north coast of France from naval attack and, as soon as Germany had declared war on France, Britain's involvement was inevitable.

Close had fully prepared the Ordnance Survey for its war-time role but although the department was immediately placed at the disposal of the War Office and the Admiralty, the first demands were for men and not maps.

The Ordnance Survey immediately lost sixteen of its twenty-two officers to war duties, although six officers were brought back from retirement to help out at headquarters. One officer, Major E M Jack of the Geographical Section of the General Staff at the War Office (later Director General) was attached to the General Staff at British GHQ in France

Use of Lucas daylight signalling lamp for triangulation. The telescope and plane-table were used to obtain a rough alignment.

'Express delivery' of maps to the front line.

to advise on mapping. Almost all the non-commissioned officers and sappers were sent on active duty within a short time.

At the outbreak of war the civilian staff numbered 1721; of these, 969 were aged over 40 and too old to enlist, 141 were women and there were 87 lads under the age of 18. Of the remaining civilians eligible to volunteer, two-thirds of them had done so by June 1915 although, as a number were declared unfit for active service, the final volunteer force in the first year of the war was only 285 men.

The Ordnance Survey's first preoccupation was with providing a reliable ranging method to help the artillery hit their targets. The Germans had been observed dropping smoke bombs or silver paper over targets from aeroplanes to give the position of batteries to their artillery and, in October 1914, Captain Winterbotham (also to be a Director General) was placed in charge of a section formed to explore these methods. After trials on Salisbury Plain, and the adaptation of three theodolites to suit the purpose of fixing the position of an aeroplane, the 1st Ranging Section, consisting of four men, Winterbotham and a lorry, embarked for France in November 1914, the first survey unit to be sent out by the Ordnance Survey.

Early experiments in France were disappointing as pilots had difficulty in determining when they were exactly over the targets, but an experiment in which sights were added to the fuselage of the aeroplanes beside the pilot helped to improve the positioning accuracy. By March 1915 greater sophistication had been obtained in the form of a simple wireless message transmitted from the plane to a heavy

artillery battery when the plane was over the target. The observer on the ground had to keep the aircraft in view through the open-sights on top of the theodolite, or, if more skilled, by viewing the aircraft through the theodolite telescope; a difficult task with a moving target. At the moment when the aircraft was over the target and the wireless message received, the telescope would be clamped and the bearing read off. With readings from two or three independent sources, the position of the aircraft and thence the enemy gun-position could be quickly computed. The Flying Corps had begun such transmissions on the Aisne in September 1914, but development had been slow.

Winterbotham earned himself the greatest respect from the gunners early in the war. He told them in which direction and at what elevation to fire their guns and with unerring regularity the shells hit their distant and invisible targets. At this time ranging techniques were not widely understood by artillery officers and they nicknamed him 'the astrologer', which stuck for the rest of the War. Three survey sections had been formed in readiness for the war but these were disbanded on its outbreak as they were not at first considered necessary for operations in countries which were already well mapped.

The Germans made a substantial invasion into France, but were checked by their need to divert forces against Russia. Around the same time they changed their strategy to an eastward sweep north of Paris instead of an envelopment of the city. This allowed the French to regain some territory but attempts to force the Germans to retreat from France failed and for the next four appalling years the Western Front remained almost static.

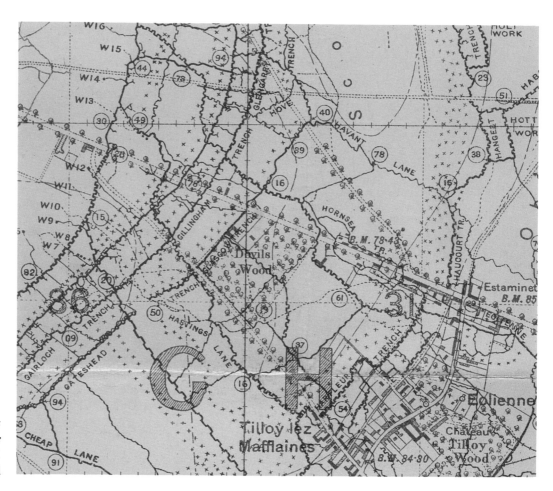

*Part of the trench map of Arras
(51b NW3) printed by Ordnance
Survey in 1917.*
Peter Chasseaud

Different tactics were needed to fight this sort of war and the struggle

early assumed the character of a siege. Intricate and extensive systems of entrenchment, strong and concealed battery positions, trench mortars and machine guns, resulted in a corresponding growth of accurate and scientific gunnery. For this purpose, an accurate large-scale map was essential, and as such a map of France did not exist, a new one had to be made.

The 1st Ranging section was split up with just two observers remaining at their original duties while the others, under Winterbotham, were joined by a further fifteen surveyors for mapping duties. Belgium was already well mapped at a scale of 1:20 000 and the plan was to extend this over part of northern France using the same projection and sheetlines but with the adoption of the French triangulation.

At this scale, a cruder and speedier method of survey could be employed than for normal peacetime work. The

surveyors used plane-tables in a method that had been known to cartographers for centuries. The equipment consisted of a tripod on which a flat board was placed. A sheet with known details plotted, such as triangulation points, was pinned to the board and an alidade, a simple device consisting of a metal ruler with a sight at each end, was placed on the board. Having identified his position and orientated the board, the surveyor would line up the sights of the alidade to observe an unmapped feature, such as the corner of a building. Drawing a line along the ruler then gave the direction, but not the distance to the object. By re-sighting onto the same feature from another place, a second line could be drawn and the intersection of these would give the position of the feature. Observations from a third position verified the point.

From 1915 survey work in France was continuous until the end of the War. The surveyors were split up to form topographical sections with each of the three armies in the field, and, as well as supplying trained staff, the Ordnance Survey enlisted and drafted abroad an additional 800 topographers, observers, draughtsmen and printers.

Overseas and over there

By the end of 1917 the constant demand for new editions of trench maps and growing concern about possible disruption of supplies from England led to the decision to form the Overseas Branch of the Ordnance Survey (OBOS). A factory site at Wardreques, near St Omer, France, was chosen, partly because of the suitability of the building, but also because the Aire Canal, which passed by the site, enabled supplies from England to be conveniently delivered to the factory by barge.

A unit of 149 people, including forty-six women from Queen Mary's Army Auxiliary Corps (QMAAC) were mobilised and housed in hurriedly erected wooden huts and a hostel. By the end of the first week in March 1918 four printing presses were running at full capacity. On 21 March the German Army began their offensive on the Somme, putting out of action two of the four field survey companies. As a result heavy demands were made on OBOS for maps and for two weeks the staff worked flat out to produce 300 000 maps.

The staff took advantage of the canal for bathing once the weather was warm enough, but with the summer heat the action close to Wardreques also began to hot up, and a staged withdrawal of OBOS was made to a site at Wimereux near Boulogne. By careful planning, map production continued without interruption and the wooden buildings were dismantled and re-erected at Wimereux. Shortly after their departure from Wardreque three bombs fell exactly on the former site of the hostel.

Printing maps at Wimereux in France during the First World War.

Conditions at Wimereux were spartan and the work exhausting, but, believing that they would be there for some time, the staff settled in and did their best to make the place homely. A piano was procured and QMAACs hosted dances ('Officers of the OS cordially invited') in the recreation hall.

However, there was little time for socialising. On 8 August, the final allied offensive began and continuous shift-work by an increased staff was necessary to meet the massive demand for maps in the final stages of the war. The signing of the Armistice on 11 November brought the need for trench maps to an abrupt end, but the machines were turned over to a new use, printing small-scale maps of Germany, for use by the allies.

Although only in existence for the last stages of the war the Overseas Branch of the Ordnance Survey printed almost 3 million maps.

But the surveyors were not just making a general map of the country: they were plotting the position of trenches, machine-gun and mortar emplacements and batteries of both the allies and the enemy. For the first time, photographs taken from aeroplanes were used in earnest to provide details for, and to revise, maps and although the problems of flying at a definite height and ensuring the camera was vertical had yet to be overcome, the photographs were good enough to enhance pre-war maps of Belgium with trench and enemy gun positions. The maps of France were so poor they had to be entirely remade. This involved checking the triangulation and compiling cadastral and other plans onto the trig. framework, adding detail and revising from air photographs. The surveyors and artillery worked closely together to improve the chances of heavy and allied gunfire reaching its target. Offensives were launched from the trenches after intensive artillery bombardment to break down opposition to the advancing troops, but fire from dug-in enemy machine-gun emplacements and artillery cut down the advancing men in huge numbers.

Flash-spotting and sound-ranging were the two main techniques used to establish an enemy gun position. Flash-spotting entailed just that: four observers in different positions on the front line would observe with their theodolites the flash of a heavy gun firing. As the observers were a known direction and distance apart from each other, they could supply the angle of the instrumentally observed flash from their individual positions, and fix the position of the gun by intersection. Early flash-spotting was inexact and unreliable, although techniques were much improved by the development of 'flash and buzzer' boards which ensured synchronisation and the concentration of observers on the same flash.

For sound-ranging, a number of microphones were stationed at known positions. Each would register and transmit to HQ the exact time at which they received the report from a gun, and the distance of that gun from each microphone, and therefore its position, the point at which the sound arcs intersected, could both be calculated. This technique was usable in all weathers and in 1916 twenty sound-ranging sections were formed and attached to the field survey companies. Their success resulted in the Germans having to employ cover fire from adjoining batteries to confuse the observers, just as they used dummy flashes to deceive the flash-spotters.

Increasing sophistication of the mapping of enemy positions and understanding the importance of survey work led to the possibility of surprise attack. Previously the enemy was alerted to an imminent advance by preliminary fire to disable their defences, the artillery finding their target by trial and error. However at Cambrai in 1917, '381 tanks, followed by a relatively small proportion of infantry, rolled forward in the half light upon the astonished Germans, without even the courtesy of a preliminary bombardment to announce their coming.' The secret was in a system of 'predicted fire' where each enemy heavy and siege battery was located and its position plotted on an 'artillery board'. The allied batteries were each supplied with one of these zinc-covered boards on which their own position was marked with large graduated arcs radiating from that position. The allied gunners were then able to calculate bearings and distances and fire with accuracy at their targets. In total 12 000 artillery boards were supplied by the Ordnance Survey during the war.

Interesting, and effective, though these advances were, nothing, it seemed, could stop the slaughter of soldiers on both sides or break the stalemate of the Western Front and at the beginning of 1917, the position of the front remained little changed from that of 1914.

Levelling at an opened fundamental bench-mark, constructed before World War I.

The home front

The demands of war on the depleted Ordnance Survey staff at Southampton meant that the normal work of the survey was much reduced. The issue of maps to the public was restricted and, where they were thought to contain information of use to the enemy, they were not issued except to public bodies and government departments. Similar restrictions applied to privately produced maps whose publishers had to send a proof copy to the Director General of the Ordnance Survey to obtain permission for publication.

Five new printing presses were installed in November 1914 and, by 1915, twenty-two presses were wholly at work on producing war maps. Non-war duties were cut to a minimum, not only to release staff for war production, but to cut the cost of the Ordnance Survey to the Government which needed funds to fight the war. Despite losing men overseas on war service, these economies meant that an additional 250 civilians had to be discharged.

At the end of 1916, a new division was created for making relief models of the trenches and fighting areas. These were sent out at an average of thirty-six a week to France and, by the end of the war, about a thousand had been dispatched. A further substantial number were made for home use by the War Office and for use by the US Senate and House of Representatives just prior to and after the American entry into the War in 1917.

Maps printed by Ordnance Survey were taken by steamer to Le Havre and distributed from there to wherever they were needed. Ninety per cent of all maps used in France

A scientific renaissance

In 1909 growing unease over the accuracy of the existing triangulation framework prompted the measurement of a new base line which could be used to perform a mathematical test of the framework. The site chosen was near Lossiemouth, on the southern slope of the Moray Firth.

Base measurement techniques had improved, with the discovery of a nickel-steel alloy called 'Invar' which had a very low coefficient of expansion and the great advantage that it could be made into wires or tapes. When suspended 'in catenary', draped over supporting tripods and a specified strain applied by means of a weight, the amount of sag in the tape could be compensated for mathematically.

The test of the framework revealed that an average error of about 1 inch in 1 mile could be expected in the old triangulation network, representing a difference of only 25 yards in the distance from Shetland to Dover. Geodetically, it wasn't worth the effort of retriangulation, as the effect on national mapping would have been minimal. However, larger localised errors were found to exist and these were to dog surveyors for some time.

Close also decided that the old triangulation marks should be found and preserved before they disappeared. These were often a stone or tile with a hole in, buried a few feet below ground, and Close set about having primary points replaced with a mark on a buried concrete block that would 'easily last a thousand years'.

Bench-marks were also in danger of disappearing, as early levellers had cut marks on 'any wall or building which came handy' and many had disappeared altogether. This prompted the second geodetic levelling for which 115 fundamental bench-marks (FBMs) were constructed between 1912 and 1915. However, only eighty-six were initially used, due to economy measures after the war. With their surrounding iron railings and foot high pillar, the FBM has the appearance of a grave and one, just outside a churchyard, had flowers placed on the chamber-cover for several years!

The FBMs were supplemented, at about 4-mile intervals, with another new type of mark, the flush-bracket, so called because they were fitted flush with the vertical surface of a wall. Cast in brass, each had a unique number and they were placed for preference on a permanent structure such as a church or public building. For rock and other horizontal surfaces brass bolts (inscribed with OSBM BOLT) were used instead. Levelling was completed in 1921.

The second geodetic levelling of Scotland was started in 1936, suffered from the interval of the Second World War, and was completed in 1952. Disappointingly, the final Scottish results failed to reach international standards.

After the First World War, Close appointed a scientific research officer, H P L Jolly, one of whose first tasks was to assist the Royal Society with a survey to measure the angle of variation (or declination) between true north and magnetic north around the country. As the position of magnetic north varies, following a pattern of moving slowly westwards for many years and then swinging back eastwards, the survey had to be repeated at intervals. Magnetic north was found to vary with the position of the observer around the country, and to be affected by mineral rocks underlying some parts of the land.

Using the results of magnetic surveys, Ordnance Survey produced physical maps showing 'isogonals' – lines of equal magnetic variation across the country, similar in appearance to the familiar isobars of a weather chart. All Ordnance Survey small-scale maps still carry a note describing magnetic variations. Responsibility for magnetic surveys, however, passed to the Institute of Geological Survey in 1982.

From 1927 Jolly was also involved in a gravity survey to determine variations throughout the country. The survey relied on timing the swing of a pendulum and Jolly designed new, lighter apparatus for these surveys. Differences found in gravity across the country were very small with, generally, a small increase in the force of gravity observed near the coasts.

Jolly found that his presence was tolerated rather than supported by the military officers. Winterbotham disparagingly summed up Jolly's work as 'Odd matters for international Unions' and 'reviews for this or that scientific journal'. But Jolly was more than just a scientific figurehead and the work carried out in his term of office, although often more interesting than directly useful to the department, was of both national and international scientific importance.

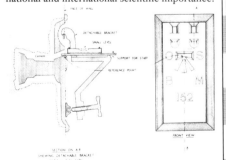

Manufacture of flush-brackets in the Ordnance Survey workshops for the second geodetic levelling.
Right: diagrammatic view of a flush-bracket.

were supplied by the Ordnance Survey. The system was a model of efficiency and, in May 1916, the Commander-in-Chief of the British armies in France commended the work and commented, admiringly, that 'I can now count on obtaining an issue of as many as 10,000 copies of any map within one week of sending it home for reproduction.' This service was enhanced by the printing of increasing numbers of maps in the field by the survey companies, and later in the War with the setting up of Overseas Branch of the Ordnance Survey (OBOS).

During the War 10 million people lost their lives, including about 750 000 from the United Kingdom and a further 200 000 from the Empire. There are sixty-seven names on the Ordnance Survey roll of honour, a mere drop in the ocean of wasted lives. But this figure represents about 6 per cent of the total number of men sent from the Ordnance Survey to serve overseas in the Great War.

A total of 32 872 000 maps, plans and diagrams were supplied by the Ordnance Survey to the forces in the war years, at an estimated cost of 1½ million pounds. In recognition of this and the vital ranging work done by the Ordnance Survey, a captured 105 millimetre German gun was presented in 1920 by GHQ in France. This 4-ton trophy was placed in front of the South Range buildings at London Road, Southampton.

The South Range of Ordnance Survey's Southampton Office, c.1920, with the captured German gun on view.

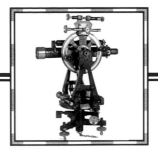

9 THE LEAN YEARS

After the First World War

Close described the attitude of the Ordnance Survey immediately after the War as 'confident'. The department had met every demand placed upon it and although some difficulties were expected as it once again settled down to its peacetime role, these were faced with optimism.

The map revision programme was, unsurprisingly, in arrears but, in order to save money, all government departments were told to cut their costs and Ordnance Survey was no exception. As a consequence the large-scale map revision period was extended from twenty years to every forty years where the population was less than 100 persons per square mile. This ruling affected about 40 per cent of the United Kingdom and allowed the survey to be maintained by less than 1500 staff. In 1914, staff numbers had been just over 2000.

Staff came back from the forces in dribs and drabs and by March 1920 all except a score had returned. Absorbing 'demobbed' personnel whilst adhering to the reductions decreed by the Treasury, it became impossible to avoid discharging staff and ninety people lost their jobs. The principle that no man who had served in the armed forces would be discharged was strictly adhered to, but Close knew that 'however considerately discharges may be carried out, they do always inflict hardship'.

Unrest, caused by resettling civil assistants finding that, after fighting for their country, they were 'employed under less favourable conditions than formerly', was quickly defused by Close who was approached with this problem by the new Whitley District Council. The Council was formed in 1920 to deal with matters which were within the jurisdiction of the Director General, and it was seen by staff as a great success that the complaints were dealt with so promptly.

'Whitleyism', as it became known, took its name from a committee chaired by the Right Honourable J H Whitley, in 1916. It had recommended that a system of Joint Industrial Councils should be set up for the purpose of bringing

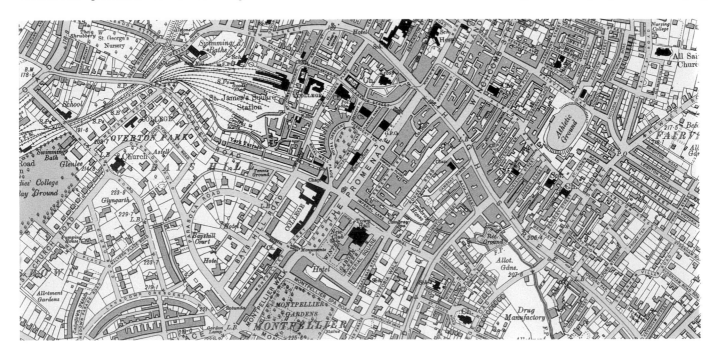

Extract from the 6 inches to 1 mile (1:10560) Cheltenham town map published in 1921.

O G S Crawford

During the First World War, Osbert Guy Stanhope (OGS) Crawford was ordered to deliver some maps from France to Charles Close. After quickly disposing of the official business, they spent the rest of the interview discussing archaeology, which was for one a hobby and for the other a way of life.

Close initiated a scheme whereby he issued 6-inch maps free, to qualified persons, in return for the use of their added archaeological information. After the war Crawford became a keen participant in this 'honorary correspondent' scheme and, as his interests were mostly in southern counties, he became a familiar figure at Ordnance Survey. In drawing errors to the attention of Close, he became at length 'a sort of voluntary field worker'.

In 1920 Close offered Crawford a permanent position at a small salary, which he accepted. However, his arrival, at a time when the department was having to drastically reduce its staff, was greeted with something approaching outrage by the military staff who generally thought archaeologists were 'a few isolated eccentrics and cranks' and for whose work 'they felt a politely veiled contempt'.

Crawford took a disarmingly practical, almost commercial approach to archaeology and did much to popularise the subject. He had direct access to the Director General who was planning an Historical Map of England. Close proudly showed a sample to Crawford who recalled that 'The result was an appalling amalgam of history and prehistory which contained also many errors of a historical and archaeological kind.' Crawford tactfully persuaded Close that it would be preferable to have a series of physical base maps, upon which details of one historical period at a time could be shown.

Crawford's work, being 'unimportant', was always at the end of the queue and he claimed that 'trying to get a move on in the Civil Service . . . was like trying to swim in a lake of glue.' Close had retired by the time the base map was ready, and when Crawford produced a model

O G S Crawford, Ordnance Survey's first Archaeology Officer.

for a map of Roman Britain to be overprinted on the map and submitted it to Jack, the new Director General, he received a reprimand for compiling this without official sanction. Approval, though, was given for the map to go ahead.

'Roman Britain' was published in August 1924 and the entire stock of a thousand copies sold out in a few days. The press praised it as 'one of the most wonderful maps ever produced' and the map continued in print through many editions for over sixty years.

The production of specialist maps was not the original purpose of Crawford's appointment, which was in fact 'to reduce to order the chaotic mixture of antiquarianism and speculation that disfigured the Ordnance maps, and to bring it into conformity with existing knowledge'. Some of this work could be done in the office, but Crawford was adamant that he needed to visit archaeological sites in person and this was often done, alone, by bicycle. Crawford spent long periods away from the

office establishing a network of archaeological contacts and greatly extending Close's system of honorary correspondents.

Crawford's name is often linked with the discovery that photographs taken from the air could reveal traces, not visible from ground level, of man's earlier habitations. Crawford gave the credit for the idea to Air Vice-Marshal Clark-Hall and Dr Williams-Freeman, but admitted that he decided to create a monopoly of the technique, using the resources of Ordnance Survey, so that all archaeologists could gain access to the library of photographs. Crawford obtained thousands of negatives of surplus photographs from the Royal Air Force from which the true nature of the prehistoric field systems were revealed for the first time. A joint air photography expedition with Alexander Keiller resulted in a book published as *Wessex from the Air*, in 1928.

The outbreak of war in 1939 inevitably almost halted archaeological activity. Crawford decided, against orders, to move his records to a safer place. The last two vans stood loaded and ready to leave London Road when they were destroyed where they stood in the blitz of November 1940. As well as archaeological records, Crawford also lost his own personal library which he had kept at the office.

The archaeology branch disbanded for the duration of the war and Crawford filled in his time by working for the National Buildings Record. This aimed to photograph buildings of historic interest, in danger of being destroyed by bombing. At the end of the war Crawford, who had almost reached the age of sixty, decided to retire.

While he was at Ordnance Survey, Crawford founded the periodical *Antiquity* which is still published to this day. Another enduring publication is the book *Field Archaeology in Great Britain* which 'began as a simple printed sheet of foolscap, which I wrote in a pub at Llangorse in Brecknockshire in 1921. Later I rewrote it; it was bound in a paper cover and sold for sixpence, and proved very popular.'

together employers (official side) with employees (staff side) for negotiation. The Whitley Committee suggestions were aimed at use by general industry but were taken up with enthusiasm by civil servants in all government departments. The benefit at Ordnance Survey was most welcomed by the civil assistants who were, at last, given a recognised avenue to express their grievances and for participating in negotiations affecting their own destiny.

Paying its way

A Select Committee on National Expenditure in 1918 raised the question of how far the Ordnance Survey could become self-supporting in terms of earning sufficient revenue to cover its costs. Close soon formulated an opinion as to what was, and what was not, possible. Some branches, such as the boundaries department or the levelling section, could never

SCALE—1 INCH TO A MILE.

PRICE ONE SHILLING & SIXPENCE.
(NET).

Map cover design, 1910. Roger Hellyer

pay their way, but small-scale maps were successfully sold in large quantities by other publishers. Many of these were based on Ordnance Survey maps, so why did the Ordnance Survey maps themselves not sell in similar quantities?

This was one of the questions asked by the Olivier Committee, who had met in 1914 to consider the selling arrangements for small-scale Ordnance Survey maps to the public. Since 1905 one map agent, Fisher Unwin, had been

responsible for all of the small-scale maps but, during the nine years of their agency, sales revenue had only increased slightly. At the Olivier Committee proceedings, the Ordnance Survey view was that this was the fault of the agent, but Fisher Unwin claimed that he had done his best with the maps, which lacked the popular appeal of Bartholomew's publications.

Ordnance Survey maps suffered from numerous disadvantages when compared with those produced by commercial publishers. The packaging was drab and the white or red covers quickly became soiled and unsaleable. Booksellers were reluctant to display them for these reasons, especially at railway bookstalls, and their protective covers somewhat discouraged the potential purchaser from opening the maps.

The maps themselves depicted the road network using a method that may have been acceptable when cars were less common but which was now frankly old-fashioned. Bartholomew's maps were far superior in this essential aspect. To make matters worse, they and some other map publishers had fallen into the habit of calling their maps 'Ordnance maps', despite this being expressly forbidden under the 1911 Copyright Act. Bartholomew's could also supply maps to the trade on a sale-or-return basis, a practice that was normal in the trade but which, to Fisher Unwin's chagrin, could not be entertained by the Ordnance Survey because of its status as a government department.

The Committee recommended that the contract with Fisher Unwin should be terminated as soon as possible, but the intervention of the war in 1914 led to the report being shelved and Fisher Unwin continued as agent until 1919. In 1920 Close, who seemed to have taken a particular dislike to Fisher Unwin, remarked that:

> The introduction of a wholesale agent was a mistake, and since his elimination the sales have gone up by leaps and bounds. Hundreds of retailers are now selling Ordnance Survey maps who had never heard of them in the time of the agent. 1500 monthly accounts have been opened.

Popular maps

The Olivier Committee laid down a number of guidelines for improving sales, including a recommendation that more attractive cover designs should be used, and that the department should produce adequate and more effective advertising material.

The content of the small-scale maps themselves was also reviewed in the light of the criticisms made by Fisher Unwin and other witnesses at the Olivier hearings. As a direct result, a new revision of the 1-inch map series was begun with

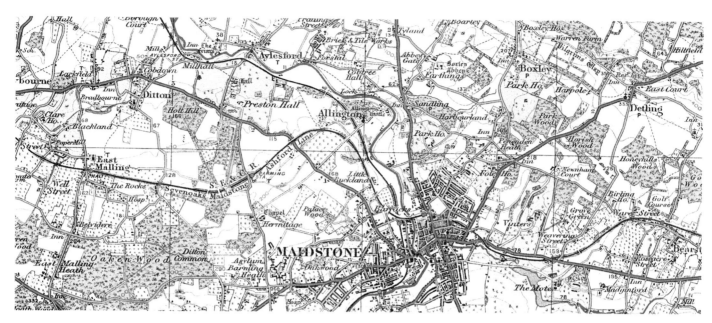

Part of the 1-inch Popular Edition of Chatham and Maidstone (sheet 116), published in 1921.

the express aim of making the maps more appealing to the public. Road information was improved and divided into eleven different classifications, giving information about road widths and quality and types of surface. In the interests of reducing clutter on the map, parish boundaries were omitted. Contours, at 50-foot intervals, were used to depict relief and the whole map was designated the 'Popular Edition'. The sheet sizes were enlarged and the number covering the country was reduced to 146 of which 83 were published by 1922.

Ordnance Survey had to change its sense of values, and the need to make money forced the department to seek expansion into new markets. A new series of maps was designed to particularly appeal to holiday-makers. These Tourist Maps and special District Maps showed the whole of a holiday area on one sheet and the first, the Tourist Map of Snowdon, was published in 1920. The popular 1-inch scale was retained but relief was shown by ideas carried over from earlier engraved maps: a clever combination of hachures, contours and layers which gave dimension and depth to the mapping.

Sales swung sharply upwards to a degree which surprised Close, especially as the price of the maps had been substantially increased. He described the effect as 'curious' and gave a full measure of credit to the new attractive cover designs by Ellis Martin. Close was so proud of these that a selection of them was entered into the Exhibition of British Industrial Art in 1921.

With its new 1-inch Popular Edition and Tourist and District Maps the Ordnance Survey finally hit upon a formula which was both appealing to the map-buying public and which met with full approval, as a military map, from the War Office. The Tourist Map range was rapidly expanded and the measure of Ordnance Survey's new commercialism can be gauged by a sudden willingness to use non-geographical descriptions as map titles (Burns' country and Scott's country, for example), a practice which would have been unthinkable in the past.

Copyright and the half-inch map

The Olivier Committee recommended that the 1911 Copyright Act should be enforced to stop commercial firms illegally using the Ordnance Survey name on their publications. Opinions on copyright fell into two camps. There were those who believed that, because the Ordnance Survey maps were compiled at public expense, publishers should be allowed to freely use the information that they, as taxpayers, had already paid for. The Government, however, took the view that it was in the interests of the taxpayers to enforce the copyright. The argument ran that if this was not done, then numerous cheap copies of the maps, or rather the most popular maps, would be produced by private publishers. They would reap a large profit, but the genuine Ordnance Survey maps, being undercut in price, would not sell. Less money

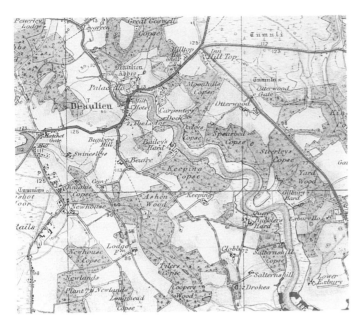

Part of the 1920 Tourist Map of the New Forest.

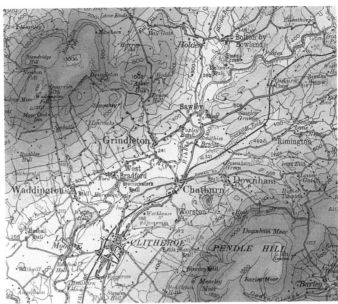

Extract from sheet 8 (Preston) of the ½-inch series: colour 'laid on with a trowel'.

would return to Ordnance Survey and the expense to the taxpayer of making the maps would therefore increase.

Generally, since Mudge's first skirmish with commercial publishers in 1816 there had been few major problems with illegal copying of Ordnance Survey maps. The Copyright Act of 1842 had codified the Government's position and each case of infringement, or application for permission to use Ordnance Survey material, was dealt with on its merits.

From 1888 the note 'All rights of reproduction reserved' was printed on Ordnance Survey maps, but the Dorington Committee of 1892 recommended a liberal approach and suggested that maps based on Ordnance Survey maps should have 'some *bona fide* difference', such as in scale. In these cases permission to reproduce was usually granted. A payment was to be made for the privilege of copying the map but Dorington thought that 'this sum should be rather an acknowledgment than a substantial payment'. This encouraged commercial publishers to produce the popular maps that Ordnance Survey did not itself at the time, intend to make. However, once taxpayer's money was being spent on producing popular, attractive maps in competition with commercial publishers, the policy began to look less sensible.

In addition to being allowed to use Ordnance Survey material cheaply, overt and inferred claims were made by some publishers that their maps were 'Ordnance' maps, thus capitalising on the Ordnance Survey's reputation for excellence. This confused the public and eventually, in 1901, a strong warning, published in the *London Gazette*, was directed

against anyone implying that their maps were produced by the Ordnance Survey. The warning was widely ignored.

The copyright position was particularly delicate with regard to Bartholomew's, as the War Office was in 1901 using large quantities of the Edinburgh firm's ½-inch maps which had originally been reduced from Ordnance Survey maps. They were much improved, with relief shown by layer colouring and a new road colouring method, but no permission had ever been granted by Ordnance Survey for use of the mapping. In reply to objections raised by Ordnance Survey, Bartholomew's argued that, as a Government department was purchasing the maps, they thought that tacit permission had been given. In 1901 when the War Office wished to purchase more of these maps from Bartholomew's, the Director General of the Ordnance Survey commented that 'it is unfortunate that the War Office should be purchasing large numbers of maps from Messrs Bartholomew's at a time when the action of that firm has obliged the Board to threaten to restrain its basing its maps, as it does at present, on those of the Ordnance Survey.'

As a direct result, the Treasury gave permission in 1902 for the Ordnance Survey to prepare and publish its own ½-inch scale maps of England and Wales, and the War Office placed no more orders with Bartholomew's for these maps.

The Ordnance Survey ½-inch map was reduced from 1-inch mapping and at a first attempt was inferior in appearance to Bartholomew's map at the same scale. Published in colour in 103 small sheets, it was fully available by 1906. A later edition used larger sheet sizes but further experimentation with colour-layering was not totally successful. Where relief was less prominent or detail less crowded, the design worked well, but in hilly areas the 'colour was laid on with a trowel and some of the sheets were quite hopeless'. A revision of the ½-inch series was started in 1932 but the sheets were produced slowly, a casualty of the general lack of resources available in those years.

After the Copyright Act of 1911 the wording used on Ordnance Survey maps became 'Crown Copyright reserved' and a set of rules governing the administration of the copyright was published. However, infringements continued and in 1913 the Ordnance Survey decided to try out its newly defined powers in a careful test case against H G Rowe and Co.

'Rowe's New Road Map for Cyclists and Motorists' was no more than a direct photographic reduction of an Ordnance Survey map. It sold at just 3*d*, undercutting the map from which it was copied, and was a clear uncomplicated case of infringement of the Copyright Act. The court found for the Ordnance Survey and Rowe's had to destroy all copies of the map and the plates from which it was printed. Ordnance Survey publicised the case in appropriate journals to serve as a warning to other publishers, and the opportunity was also taken to publicise the fact that permission to copy an Ordnance Survey map would not normally be withheld, provided the rules, which publishers were urged to study, were complied with. Free permission was usually granted for educational or scientific book illustration.

Relations with the trade over the copyright arrangements remained fairly amicable until after the First World War, when the Committee on National Expenditure decided that a royalty should be applied to Ordnance Survey maps. After 1 July 1918, every time a map was copied the publisher had to pay a small fee for the rights. The situation was made worse for commercial publishers after the Geddes Committee in 1922 insisted that royalty payments for copying Ordnance Survey maps should be 'substantial in every case'.

Faced with the double 'insult' of Ordnance Survey producing its own popular maps which enticed customers away from their own hugely popular products, and having to incur the expense of a new royalty on their own maps, Bartholomew's felt that they were being deliberately squeezed out. They canvassed the trade and, finding that their views were shared by other publishers, they lobbied against the new rules, accusing Ordnance Survey of being hostile to private enterprise and attempting to control it by aggressive methods. Unwillingly, Ordnance Survey found itself drawn into a battle over its right to protect its own products from piracy.

Understandably, no commercial publisher liked having to pay for what they were used to having free and various excuses were offered to try and avoid payment. Some publishers claimed that they thought the royalty payments were introduced for the duration of the war only and others tried to claim exemption by saying that the maps were produced before 1918, when this was not the case. Revenue from royalties did increase, however, and by 1926 almost £4000 was generated by these charges.

The main agitator against the system of royalty payment was Bartholomew's. Cartography is usually a gentlemanly business and Bartholomew's had long held a respected position as a major map publisher. This generated a natural distaste for battle in open court as it was felt that two cartographers should be able to reach amicable agreement. Negotiations were accordingly opened between Bartholomew's and the Ordnance Survey but these proved increasingly difficult and protracted, and at times acrimonious.

Slowly Ordnance Survey won its battle to prevent unauthorised use of its name by other publishers. But it must be said that the problem had been partly of its own making, the Survey having, as Bartholomew pointed out in one letter, allowed his firm to use a map title for thirty years without objection.

Map publishers took a long time to accept the Ordnance Survey as a serious contender within the map trade and it was 'strongly felt that the Government with the aid of a parliamentary grant is not entitled to enter into commercial competition with the existing printing industry of the country'. However, Ordnance Survey had already begun to savour the rewards of commercial success and the Treasury was observing with satisfaction its increased sales revenues and royalty payments. No amount of lobbying by Bartholomew's and other firms could now stem the tide of the new popular maps from Ordnance Survey.

Geddes

The final year of Close's directorship in 1922 was the year of the 'Geddes Axe' in which drastic cuts were made in public expenditure. No exception was made for the already slimmed-down Ordnance Survey and the Geddes committee recommended that the twenty-year revision cycle for large-scale plans should be confined to those areas where considerable change had occurred since the last revision. The cost-saving was estimated at £30 000 a year and a staff cut of 143 was recommended. Taking into account the separation of the Irish Survey resulting from the partition of Ireland that same year, this brought the staff complement down to 1000.

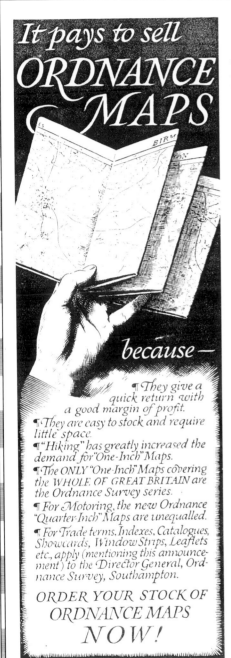

It pays to sell ORDNANCE MAPS *because—*

¶ They give a quick return with a good margin of profit.

¶ They are easy to stock and require little space.

¶ "Hiking" has greatly increased the demand for "One-Inch" Maps.

¶ The ONLY "One-Inch" Maps covering the WHOLE OF GREAT BRITAIN are the Ordnance Survey series.

¶ For Motoring, the new Ordnance "Quarter-Inch" Maps are unequalled.

¶ For Trade terms, Indexes, Catalogues, Showcards, Window Strips, Leaflets etc., apply (mentioning this announcement) to the Director General, Ordnance Survey, Southampton.

ORDER YOUR STOCK OF ORDNANCE MAPS *NOW!*

The first sales representatives

Close realised that to sell the new popular maps effectively it would be necessary to adopt commercial trade practices and he decided to appoint two 'map travellers', Gerald Chamberlain and Mr P Kennedy, both men who had served abroad in the First World War 'with success and some distinction'. For this Close offered a salary of £200 plus travelling expenses. Mr Chamberlain recalls:

My first thought was 'means of travel' and I suggested that a small car would be the most satisfactory . . . One was brought to the entrance gate but never entered. It seemed that no precedent could be found. Finally it was decided that I should be provided with a supply of 1st class railway travel warrants and the appropriate rubber stamp.

On arrival at each town Mr Chamberlain had first to walk around to find a hotel. Once settled, he would order a taxi to take him to either a named stationers or the town centre but, after that, travel was on foot for the rest of the day. Despite this inconvenience Mr Chamberlain's first round of visits was quite successful, but when he called again:

I was met with widespread angry complaints. Maps of which I had been authorised to promise delivery had not been delivered . . . After three weeks of frustration I returned to base and sought an interview with the Director General. He was equally dissatisfied and asked me to put forward suggestions to improve matters. I proposed that a separate office be set up,

staffed by a clerk and typist, which would become a medium between the public and officialdom. To this he readily agreed and promised to arrange accordingly. There must have been difficulties to overcome, for matters remained unresolved. After a further three months of frustration I asked the Director General if I could be relieved of the appointment and given an alternative post. Fortunately a vacancy had occurred in the Levelling Dept.

Mr Kennedy decided to ride out these difficulties and, eventually, a smooth-running system was developed with two representatives being almost continually on the road from February to October. The winter was spent stocktaking and preparing advertising material and taking their annual holiday. Cars were eventually, grudgingly, supplied on the understanding that these would be garaged near the office and not driven home by the representatives.

It was 'practically impossible' to find an appropriate civil service grade in which to place the representatives 'as there is no other grade with similar duties', and for some time they were classed as storekeepers, which they patently were not. Neither were they ever employed on a commission basis, as it was feared that this would lead to overstocking of retailers with maps. Instead the representatives concentrated on making sure that retailers were adequately stocked, assuring shopkeepers that a postcard request would bring any Ordnance Survey map by return of post.

Trade advertisement by Ellis Martin.
Tim Nicholson

Ellis Martin

Ellis Martin was thirty-seven when he returned from the war after being employed with the Tank Corps in drawing sketch maps of marshy ground to aid the transport of heavy military vehicles. Martin's commanding officer had suggested that he should apply for a job with the Ordnance Survey when the war was over, and in 1918 the department issued a Christmas card designed and painted by Martin.

Ellis Martin, a Plymouth man and student of the Slade School of Art, was already an established commercial artist with a growing reputation before the Great War interrupted his career. Although a freelance, he worked for lengthy periods in a retainer capacity with such firms as W H Smith and Son and Selfridge's in London. His vigorous railway posters adorned the very W H Smith station bookstalls which had been so uncooperative in selling Ordnance Survey maps before 1914. In 1919, he was engaged by the Ordnance Survey as its first professional artistic designer with a brief to produce pictorial covers and point-of-sale material which would sell maps. His impact was immediate, and in the 1921 Annual Report, the Director General was recording the highest map sales 'in the history of the Ordnance Survey'. In a glowing tribute, Close acknowledged that this happy state of affairs was largely due to Martin's map cover designs.

Martin was not the only artist at work on map covers, although he was the only full-time designer. Close found a number of able amateur artists among his own staff, and Arthur Palmer, a photo-draughtsman who had joined the department in 1891, was to be the most prolific of the part-time artists. He designed a series of Tourist and District Map covers which had the quality of evoking a bygone age. Colourful in a gloomy, murky sort of way, they displayed the last vestiges of an outmoded art-nouveau style, especially in Palmer's attractive, limpid calligraphy.

However, Martin, with all his powers as a keen observer and expert painter, was not hemmed in by any feelings of the past so far as artistic style was concerned. His pictures are certainly evocative of the times, but they moved with the times. A drawing of a cyclist on a hillside, produced for the 1-inch map of 1919, is a perfect cameo of the period: the cyclist is in Norfolk jacket and plus-fours, with a tweed cap on his head. Fourteen years later, when the next edition of the 1-inch map was published, we are back on the self-same hillside, but this time the figure is a hiker, his knapsack on his back and his sleeves breezily rolled up. With a minimum of effort, Martin had captured a more liberal age than had existed when he painted his stuffily dressed cyclist.

One of Martin's most important assignments was to design a war memorial for those members of Ordnance Survey staff who had lost their lives in the war. The memorial took the form of two large stained-glass windows which were mounted over the library of the South Range in the London Road headquarters. These beautiful windows were destroyed during the Second World War. By then, however, Martin was no longer employed by the Ordnance Survey: in a pre-war economy drive, Martin's post was abolished and he was, in effect, made redundant.

Martin's map cover designs were mimicked by other publishers, but no other map cover artist anywhere ever matched his flair and sheer artistic skill. He was a master of his genre, and his work was the embodiment of that strange era of intense leisure pursuit which existed between the wars. Ellis Martin died in a Sussex nursing home in 1977 at the age of ninety-six.

Ellis Martin's cover design for a number of the 1-inch maps of the 1930s.

Map cover designs of the 1920s and 1930s. The Peak District cover is by Arthur Palmer, the other two by Ellis Martin.

Close reasoned that although staff numbers were considerably lower, so hours of work, leave and allowances had, over past years, been improved and that the whole process should be regarded as 'Reduction of staff accompanied by improvements of conditions'. He argued that the country was only willing to pay a certain sum for the survey and if individuals were to have more money, then there must be fewer of them. This must have made cheerless reading for the staff. Close seems to have been resigned to the cuts and even warned that if pay increased further then more reductions might have to be made.

The good relationship between management and the staff, military and civilians, suffered under the cuts and Close sadly observed that the early industrial peace which had marked the first years of his directorship could not be maintained. For Close himself, affection and respect ran deep. Knighted in 1918 for his services during the war Sir Charles was known to his staff by the nickname 'Daddy' and was particularly kind, understanding and appreciative of the changes that active service in the war had made on many of the employees.

Ireland after Colby

When Colby returned to mainland Britain in 1838 he left control of the Dublin office in the capable hands of Larcom, one of whose first successes was a railway map of Ireland at a ¼-inch scale (1 inch to 4 miles). This combined Ordnance Survey triangulation and mapping with information for those southern counties as yet unsurveyed by the department compiled from other sources. Colby decided not to publish this hybrid map under the Ordnance Survey name and it was published by Larcom and Griffith. The map was convenient, showing the whole of Ireland on six sheets and it continued in use until the Ordnance Survey finally published an 'official' map at this scale in 1887.

In the 1840s the Irish survey was threatened with complete closure when the task it had originally been created to carry out – measuring the townlands – was finished, but Larcom and Colby successfully lobbied for the Survey to continue, although in 1846 the Treasury ruled that 'every practicable reduction may be made in the expense'.

In mapping terms, Ireland was so far ahead of England that the Battle of the Scales left the Irish Survey more or less untouched. In fact it was argued that the 6-inch survey of Ireland was so exact that any publisher could make a 1-inch map from it. Eventually, after repeated protests, and in the interests of uniformity within the United Kingdom, the decision was taken in 1852 to allow the Ordnance Survey to publish a 1-inch map of Ireland; but, for economy, without hill features.

When Henry James took over as Superintendent of the Ordnance Survey he advocated that Irish maps should follow those of Great Britain in terms of scale and style. However, while Ireland remained so far ahead there was no question of replacing the 6-inch mapping

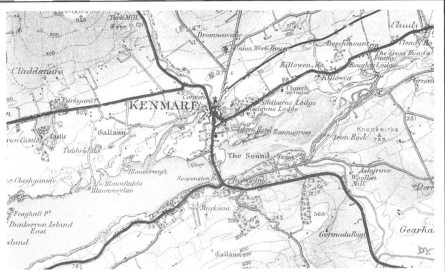

Part of the Killarney District map of 1913. Subsequent Tourist and District maps and the 1-inch 5th (Relief) Edition were based on this style. J R P Browne

with the 1:2500 agreed for Great Britain, and in 1868 the Treasury agreed instead to a revision of the existing Irish maps at the 6-inch scale.

In 1881, the Irish Land Act was passed under which the Land Commission could purchase estates for sale to tenants. Sales of Ordnance Survey 6-inch maps increased dramatically and revision work became a higher priority. Many farms, however, were small and the maps were not detailed enough to be practical. Further pressure for larger-scale mapping came in 1885 with the passing of the Ashbourne Act. Under this Act tenants were allowed to borrow the full price of their farms on favourable terms, an opportunity taken by many farmers. Charles Wilson, then head of the Irish Survey, persuaded the Treasury in 1887 that maps of Ireland at 1:2500 scale were now a necessity.

As it became obvious that Home Rule for Ireland was finally to become a reality, and that

the Irish Survey would pass out of the control of the Ordnance Survey, a certain apathy became apparent in the treatment it was given from Southampton. The Irish Survey, with its slow-selling and unprofitable maps was seen by Charles Close as a burden which he looked forward to shedding and, from 1912 onwards, little innovation was encouraged.

On the first day of January 1922 responsibility for the survey of the six counties which made up the new province of Northern Ireland was transferred to the Government of Northern Ireland and on the first day of April the same year, the remaining twenty-six counties were handed over to the Provisional Government of the Irish Free State (later to become the Republic of Ireland).

The three autonomous Ordnance Surveys remain on good terms and the productive and happy Mountjoy years are not forgotten.

In 1921 he contributed a series of articles to the *Royal Engineer's Journal* about the origins and first years of Ordnance Survey. These were later collected into a book and published as *The Early Years of the Ordnance Survey*.

Close's retirement can scarcely be described as such, for from 1922–8 he was secretary of the International Geographical Congress, and later President up to the Second World War. He remained on the council of the Royal Geographical Society for thirty-five years, resigning at the age of seventy-five. He was always modest about his achievements and took an immense interest in a wide range of subjects apart from cartography. In 1938 he took the name Arden-Close in compliance with the terms of a bequest. He died in 1952, survived by his wife for only three months.

The end of engraving

The first task facing Colonel Evan Maclean Jack when he succeeded Close in 1922 was the unpleasant one of implementing the measures of the Geddes Committee, and in particular their instruction to cut staff numbers to 1000.

At first all scales of maps had been engraved, but since the 1850s large-scale maps had been produced by photographic methods. However, for many more years it was felt that the fine linework of the 1-inch map still required production by engraving. It was probably obvious that engraving would become out-moded at some point, but in 1920 the engravers had been assured that reductions in their department were not envisaged. Indeed steps had been taken to adapt the use of engraved copper plates to colour printing methods. These were almost complete for the whole of England, and the engravers must have felt reasonably secure in the belief that the 1-inch map would continue to be produced by engraving methods for the time being.

However, alternative methods were already under examination and Lieutenant Colonel W J Johnston, by 1921 in charge of the publication division, had come to the conclusion that, for both economic and aesthetic reasons, the coloured Popular Edition would be better produced by redrawing, with reproduction by heliozincography. As part of the drive to reduce staff numbers to 1000, it was therefore decided to abolish the engraving department. When these plans became known, there was justifiable anger amongst the twenty-five engravers who felt they had been misled by the management. Jack was sympathetic but, although he patiently negotiated with them over the terms for their dissolution, he had no choice but to stand firm on the issue of the abolition. This was an emotive crisis with accusations from the engravers and their union of betrayal by the department and charges that

Ordnance Survey were adopting 'Victorian methods of administration'. The cuts were nevertheless implemented and by July 1923 the engraving branch had been phased out and the staff transferred to other duties, except for one solitary engraver who was retained for Admiralty work.

The case of the engravers was not Jack's only problem: the reductions affected all staff and reduced the promotion prospects of those who remained. This, and the nil recruitment policy, caused widespread dissatisfaction. The situation was aggravated by any vacancies that did occur being taken by former Royal Engineers who, having completed their military service by about the age of forty, could then settle down to a civilian career at Ordnance Survey for a further twenty years. Bad feeling between military, ex-military and civilian staff was the inevitable result.

Jack dealt with many of the grievances through the new Whitley system, agreeing to a number of changes requested by the civilian staff. The most important of these was the abolition of the daily rate of pay for work. Although piecework had by now been abandoned, daily pay rates and irregular pay increments remained and when Jack substituted annual salaries and regular increments it hammered home the last nail in the coffin of Sir Henry James's hated pay policy.

In the whole of Jack's eight-year term as Director General he was unable to procure any increase in staff numbers above the 1000 limit imposed by the Geddes Committee. The achievements of the Ordnance Survey were accordingly restricted.

New maps and cost-cutting

In 1924, Ordnance Survey was investigated by a Committee of Inquiry into government printing establishments. The Committee made the shock recommendation that responsibility for all map printing and the sale of maps should be transferred to the Stationery Office. Jack later recalled with horror that 'The proposed change would have had a disastrous effect' but 'fortunately was not approved, and I trust that it will never be revived'. A further recommendation that a costing system should be adopted by the department was accepted and trials were begun with alacrity and a profound sense of relief that the greater evil had been averted.

The abolition of engraving of the 1-inch map gave the opportunity for another review of its content. The design of the Fifth Edition was approached with 'free and unbiased minds, retaining what was good in the old map, but discarding that which was bad, or that which had been retained simply because it was done by the engravers'. The overall style of the map was maintained, but improved writing and symbols were incorporated, as was a system of solid black building depiction

Ordnance Survey map on Place's waterproof paper, c.1933.

optimistically thought 'Most adults in the nation became familiar during the war'. The usual interval for revision, of fifteen years, was kept as a standard, but intermediate revision was made to update the road information which was rapidly changing.

Sales of maps steadily increased, helped by the attractive cover designs by Ellis Martin and others, and by a spirit of adventure, and a willingness by Ordnance Survey to try new products. This era saw the publication of several 1-inch Tourist and special District maps including 'The Trossachs and Loch Lomond' and 'The Wye Valley', and an extension of the archaeological and historical series to include titles such as 'Roman Britain' and '17th Century England'. An experiment was also made in printing on a waterproof paper invented by Colonel C O Place, a Royal Engineer. Difficulties were experienced in the printing process but the resulting map was amazingly tough and capable of withstanding a wash with soap and water and being ironed! A note inside the front cover invited purchasers to send their comments on the map to the Director General. A high wastage rate in printing and a high price unfortunately caused the early demise of this promising method.

One of the strangest maps ever produced for the general public was published in 1927. Valid for use only on one day, it showed the projected path of the shadow during the total eclipse of the sun on 29 June that year. Prepared in co-operation with the Royal Society and Royal Astronomical Society, this oddity attracted much press and public attention – not all of it favourable as, on the eve of publication, a number of scientific errors were found in the calculations.

The revenue from sales of over £60 000 in Jack's last year of office was double the pre-war figure and was considered satisfactory taking into account the troubled economic state of the post-war years.

Economies also prompted innovation and considerable effort was made to reduce costs, turning attention to items which had received little consideration in the past. For instance, it was discovered that no systematic examination had ever been carried out of the chemical requirements of map photography and production. This was accordingly undertaken and an early success was made by Colonel J E E Craster who invented a method of recovering much more silver than before from the photographic processes. The silver was sold to reduce the chemical bill. Professional help was sought from the Scientific and Industrial Research Department who examined the chemicals used in the reproduction processes, and they assisted not only in cutting costs but in substituting less poisonous compounds (the use of hyposulphite of soda instead of cyanide of potassium, for example) and helping to create a safer working environment.

in built-up areas, which replaced the old method of cross-hatching. The opportunity was also taken to place both Scotland and England on the transverse Mercator projection. (Previously Scotland had been cast on the Bonne and England on the Cassini projection, creating a mismatch at the Scottish border.) Parish boundaries which had been removed from the maps in Close's day were brought back to stem the flood of complaints that had greeted their disappearance, and the boundaries of National Trust areas were also added. A 5000-yard grid was laid over the map for referencing by eastings and northings, a system with which Jack

Not all economies worked to the staff's advantage and, although a system of humidity control in one of the printing rooms improved map registration and cut the numbers of spoiled maps by reducing paper stretch, the system had the unwelcome effect of making 'a cold day feel colder and a hot day hotter'.

Mechanisation of processes previously done by hand and a 'work study' of the production flowline also led to greater efficiency and higher output. One notable innovation was a map-mounting machine invented for Ordnance Survey in 1927 by the Practical Machines Company. Once a number of teething problems were sorted out, it was highly successful and soon adopted by other mapping organisations.

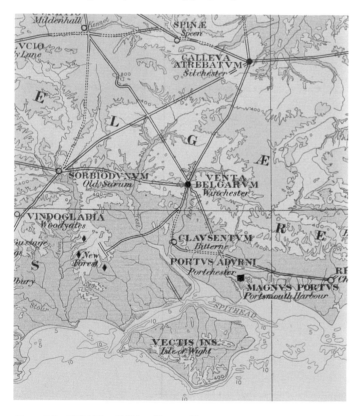

Part of the 1924 First Edition 'Roman Britain' map.

This Ellis Martin cover design was used for the Third and Popular Edition of District and Tourist maps, c.1932.

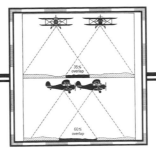

10 AT WAR AGAIN

Dry rot

Considerable effort, in Jack's term of office, had been put into the search for new and more efficient methods of production, but no technological breakthrough was made. Although small-scale maps kept up an illusion to the general public that the Ordnance Survey maps were up to date, large-scale revision was falling behind. Winterbotham was acutely aware of the situation and with his usual talent for allegory concluded that 'The drawing room is neatly papered with good small-scale maps, the rest of the house is beginning to show dry rot.'

The 1920s and 1930s were notable for an explosion of building activity. New roads, houses and industrial estates transformed the fringes of towns but the output of revised Ordnance Survey large-scale plans recording these changes, fell dramatically.

From 1928 the plans that were taken up were those where most change had taken place since the last revision. The more change there was on a sheet, the longer it took to revise, so fewer and fewer plans could be surveyed and published each year, and Ordnance Survey fell ever more behind.

Harold St John Lloyd Winterbotham succeeded Jack in 1930 as Director General, after being away from the department for eight years. This had been mainly spent in the post that Jack had vacated as Head of MI4 (Geographical Section, General Staff). Winterbotham was a complete contrast to Jack. A man of action and outspoken, he had an opinion on everyone and everything, a talent for witty observation and tremendous energy and enthusiasm. On returning to Ordnance Survey he was dismayed by the poor progress made towards bringing the large-scale maps up to date, but was confident that he could improve the situation. He considered Jack to have been wrong to quietly accept the Geddes cuts, and that with his 'outstanding honesty of purpose and loyalty to a mistaken policy . . . did not save the country money. He cost the country a cool million.'

Winterbotham explained in his first annual report that Ordnance Survey was failing to provide a useful service. Each morning post, he claimed, brought requests such as 'I am directed by my Council to ask if it is now possible to undertake the revision of the 1:2500 scale plans of this

Brigadier Harold St J L Winterbotham, Director General 1930–35.

district.' and 'The Council are requiring plans for town planning purposes, but they are unable to afford to pay for special plans.' As Ordnance Survey could not provide the plans needed by local councils, they began to make their own, sometimes using retired Ordnance Survey employees. These revisions, based more often than not on old distorted paper sheets and compiled without proper checks or field control, were generally of poor quality and the plans were suitable only for their immediate task. Saving money at Ordnance Survey merely resulted in a shifting of the cost of survey from a national government department to the local councils, or as Winterbotham saw it 'taxation falls even if rates increase.'

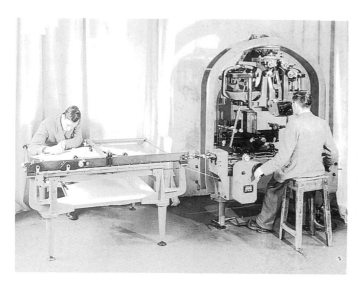

Wild A5 stereoplotting machine, c.1937.

Air photography

Every avenue for increasing production was explored, the greatest promise seeming to lie with air photography, a technique first used in the First World War. But there was a world of difference between rapid mapping of trenches and detailed and accurate peacetime survey work, and the technique proved difficult to adapt. Winterbotham was involved from the beginning, first as Ordnance Survey representative on the Air Survey Committee and then representing MI4 on the same Committee. At the end of his term as Director General he claimed to 'have done more about this air photo business than any other Englishman'.

Air photography experiments were begun in the early 1920s, with estuarial surveys of the River Duddon in Cumbria and Poole Harbour on the Dorset coast. These areas were chosen because mapping the water channels on the ground was 'difficult and often dangerous'. Unfortunately the photographs supplied were poor quality because of bad weather, and the trials were largely unsuccessful. A new attempt was made in 1926, this time on a more scientific basis, by revising an area near Eastbourne both by conventional ground methods, and from air photographs. From this Jack, by now Director General, concluded that the photographs were sufficiently accurate for survey purposes and would save staff time on the ground. However, after a few more years without real progress being made, Jack began to lose heart in the project and generally thought that it was 'unlikely that, for the special conditions of Ordnance Survey revision, air photography will be of great value or economical'.

Successful air photography depends on cloud-free skies and it was soon found that the incidence of days suitable for flying only amounted to around one month each year. The photographs obtained could not, of course, show names or boundaries and they were less helpful than anticipated because of information being hidden in shadows or roads obscured by overhanging trees. Surveyors still had to go out on to the ground to fill in the missing details. In addition the photographs had to be 'rectified' before use in order to take account of the angle of the aircraft, and therefore the camera, when the photographs were taken.

Winterbotham considered that the 1925–7 experiments were 'ill judged' mainly because it was 'obvious' that the cost for rural revision by air would be more than by conventional revision methods. In his opinion it was the expanding urban areas that should have been flown, but even here the gains made by using air photography were disappointing.

However, progress was made, albeit slowly, and by 1934 some eighteen staff were fully employed on air revision, partly because of a fortunate copyright infringement by a private firm called the Air Survey Company. They had been using Ordnance Survey plans as a basis for rectifying their photographs and, in return for permission to continue to do so, an agreement was made that they would supply free copies of the rectified photographs to Ordnance Survey. The revision of Middlesex was largely based upon these photographs.

A rectified photograph could be placed in an epidiascope, which projected the image of the photograph upwards on to the underside of a flat ground-glass screen. The image could be enlarged or reduced and tilted about two axes to produce a match to a surveyor's working plan laid on the screen. Detail was traced on to the plan directly from the air photograph image, a system which was adequate where relatively small changes were to be made to an otherwise fairly complete plan.

Using photographs as a starting point for maps was an altogether more difficult procedure, and essential research was carried out at Ordnance Survey under instruction from the War Office Air Survey Committee. Stereoplotting machines allowed two overlapping air photographs to be seen by the operator through an optical viewer, as a single three-dimensional image. The operator was able to see a superimposed 'dot' held within the optical system of the machine and apparently 'suspended' over the three-dimensional image. The 'dot' could be moved up and down, left and right and backwards and forwards. As the 'dot' was traced over the three-dimensional image it directed a pencil, through a system of rods, screws and levers. The shapes of houses, roads, paths, hedges, fences and so on could be traced on to the map, except where shadows were too deep on the photographs for the machine operator to see clearly. These techniques were still experimental when they were abruptly ended by the destruction and damage of the stereo-plotting equipment during the Second World War.

=== **I wish I could stay** ===

Winterbotham's own retirement seemed to take him by surprise. He was of retiring age, fifty-seven, but perhaps hoped to have been kept on for a further year or two to see through the expansion of staff numbers that he knew was about to happen. He left for his successor, Brigadier Malcolm MacLeod, a detailed set of handover notes giving advice about current problems and personalities, and setting out the plans he had for the future expansion of the Ordnance Survey: 'If this is a daydream does it touch you? . . . I wish I could stay to see it.'

Winterbotham's early optimism that he could turn the survey round and get permission to increase staff sufficiently to clear the arrears of work had turned to frustration as he failed to achieve his goal. Staff numbers had increased by 150 in his four years of office, but what Winterbotham was seeking was a real expansion of 500 or 600 staff. He regretted the lack of enthusiasm at the Ministry of Agriculture and Fisheries, and the isolation of Southampton from London. Of the Minister himself he wrote 'Not once, has he seen the Ordnance Survey, not once has he asked for first hand evidence', and complained that 'after four years I am no nearer driving the truth home than when I started.'

To be fair to the Ministry, there was probably little they could do during much of Winterbotham's term of office. In 1929 economic collapse began in the USA, spreading to all countries and resulting in massive unemployment as whole industries ground to a halt. In Britain an emergency, all-party government was formed to cope with the financial crisis and, amongst other measures, they announced massive cuts in state expenditure. Against this background the problems of the Ordnance Survey had to be considered a very low priority.

Obsessed with the historical perspective, Winterbotham considered that detailed records, not just of nationally important events, but of the 'thousand and one matters of our wide activity' should be made in the hope that 'we shall, perhaps, cease those frequent irrational changes of minor policy . . . which are dictated by ignorance of why existing method had been found desirable.' He was anxious that something should be written down before the knowledge was lost and compiled the history of the large-scale plans himself, as a professional paper. In his handover notes he hinted 'I have finished "the plans". I would welcome the job of "the maps" when I go.' MacLeod chose not to invite him to compile this and instead

Field section, c.1934, receiving instructions for the day's work.

Winterbotham wrote *A Key to Maps*, a small popular book about the general use of maps. Written in his easy, humorous style the book ran to several editions.

=== **MacLeod** ===

MacLeod was noticeably lacking in overt humour, and how much notice he took of Winterbotham's legacy of advice in the handover notes is open to conjecture. Certainly he was a man with very definite views of his own, who was unlikely to take kindly to attempts by a former Director General to rule from retirement. Winterbotham continued to closely follow the progress of the Ordnance Survey, and his ability to pass caustic and public comment about particular aspects of policy with which he disagreed led to MacLeod having to ask him to 'Keep off the grass', on more than one occasion.

MacLeod was born in India in 1882, but traced his family back to the Raasay (an island off Skye) branch of the clan MacLeod. He had a distinguished academic career, collecting both the Pollock and Queen Victoria gold medals at Woolwich. MacLeod was also an accomplished sportsman, his ambition to become skipper of the Royal Engineers Rugby XV shaping his choice of posting. He not only achieved this aim, but was also invited to join the famed Barbarians rugby team, which he had, regretfully, to turn down. As well as rugby, MacLeod played football and tennis to county standard.

During his service in the First World War, MacLeod, in command of the 4th Field Survey Company, had been responsible for many new developments in the production of

The smallest scales

The Quarter-inch map

Work first began on deriving a ¼-inch map from the 1-inch in 1859, but insufficient resources delayed its completion until 1888. This map was heavily criticised by Henry Crook who described it as 'bad in design, bad in execution, entirely obsolete ... and grossly inaccurate in places with regard to natural detail'. The Second Edition, addressed some of his complaints and was available for the whole country in twenty-one sheets by 1918.

The Third Series of the early 1920s was published both in map and atlas form, the first venture into this field for Ordnance Survey. Added emphasis was placed on the road network, and contours, enhanced with colour layering, were substituted for hill-shading.

In the 1930s, Winterbotham decided to 'go baldheaded for that large audience, the motorist of tomorrow'. The maps of this Fourth Series were strikingly different in format, being in their folded version long and thin for ease of use in a car. Green was used solely for woods and relief was shown by layer tints in buffs and browns.

The Ten-mile map

The main efforts of Ordnance Survey have always been concentrated on maps of the prescribed scales such as the 1-inch, the 6-inch and the 1:2500, but indexes showing the layout of sheetlines within these series, were often useful maps in their own right.

The 10-mile (1 inch to 10 miles, or 1:625 000) evolved in this way and was first engraved as an index for the 1-inch maps as early as 1817. However, the 10-mile map was not available as a topographical map until 1903, when it was produced both in outline, with coastal water in blue, and as a coloured hill-shaded map, printed in twelve sheets.

Revenue from the sale of these maps was never very significant, slipping to just under £20 in 1912. However, the map was continually in demand as a base on which statistical material might be overprinted, and many thematic maps were produced at this scale, especially for other government departments.

The map was revived in 1926 in three sheets 'without the least reference to public convenience' and there remained no real attempt to sell the maps, 'but rather a gracious permission to buy them if you took the trouble to find out for yourself how to get a copy'.

Part of the ¼-inch Fourth Edition, sheet 3, north east England, published 1935.

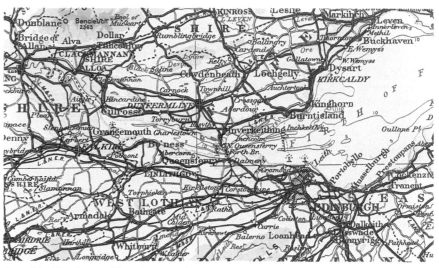

Part of the 10-mile map of Great Britain, North Sheet, published 1936.

Winterbotham perceived that the increasing number of cars on the road created a demand for a useful motoring map. Other map publishers already produced road maps in profusion, but Winterbotham made the Ordnance Survey road map superior by close consultation with the Ministry of Transport, who adopted it as a definitive record of their roads. The map was published on just two sheets in the 1930s and frequent changes of road information led to numerous revisions of this *Road Map*.

The International Map of the World

The concept behind this project was to have complete coverage of the world with mapping, to a uniform specification, at a scale of 1:1 000 000. Ordnance Survey published its portion, covering the United Kingdom, in 1905 and was later unanimously elected to serve as an advisory centre for participating countries. The war prevented any further work, but in the 1920s interest steadily increased as more countries contributed finished sheets to the map. By 1929 it was sufficiently complete to be used for long-distance flying and had also found favour as a base for statistics.

The international map was unusual in that it transcended all national boundaries. The sheets were produced by the country which had the largest amount of territory in the area. Thus France produced the Paris sheet which included Kent, and Britain the London sheet which included parts of Brittany and Normandy. Each sheet contained a standard 6° of longitude by 4° of latitude. Ordnance Survey published a map of Great Britain to the international standard in 1932 using the appropriate parts of seven of the international sheets.

Major General M N MacLeod, Director General 1935–43.

maps in the field. This left him with very definite ideas about the role of survey during war.

MacLeod joined the Ordnance Survey in 1922, and advocated the setting up of the 19th Field Company as a military training unit, with the intention of preparing REs in survey techniques for war conditions. However, his views were out of favour, as at the time 'General Staff were more interested in the development of tanks', rather than the combination of survey and artillery bombardment MacLeod advocated, and which had been so successful at the Battle of Cambrai in 1917. Winterbotham, as Head of MI4 (GSGS) at that time, did not support the scheme. MacLeod refused to let the matter rest and lectured and published articles about surveying, artillery and the necessary training.

However, it was not until 1929, when he succeeded Winterbotham as head of MI4, that he could put his ideas into action. The 19th Company finally came into being in 1930, and thereafter all Royal Engineer officers spent six months training in trigonometry and topography in the Company,

before joining Ordnance Survey. Perhaps not realising that MacLeod was behind this set-up, Winterbotham, in his handover notes to MacLeod, committed a serious *faux pas* in a humorous review of what he saw as the folly of this unnecessary company.

Winners and losers

Several Acts of Parliament passed from the mid-1920s required public authorities to use up-to-date maps, to comply with the terms of the Acts. The 1925 Land Registration Act was the first of these but, by 1928, Ordnance Survey was taking so long to revise any plan specifically for compulsory registration that the problem became the subject of an inquiry. As a result a payment to Ordnance Survey of £3000 a year was authorised, to be made by Land Registry for the employment of temporary extra staff. The money was never actually paid, but the Treasury allowed an equivalent increase of manpower, of sixteen men a year. Most of the Land Registry work was in suburban London and, although helpful, the extra manpower was still inadequate to cope with the Land Registry work.

Winterbotham believed that the demands made by Land Registry constituted a high priority, as their needs had been one of the major factors for the final settlement of the Battle of the Scales. Whereas, in the early days, the Ordnance Survey's *raison d'être* had been mapping for military purposes at 1-inch scale, Winterbotham now believed the main task was the supply of 'cadastral' mapping for civil needs. He went to great lengths to help the Land Registry, even to the point of closing down a survey office in Norwich and relocating it in London, specifically to build upon the relationship between the two departments. He also saw this as a means of providing a toehold in London which might by its accessibility bring relations with the Ministry of Agriculture and Fisheries to an improved state.

Cases from Land Registry requiring survey work were passed on a daily basis to the London Office for sorting and sending out to the appropriate field office. A special mobile force, using cars, tackled the London cases from that office. The time limit allowed for dealing with a Land Registry case was six days, after which an explanation had to be made to excuse its lateness. These measures showed that Ordnance Survey was capable of dealing very effectively with Land Registry. Difficulties were envisaged when, and if, compulsory registration was extended to more counties but Winterbotham saw in this the means of salvation for Ordnance Survey, believing that the Ministry would be unable to refuse to increase staff under such circumstances.

Further pressure was made on Ordnance Survey resources by the Town and Country Planning Acts of 1925 and 1932 which required councils to illustrate their planning schemes with maps. Ordnance Survey was simply unable to meet this demand and consequently planning schemes were held up because the maps were unavailable. Land registration needs were confined to a relatively small area, but town and country planning requirements made the problem visible nationwide.

The need for maps was beginning to overwhelm the need for government economy and in 1935 an investigative committee under Sir John Davidson was set up to consider what should be done. Out of the four problems they were set, they decided that two were urgent. These were the immediate needs of the Town and Country Planning Acts and a review of copyright regulations. The other two problems were the longer-term questions of how large-scale plans should be brought up to and kept up to date, and a general review of map scales and styles. What was absent from their terms of reference was any mention of how Ordnance Survey maps should be made to answer for the needs of compulsory land registration.

It was found that about 4500 plans needed urgent revision, of which 1400 needed 'substantial' revision. MacLeod advised the Committee that with current resources only 200 plans a year could be produced but suggested that a partial revision could be made, updating only the details essential to town planning. This would allow the 1400 plans to be cleared within two years but could even then only be achieved if all normal revision work was suspended. The Committee agreed that a partial revision was the answer and to prevent the undesirable consequence of further arrears in normal revision work they authorised the much wished for increase in the staff complement of Ordnance Survey.

The Committee had considered carefully the question of the practicability of air photographs being used, instead of conventional methods for map revision, but concluded that 'to rely solely on air photography to cover a vital stage in map revision would be a risk that could not be justified.' This caution was prompted by the failure of an air survey trial covering the Birmingham area, but the Committee felt that air photography was a future way forward, and recommended further experiment.

This happy state of expansion had not considered the needs of Land Registry. Winterbotham's special relationship with them had been carefully nurtured believing, as he did, that when compulsory registration was brought in for more counties this would provide the impetus for Ordnance Survey expansion, but suddenly town and country planning was the new priority. MacLeod seemed particularly unsympathetic towards the Land Registry and in 1935 declared that Ordnance Survey could not undertake to revise any more whole counties, in anticipation of land registration. This was perceived by the Land Registry as a betrayal, and a deep rift developed between the two departments.

It was not that MacLeod did not want to co-operate with Land Registry, but he saw their requirement, by comparison with town and country planning needs, to be less urgent. He was also dissatisfied with the fact that, in urban areas, 1:2500 plans had to be enlarged photographically to 1:1250 for Land Registry, which ran counter to the long accepted practice of always surveying at the largest scale required. MacLeod's view, given to the Davidson Committee, was that it would be more sensible to survey these urban areas at 1:1250 scale in the first place. He even suggested that the extension of compulsory land registration should be postponed until this was done.

The Land Registry vehemently disagreed, pointing out that the maps were not used as conclusive evidence of property boundaries but only for the identification of registered land. MacLeod's proposal would mean both a very long wait before they could proceed with their task and a vast increase in the cost of the mapping to Land Registry. However, postponement of compulsory registration became unavoidable as the Davidson Committee agreed that town planning was the mapping priority, and that the resources of Ordnance Survey should be directed, in the first instance, towards this.

No exemption

The right of Ordnance Survey to charge copyright royalties to commercial publishers who reproduced its maps for profit was largely established by 1935, but there remained a particular problem with local authorities who had to use Ordnance Survey maps for public purposes. These ranged from complying with Parliamentary regulations in the submitting of proposals for town planning, to drafting out schemes for street-lighting and public transport.

In 1925 it was agreed that local authorities had a special case, and they were permitted to copy Ordnance Survey plans free of charge, on the understanding that copying the maps in bulk would not take place. This proviso was widely ignored, and instances of 'editions' of more than 500 copies came to Ordnance Survey notice. Perhaps more damaging than the number of maps being copied by the local authorities was the fact that the copies often excluded the Ordnance Survey Crown copyright notice. These unmarked maps were found to have been extensively copied for private interest, without payment of royalties being made.

Civilian recruits being taught 'detail surveying' by a non-commissioned officer.

New rules introduced from 1932 restricted the local authorities to making, without notification to Ordnance Survey, only a dozen copies of each map. If notification was given, they could make up to fifty copies without incurring royalty charges, provided that these contained the desired acknowledgements of source and copyright, and that they were printed by the local authorities themselves. These regulations were unworkable. They had been made without reference to the fact that most local authorities contracted their copying to private firms. It was also considered unfair that other corporate bodies using the maps for public purposes could not claim exemption from royalty payments.

In general Davidson could see no good argument for allowing local authorities any exemption from copyright royalty payments. Indeed, he argued that if the Ordnance Survey maps were unavailable, then 'a very substantial expense would be thrown upon local authorities' to provide their own surveys.

Davidson recommended that all users of Ordnance Survey copyright material should pay royalties, and that exceptions should be allowed only 'very sparingly' for nonprofit-making learned and scientific publications, and only then when a small portion of map was used. To ensure that loopholes were closed, private printers with contracts for local authority map reproduction had to obtain a special licence from Ordnance Survey, and to keep record copies of all reproductions made. These could be inspected at any time. This review of the copyright rules doubled the revenue received from royalty payments within the next three years.

A new charter

The Davidson Committee made their interim report in 1935, but took a further three years to consider the two longer-term problems they had been set. MacLeod and Davidson were both aware that the recommendations made on the remaining issues of revision procedure for large-scale maps, and the review of scales and styles of maps, would be laying down a framework for the next half century. Both were deeply concerned that the right decisions should be made.

Davidson invited MacLeod to see him privately before the Committee formally began its work, and discussed with him 'the future of your show'. At this and other meetings the two men found ground on which they could immediately agree. This was helpful to MacLeod as he could, for instance, begin the retriangulation of Britain in full confidence that it would meet with the Committee's approval.

The Committee also got off to a good start on the question of scales. It was unanimously agreed that the 1:2500 scale was the ideal scale for the national plans and should be retained. However, MacLeod, pointing out that this was a decimal scale, advocated that all other scales should be divisions or multiples of it. Thus his next suggested scale was 1:12 500 into which twenty-five 1:2500 plans would fit. From here he went to 1:25 000, 1:50 000, 1:125 000, 1:500 000 and finally to 1:1 000 000.

Davidson agreed that to have the scale related in ratio was desirable 'if it were possible to wipe the slate clean and start afresh, but we have had to consider that there already exists a well-established series of scales'. Some consultation was made to see if a 1:12 500 scale would be preferred to the 6-inch (1:10 560) but although no difficulty was perceived by potential customers neither was there 'evidence of any wide-spread desire for such a change'. On balance Davidson decided that it would be best to retain the tried and tested 6-inch map scale.

MacLeod did manage to convince the Committee of the merits of national cover at the 1:25 000 scale. He believed it would 'undoubtedly have considerable civil value and . . . enjoy a good sale'; he thought it might possibly 'eventually replace the six-inch'. The 1:25 000 scale was greatly desired by the War Office who had, for some years, considered it ideal for tactical manoeuvres, and essential for training. A number of sheets had already been produced by Ordnance Survey at

the expense of the War Office who were of the opinion that they would like the whole country mapped at this scale as soon as possible, 'were unlimited money available'.

MacLeod's loyalties may have been divided between the military advantages of the scale and the question of genuine need of the map for civil purposes. By this time war was perceived to be a real possibility and, although the War Office needed the 1:25 000 maps, they couldn't afford to pay for them. If evidence could be found that the maps would be of use to the general public, then the cost would be borne by Ordnance Survey. In the event, the scale was agreed, not only for military benefit, but also in the belief that it would prove particularly suitable for walkers and educational authorities.

The Davidson Committee could see no reason for changing any of the scales of mapping at 1-inch and smaller and recommended that all should be retained. Some discussion did take place over MacLeod's suggestion for substitution of a 1:50 000 scale map for the 1 inch, but once he had lost the argument for the 1:12 500 MacLeod could see no advantage in pressing for the 1:50 000 scale, especially as such a change would be very expensive. Prophetically he did, however, express the view that it 'might be considered at a later date'.

A keen recruit taking seriously the need for exact measurement, despite the unpleasant conditions.

The Committee also considered the introduction of a new large scale of mapping for urban areas. Land Registry and local authorities had made it clear that the 1:2500 was inadequate in these town areas. Although generally in favour of a scale of 1:1250, Davidson recommended that the revision at 1:2500 should take priority. When this was nearing completion, further investigations into the desirability of the 1:1250 should, the Committee thought, then take place.

The review of map styles included in the Davidson Committee's terms of reference did not result in any recommended changes. After examination of evidence they concluded that it was both 'unnecessary and undesirable for us to recommend any changes ... for such questions fall more properly within the scope of the Director General.'

Continuous revision

In spite of the measures to accelerate revision introduced as a result of the interim Davidson report, by 1939, 50 per cent of the plans were still more than twenty years out of date.

MacLeod favoured a system of continuous revision. This abandoned the concept of revising plans at a prescribed interval of years (cyclic revision) and replaced it with a system of change being incorporated on to a 'master' plan as soon as possible after it occurred. The revised plans would only be fair drawn and published after a certain amount of change had taken place. In the meantime the surveyor's master plan could, on payment of a fee, be copied for anyone who needed up-to-the-minute information. The Davidson Committee considered that the solution was 'ideal' and should 'be adopted as soon as practicable'. Understandably the Treasury were less enthusiastic as there was no illusion that this was a cheap solution to the problem. They were finally convinced, on the grounds that to continue cyclic revision would 'permit continued deterioration in the knowledge that at some future date it must be remedied at ever growing cost'.

MacLeod was content with the findings of the Davidson Committee, and could claim with justification that most of their recommendations were 'based on the proposals which I submitted to the Committee'. With satisfaction, he hailed the Final Report of the Davidson Committee as 'a new charter for the Ordnance Survey'.

Preparations for war

Just prior to the First World War the department had stood in a state of readiness, with maps as up to date as they could be. The situation before the Second World War was somewhat

'Penning up' after the day's surveying. The ink was kept flowing from the bone-handled pen by frequent wiping of the adjustable blade on a convenient surface, usually the fingers.

The National Grid

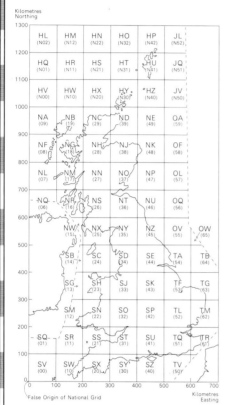

The 100-kilometre National Grid squares that cover Great Britain. Both reference letters and the numbering formerly used are shown.

One of the recommendations of the Davidson Committee was that the 1:2500 plans should be recast on national sheetlines, and on a national projection. This would also allow the use of a new standard reference system – the National Grid. Instead of the multitude of meridians, at one stage Winterbotham had counted in excess of 150 (many towns had their own), there would

be just one, running up through the middle of the country.

The projection chosen was the Transverse Mercator, a modification of the Cassini projection then in use. This projection was not new, having been successfully used by Ordnance Survey since 1929 for the Fifth Edition 1-inch map, and as early as 1821 by Gauss for his map of Hanover. However, Gauss's work was not published until 1866, by which time the Ordnance Survey was committed to its format of individual county and town meridians.

The Transverse Mercator was particularly suitable for a long thin country and especially suited to Great Britain, after the removal of Ireland from its outline. The projection also had the major benefit for mapping of stretching the topography equally in all directions, an effect known as orthomorphism.

The origin, or zero point, of the projection (the 'true origin') was selected at a point, latitude 49° North, longitude 2° west (of Greenwich). The origin of the National Grid (the 'false origin') is 400 kilometres west of the meridinal line, at 49°46′ North and 7°33′ West, a point just south-west of the Isles of Scilly. The national meridian was chosen to be the 2° West line of longitude, which is also the only National Grid line coincident with a line of longitude.

The National Grid related only to Great Britain, and, apart from the one coincident line, totally ignored the world-wide geographical referencing system of latitude and longitude. This made it easy to use, and neatly avoided the problems inherent in a grid based on latitude and longitude in the northern hemisphere, that grid lines had to taper inwards slightly towards the north, as a reflection of the narrowing of the South–North grid lines towards the North Pole.

The use of a metric National Grid had a number of advantages, not least of which was that the number of 1:2500 plans needed to

cover the country was 200 000 plans of 1 kilometre square, compared with 240 000 plans of 1000 yards square if the imperial grid was used.

The National Grid system covers the country in a series of progressively smaller squares, nesting inside each other. The largest squares, with sides of 500 km were originally referred to by numbers, but from 1951 letters (all those except I) were used instead. Each 500-km square is broken down into twenty-five 100-km squares, again referred to by letters. Within the 100-km squares are one hundred 10-km squares, and within each of these are one hundred 1-km squares. The references that can be quoted are as precise as the map scale will allow the map reader to identify, or interpolate down to, for example, 1 metre, or perhaps 0.1 metre, on a 1:1250 plan.

A further advantage of the National Grid was that it could also be used as a map numbering system, by 'naming' the maps with the grid references of their south-west corner. This was adopted for scales larger than 1:25 000.

For the general public the National Grid was only a qualified success. Most regular map users welcomed it, but the occasional map user found it complicated and confusing. One problem was remembering which figures to quote first, as the National Grid system was the opposite way round to the usual method of quoting longitude and latitude. On some of its maps, Ordnance Survey now prints a reminder of the rule to read the grid reference along the bottom (or top) of the map first, and then up the side, that is eastings followed by northings.

Tourists and motorists were found to dislike the National Grid, and preferred to buy maps with a simple reference grid relating to an individual map. In recent years these have been introduced on some Ordnance Survey maps, but in all cases the national grid is discreetly retained for anyone who wishes to use it.

different. During the parsimonious inter-war years a heavy layer of unsurveyed map detail had settled over Britain and, although a start had been made on revision, the expanded Ordnance Survey had yet to sweep up all the information on to its maps.

The expansion of staff numbers authorised by the Davidson Committee overcrowded the London Road offices and additional Ordnance Survey offices began to appear at

various locations around Southampton. Premises at Crabwood House, Maybush, were obtained, and within the spacious grounds of this private house, it was intended, in the future, to build a purpose-designed office for the Ordnance Survey. But in the meantime the house itself and a number of hurriedly erected huts served to accommodate some of the extra staff.

Responsibility for military survey at this time rested with

the Geographical Section of the General Staff (GSGS). This War Office department was headed and staffed by Royal Engineer officers with survey qualifications. Its function was to prepare and supply to British forces and War Office staff world-wide, all maps for defence, administration, training and active service. A huge library of foreign maps and survey data was also collected. In the event of a war, the organisation of survey units and initiation of mapping would fall to this office. A small but fully equipped map production unit was under its direct control, although much of the work was contracted to Ordnance Survey.

By now, Ordnance Survey had lost all responsibility for survey work of a purely artillery nature, such as the sound-ranging and flash-spotting techniques at which they had become so expert during the First World War. This had been taken over by the Royal Artillery who formed their own Artillery Survey Regiments for the purpose, but it was agreed that, during any war, the Royal Engineers would continue to be responsible for all other survey work, such as triangulation and supply of maps.

By late 1934 the evidence that Germany was preparing for war was, to military minds, overwhelming and Winston Churchill called for more spending on defence, saying that German munitions factories were already working 'under practically war conditions'. In spring the following year, new expansion plans for the Services were announced by the government including a trebling of the size of the RAF within two years. What Stanley Baldwin had termed 'our attempt to lead the world towards disarmament by unilateral example' had failed and Britain joined the new arms race.

Funds ten times the normal amount were made available to GSGS for 1936 to undertake a large programme of new mapping, mainly of north-east France and Belgium at various scales. Most of the work for this British rearmament series was allocated to Ordnance Survey for execution under a specially appointed officer. The French mapping was undertaken with the full co-operation of their own *Service Geographic de l'Armée* but, because of the neutral position of Belgium, War Office library maps had to suffice as a base for that country. Production capacity at Ordnance Survey was reviewed, and it became clear that this would be insufficient if war was to break out. Five high-class lithographic printing firms were therefore approached in strict confidence with trial map orders. Only one had printed maps before but all gave satisfactory service during the trial and this resource was held in reserve against such a time as it might be needed.

Following its non-aggression pact with Russia, Germany invaded Poland on 1 September 1939. Britain and France, who had made a commitment to defend Poland against attack, declared war on Germany two days later.

Even before war was formally declared, Britain had been living with the expectation of it for some years. Mass Civil Defence exercises had taken place as early as 1935 and in 1937 Parliament had sanctioned a massive programme of providing air-raid shelters in most towns. Over the following two years Ordnance Survey issued, on a restricted basis, specially updated 6-inch maps to local authorities in urban and built-up areas to enable them to cope effectively with air-raid emergencies. This Special Emergency (Air Raid Precaution) Edition was made by including all available large-scale revision reduced on to existing 6-inch maps. The result was a slightly untidy and less accurate map than would normally be acceptable, but it was up to date.

At war again

British forces were fully mobilised well before the invasion of Poland and this dramatically affected staff numbers at Ordnance Survey. The Survey Battalion of seventeen Royal Engineer officers and 500 other ranks was mobilised into three Survey companies and two Survey Training Units. The Survey companies stood in readiness to serve overseas with the British Expeditionary Force and the Survey Training Units merged to become a War Office controlled Survey Training Centre RE located in Wales. Up until this point, all training in survey for war had been undertaken by Ordnance Survey, and MacLeod, who had clear ideas on how such training should be organised, was extremely annoyed by this sudden takeover. In addition to the loss of the Royal Engineers, 180 reservists, territorials and militia were called up from Ordnance Survey to join their various units.

No arrangements had been made to categorise any of the civilian jobs at Ordnance Survey as reserved and, within six months, 675 of the 2495 civil assistants had been called up. Belatedly, consideration was given to reserving some posts, as it became obvious that a core of trained and experienced staff had to be retained, to ensure that the production of maps for the war was kept in full swing. Early in the war Ordnance Survey were able to recruit the skilled tradesmen it needed from civilian printing firms, but by 1942 reproduction staff were being 'directed' to Ordnance Survey as an alternative to enlistment.

The department coped with the loss of its trained men as best it could, calling retired staff back to duty and, in common with much of British industry, employing women to supply some of the numbers needed. By the end of 1940 some seventy-four 'women draughtsmen' were under training 'in the simpler classes of large-scale drawing'. Young lads between the age of 16 and 17 were also engaged and trained in basic 'map construction', and during the war over 1000 of

A direct hit

After the evacuation of Dunkirk in 1940, the Ordnance Survey headquarters at Southampton found itself potentially in the front line. MacLeod requested a move to safer quarters but the Office of Works had been inundated with similar requests and all departments were told to stay where they were.

MacLeod made contingency arrangements and secured the authority to commandeer a large modern printing works in Nottingham as a reserve headquarters. Duplicate printing plates, stocks of paper and so on were assembled at Nottingham and offices established both there and at Derby Grammar School. At Southampton some map production processes were moved into huts hurriedly built in the grounds of Crabwood House on the outskirts of the town.

On the night of 23 November 1940, three incendiary bombs fell at London Road all of which were quickly dealt with by the fifteen-strong fire party on duty. It was recorded that 'Night-watchman Sallis . . . directed the boys when to lie flat and wasted no time once the bombs had fallen in ordering them to resume operations. He was most helpful and inspiring . . . One Sapper and two Boys were wounded.'

Worse was to follow a week later when the incendiaries 'showered down in such numbers that the ARP personnel and the military piquet were unable to cope with the situation'. The fire brigade managed to attend, although overwhelmed by calls from all parts of the town. They achieved some initial success in controlling the fires, but with bombs still falling, the water supply gave out and there was little more anyone could do. Soldiers' families in married quarters on the site had a terrifying night being evacuated four times from different buildings in an effort to find safe shelter and four fire-

Blitz damage at Ordnance Survey headquarters, Southampton.

fighters were slightly hurt. The courageous action of the staff that night was recognised by the award of the George Medal to Lieutenant Jack Keleher and Boy N S Thompson RE for their conspicuous bravery and devotion to duty.

MacLeod reported to the Ministry that 'Several blocks of the buildings on the OS enclosure were completely gutted or partially destroyed as a result of incendiaries and H.E. [high explosive] shells . . .' In addition two outstations, the old public library in London Road and Marlands House near the Civic Centre, were demolished.

Many thousands of maps were lost, as well as large quantities of glass negatives, original manuscripts, the library and numerous offices. The original Ramsden 3-foot theodolite, which had been stored in a basement for safety, was said to have melted. However, as most of the war work had been transferred to Crabwood,

little delay was caused to production. On 18 December MacLeod reported that 'practically all our draughtsmen and most of our printing machines are now at work.'

Southampton suffered from frequent air attacks, the docks being a natural target, and the question of moving the department was once again taken up 'very energetically' with the War Office by Colonel Hotine. New offices at Chessington in Surrey were erected and finally occupied in 1943. The printing works at Nottingham had been commandeered for map production and so, although never used as a headquarters, remained an Ordnance Survey outstation.

MacLeod observed ironically that 'no more bombs fell in Southampton, even on and around 'D' day, while the new offices at Esher and Chessington had many narrow escapes from flying bombs and rockets.'

these youngsters were subsequently enlisted into Royal Engineers survey units. MacLeod also managed to increase the number of Royal Engineers at Ordnance Survey, firstly by accepting trainees awaiting a posting on active service and later by welcoming REs unfit for field survey duties due to injury or illness, but able to undertake light work. The number of men 'overposted' in this way swelled the numbers by up to 200 men.

In general the main contribution of the Ordnance Survey to the war was its ability to meet the heavy demand for printed maps. Once war was declared the normal civil

mapping programme was set aside as Ordnance Survey became,· in effect, 'a War Office controlled factory for map production', although it still remained under the administrative control of the Ministry of Agriculture and Fisheries. Throughout the war Ordnance Survey was the principle source of bulk map supplies for theatres of war in Europe and north west Africa. Maps for further afield were printed in countries closer to the action or by the Allies.

As well as actually printing maps Ordnance Survey also produced numerous large-scale plans and monochrome small-scale maps in the form of kodaline film negatives.

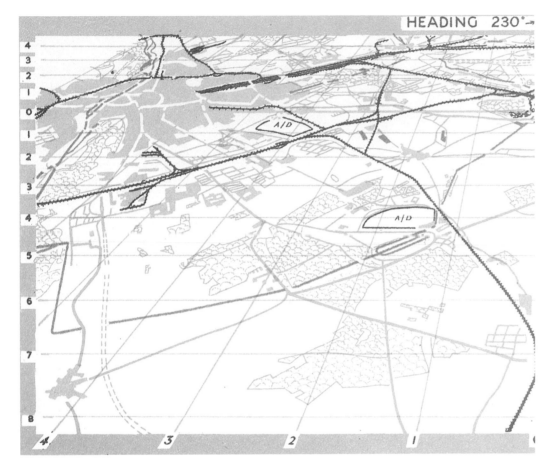

HEADING 230°

A/D

A/D

*Part of a 1943 bombing mission
map. An oblique view of the area,
as would be seen by the pilot on
his approach to the target (Allach,
near Munich) on bearing 230°.*
J R P Browne

These were supplied to field survey units who could print paper maps from them as demand dictated. These units made use of both static printing machines for larger maps and smaller mobile printing machines mounted on trailers. In the retreat back to Dunkirk these machines kept up a constant supply of maps and, as Albert Hicks, a driver with the 14th Field Survey Company, recalls,

> we managed to keep working, but when we got to within eighteen miles of Dunkirk, we found all the bridges in front of us had been blown up, and the order was given to destroy all equipment we could not carry. Cars, lorries, printing machines, etc. were all destroyed with big hammers through the machinery and engines.

All survey equipment, much of it on loan from Ordnance Survey, was lost in the retreat, except for a few theodolites which were carried to safety by hand. After they landed at Ramsgate, Albert remembers that the Survey Company went by train to Wiltshire where they received an unexpected welcome.

> We had not been there long when in came a very smart car and out stepped Queen Mary and the Princess Royal, who after a brief word with some of us, sat down behind a trestle table and as we all filed past she gave us a £1 note each. In the evening, after they had gone, we went into town to have a drink but we could not spend that £1, every drink we ordered was free, the publicans would not take our money.

The mobile map-printing units had proved their worth in France and machines were later installed into specially designed lorries for rapid deployment in war zones.

The evacuation from Dunkirk switched the emphasis from foreign to home mapping. The danger of invasion by the Germans, previously remote, suddenly became imminent and a large home defence army had to be provided at short notice with maps of all possible invasion areas. MacLeod knew that the ordinary civil maps were largely unsuitable for these purposes as gridded maps were essential for military operations. He estimated that 50 000 gridded maps of 150 different 1-inch sheets would be required, as well as quantities of gridded 1:25 000 maps. But GHQ Home Forces, which was responsible for defence, had initially underrated the importance of mapping and MacLeod found himself without guidance on which areas were to be made a priority. Urgent representations to the Director of Military Operations resulted in belated inclusion of a survey organisation within the defence force framework and the necessary maps were rapidly produced. Maps of areas most at risk from invasion were printed within two months, just in time for the expected invasion date. The 1:25 000 maps were produced by direct photographic reduction from the published 6-inch maps.

The bombing of Ordnance Survey's Southampton offices in 1940 drove the administrative headquarters into temporary accommodation in Southampton until a new specially built complex of huts could be completed at Chessington in Surrey. Map production under direct Ordnance Survey control was eventually carried out at Chessington, Esher and Waddon in Surrey, at Crabwood near Southampton and at Nottingham. Each of these branches had its own quota of draughtsmen and machinery and was more or less a self-contained entity so that destruction of one by bombing would not affect the others.

Despite the rapid expansion of printing facilities at the different Ordnance Survey sites it was necessary not only to call into service the five commercial printing firms previously approached, but also an additional thirty printers nationwide. Urgency did not allow for normal tendering formalities to be followed and, instead, a cost-plus-profit scheme was worked out with the British Federation of Master Printers. Ordnance Survey supplied the paper and the master printing plates and a standard profit of 7½ per cent was permitted to the printing companies. The department also requisitioned numbers of printing machines which were returned to their owners after the war, having given good service.

The efficiency of the map supply operation was a matter of pride to the staff. The following recollection by J J Dawson at the Nottingham works refers to mapping provided for the D-Day landings and subsequent invasion of Europe by the Allies.

When General 'Blood and Guts' Patton had swept right
across France, he sent back his message – 'Send me
ammunition and maps'. We were already engaged on a series
of 1:25 000 of Eastern France, Holland and Belgium . . .
Suddenly the pressure for these maps became more urgent
and the ordinary methods of transport (road and rail) were

abandoned. The maps were coming off the machines at about 4 pm, were packed and rushed by lorry to Hucknall Aerodrome a few miles away, from there they were flown to Tangmere and by breakfast time the next morning they were delivered to the men who needed them. In the whole four years at Nottingham that was the task that gave the greatest pleasure and satisfaction to all concerned.

The combined war output from the private firms employed under contract and the Ordnance Survey, was approximately 342 415 000 maps.

As a result of enemy action, fifty-six Ordnance Survey staff lost their lives in the Second World War.

To Members of the Ordnance Survey who are at present Prisoners of War.

We are all looking forward to the day when you will rejoin us and help to start building up again the peace-time work of the Ordnance Survey. The end of the war will find us with heavy arrears in our programme. The successful development of the post-war planning of the country will depend largely on the way in which we carry out our task of supplying the maps and plans which must form the basis of the work.

The planning of the Ordnance Survey post-war programme is in hand. In order to execute our plans quickly it is necessary to get as many of our old staff to work as possible and that their knowledge and experience of Ordnance Survey methods should be as great as possible. Not only do we expect to absorb our own old staff as fast as we can get them, but there are likely to be vacancies for others who have an interest in the work. We shall want not only trained men to go on progress, but instructors for the school. There will be a place for all of you in this scheme, and the more you have kept up your survey knowledge the better you will be able to help and the better will be your prospects.

I have consequently had prepared these notes on Trigonometrical and Detail Survey for you. I suggest that those of you in each camp who have most experience should help the ones who have less knowledge. I should suggest also that any of you who have an aptitude for instructing should take turns in holding classes in order to train yourselves as instructors.

I have already mentioned that after we have absorbed our own staff, there are likely to be vacancies for new men; so encourage people who are not old survey men to join your classes. Even if they don't join us after the war, they will find the work interesting and useful.

I hope that in addition to the value both you and the survey may get from your working on these notes, you will find that they help you to pass the time away until you come back to rejoin us.

G. Cheetham

Major General,
Director General,
Ordnance Survey

November, 1943.

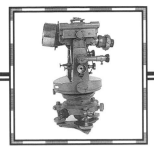

II   DAVIDSON DAYS

═══ Retriangulation ═══

Control for large-scale mapping was, until after the Second World War, provided by the triangulation framework completed in 1852. Some forty local meridians, one per county or group of small counties, were used. Each of these county areas was treated as a separate entity, accurate within itself, but there were serious discrepancies, of up to 50 feet on the ground, when plans of one county were compared directly with those of a neighbour. Various attempts were made to recompute small areas from existing triangulation observations across county boundaries, but this created even more of a patchwork effect. With urban development boom of the 1930s, it became quite apparent to MacLeod that a complete retriangulation to geodetic standards was necessary.

The task was put in the hands of Captain Martin Hotine, Head of the Trigonometrical and Levelling Division, and the subsequent creation of the retriangulation and the methods to be later employed on it, were his.

Traditionally the primary triangulation of the whole country would be carried out first, followed in turn by the secondary and tertiary triangulation. However, there was already a shortage of suitably qualified observers, and Hotine was also aware of the potential war looming. This, he knew, would take a considerable toll on Ordnance Survey staff numbers, but without the retriangulation there would be little point in embarking on a massive programme of new large-scale survey. There was a need first of all for triangulation control, and it was needed fast.

Hotine's solution was a clever and slightly unorthodox compromise. He divided the country into seven blocks or 'figures' and decided to concentrate the first season's efforts on the primary triangulation within just two of these. When the retriangulation of these two figures was completed, the computations were declared final and all subsequent retriangulation was referred to them.

The first task, started in 1935, was a 'paper recce', which involved marking up on large-scale plans the position of the primary and secondary trigonometrical stations that had been found and re-marked during Sir Charles Close's directorship, and also the supposed position of stations not found. This gave an indication of local problems such as obstruction by buildings constructed since the last observations, of up to

Major M Hotine (second from right) and three observers during the early stages of the retriangulation.

100 years earlier. From this a broad picture of the framework of triangles grew, and the need for additional and resited stations became apparent. The average primary triangle side was planned to be about 30 miles; those of the secondary triangles would be about 5 miles long.

A ground reconnaissance of the first two figures of the triangulation was carried out later in the year. During this the 'recce' parties temporarily marked the sites of the proposed trig. stations. At some sites they noted where the use of axe and slasher (and the permission of landowners) would be needed to clear trees and undergrowth, which were obstructing the observing rays to other trig. stations.

Land subsidence in mining areas, or near quarries, was sometimes a problem as the effects could translate into a sideways slide of the trig. station. The possibility of this undesirable event was minimised by consultation with colliery surveyors and the Geological Survey Department, who advised on the selection of stable sites. At mines these were often on colliery winding towers, which were not popular observing sites, splattered as they were with coal-dust impregnated heavy lubricating grease. Surveyors and observers smeared with the grime soon adopted some hastily but effectively retailored potato sacks as overclothes.

The stations temporarily marked by the recce parties, were later made permanent by the construction of the familiar 4-foot high triangulation pillar, built of either concrete and painted with masonry paint, or of local stone. The pillar builders worked ahead of the observing parties to allow time for the newly constructed pillars to settle. Primary triangulation pillars are very nearly all placed on the tops of hills or mountains, often some distance from roads or even tracks. Transporting the raw materials, sand, gravel and cement by the hundredweight, to these remote sites required ingenuity. Hired lorries or horse and cart were used as far as a road or track could be followed and then the loads were transferred to packhorses, often resorting to sheer manpower where the ground was too steep or boggy for the horses. The pillar builders were resourceful, independent men with great powers of determination. A pillar base needed to be sunk at least 3

Vanessa tube shuttering, centre tube and tools being carried to the site of pillar construction.

feet deep, representing considerable spadework in unpleasant conditions. Anything less, and it could be inclined to topple over. It is thanks to the integrity of the pillar builders that most of the pillars they constructed stand firm to this day, having withstood the unwelcome attention of frost, subsidence, lightning strike or the occasional energetic vandal.

Endless speculation surrounded the pillars' intended purpose and the surveyors employed recorded some of the more fanciful suggestions put forward by local people:

A neon light at the summit for the guidance of aircraft;
A sundial;
A searchlight or the mounting of an anti-aircraft gun;
An oil well;
In commemoration of the Jubilee.

In some places, such as the remote points in the Highlands and Islands of Scotland, the pillars were constructed as round columns, concrete being poured into a large cardboard tube, for some reason called a 'Vanessa tube'. These tubes were allowed to rot away or were stripped off, and the pillar painted at the next visit when initial observations would take place. There was an obvious saving in time and effort here, as normal pillars were constructed with wooden shuttering, which had to be retrieved by the pillar builder before the observation party arrived.

Some of the original stations had been marked by the sappers with a cairn, so that they could be easily located in the future. Over the years these sometimes acquired the status of an 'ancient monument' and became an object of local veneration. In one such case Ordnance Survey was accused of 'vandalism and removing cairns' which were 'relics of the past ages', with a plea to 'leave the ancient monuments in their original state'. There was a sudden close to the correspondence when the history became clear.

Where new trig. pillars were needed at or on recognised archaeological sites, Ordnance Survey was careful to seek advice from antiquarian authorities and eminent archaeologists, to ensure that any ancient remains were not disturbed. At prominent beauty spots, all attempts were again made to satisfy local interests. These included incorporating various devices on to the sides of the pillars, such as waymarkers, plaques and collecting boxes, and incorporating topographs (plates with directional information) on to the pillar tops.

The ingenuity of the pillar constructors and surveyors overcame most problems encountered and led to some interesting innovations, such as the 'Curry stool'. Designed by a surveyor, Mr Ernie Curry, this provided a stable triangulation station and theodolite platform in soft peat bogs. Three stout poles were driven at an angle, 120° apart, into the peat until they hit firm ground (sometimes nearly 20 feet down), and their protruding tops were covered and bound by a collar of concrete. The result was a triangulation station that, in diagrammatic form, looked like a vast milking stool thrust into the peat. In the middle of the concrete collar, which was large enough to take the outspread legs of the theodolite tripod, was the trig. bolt. The observer stood on boards, just above the concrete, arranged so as not to disturb the theodolite.

In the first 1936 'hill season' the men were divided into three parties. Each was led by an observer who had two assistants, a booker (who could also observe) and a lightkeeper-cum-general organizer. Detached from each party, at the stations being observed to, were nine lightkeepers. The lightkeepers were kept in touch with the observer's progress by prearranged morse code signals, demanding constant attention to the observer's 'leading light'. Lightkeepers had charge of the observing beacons which were powered by 6 V car batteries; these had to be kept charged if the lights were not to fail at a crucial moment. With one, or even two, of these heavy batteries strapped to their backs and often with only bicycles as transport, the lightkeepers would travel miles to a battery-charging rendezvous or garage.

The parties were deliberately given areas well apart so as not to interrupt each other's schemes, which also meant that delays due to bad weather in one part of the country might not affect progress in another. The men were indefatigable, and achieved more than had been hoped for in the first season. Altogether, 56 primary stations were occupied between April and October, giving a broad framework of triangles, most of them fully observed, extending up the backbone of the country from the Isle of Wight to the Tyne. Eleven of the stations observed duplicated those of the Principal Triangulation of the 1850s, and effectively provided continuity, as far as was possible, of geographical coordinates on old and new maps.

The theodolites used throughout the retriangulation were manufactured by Cooke, Troughton and Simms. Known as Geodetic Tavistocks (or Tavis), they were named after a conference held in 1926, at Tavistock, in Devon. The theodolites, with their 5½ inch horizontal circle (later reduced to 5 inches) and weight of 32 pounds (14.5 kg) were minuscule compared to the Ramsden 3-foot, the original geodetic theodolite, in regular use 100 years earlier. The Tavis proved very popular with the observers. They found that, provided they applied what at first appeared trivial precautions to their observing procedures, they received very few requests for observations to be repeated.

The start of the 1937 season saw a change in the working pattern, the plan being for the three observing parties to work their way up through Scotland, line abreast. The

lightkeepers, now in parties of one to three men, set up the beacon lights so that one light was actually on the pillar, while up to two others were placed eccentric from the pillar and on direct line to their respective observing stations. This way one station could, where necessary, be observed from three directions.

The 350-mile journey from Southampton and the climbs to the first observing and lighting stations, including setting up camp, took place in miserably wet conditions. But the staff made light of the deprivations. As the observer at Whitelyne Hill, in Northumbria, wrote 'beyond a wet bed, wet clothes, wet everything, there is nothing to report'.

To the west, the lightkeeper at Criffel, a few miles south of Dumfries, penned the following lament:

I'm fair foreichan speilan' up aul' Criffel ilka day,
Whilst puir aul' John S. Harrison near conked out on the way;
For luggin' batteries up a hill is no' exactly fun;
John swore the hale clanjamferie wad wey gey near a ton.

Ae nicht I spent upon that hill I got an unco fricht,
When I was gettin' spreauchled doon, the aul' mune dimmed her
*   licht,*
I waded through the heather an' tummelt owre a rock,
Then waunnert in the brecken an' got hame at fowre o'clock.

And this was one of the lower hills to climb! (John S Harrison was a local farmer.)

The work progressed well, except for the observations at Ben Macdhui in the heart of the Cairngorms, which stubbornly kept its top in the clouds, though the lower

Solitary lightkeeper.

The trig. on Cadair Idris

In 1936 the first of what would eventually number over 6500 triangulation pillars began to appear on high and exposed places around Britain. One pillar with a chequered past is that on Pen y gadair, the highest point on the ridge known as Cadair (or Cader) Idris. The pillar, 6 miles south of Dolgellau, sits astride a cairn on a big bluff mountain, typical of this area in the Snowdonia National Park.

The site was originally selected in 1804, the triangulation point being marked with a chisel-cut arrow on a free-stone block. A cairn was erected over it, both to pinpoint the mark and to support a wooden pole used for the survey observations.

In 1936 enquiries, to find the owner of the land on which the cairn stood, were made in preparation for the retriangulation of Great Britain. A trig. pillar was to be built on the summit and eventually four people gave their permission, all of them claiming ownership.

Work commenced on Monday 10 August 1936 and the tale is best told in the pillar builder's own plaintive words:

Sir
Report on Construction of Triangulation pillar at Cader Idris Aug 22nd, 1936
The above pillar was completed on Aug 22nd 1936

Mon 10th   I travelled here from Treorchy, leaving Treorchy at 10.30 am arriving here at 10 pm. Nothing done to day owing to late arrival.

Tues 11th   Went to station to see about O.S. stores, which did not arrive until late afternoon, made arrangements with contractor re material and removal of O.S. stores from station.
I inspected trig point and found only pack horses could do the job.

Wed 12th   Waiting for arrival of materials and stores and interviewing farmers re pack horses.
Nothing done to day on construction.

Thurs 13th   I have now secured horses. To day we managed to get one load to trig point and then had to give up owing to rain and heavy mists on top of Cader Idris. Before starting to day we have had to make a road up the side of

the rocks. Today we got a horse stuck in a bog. The mists on Cader are terrible every day, until the afternoon's, and cannot attempt getting up until the afternoon's.

Fri 14th   This afternoon we managed to get another load to the top of the mountain ¾ of the way to trig point, but had to leave same there owing to heavy mists and rain, we were wet to the skin and returned to digs.

Sat 15th   Weather here to day is terrible and nothing can be done. One cannot see the mountain.

Mon 17th   This morning we managed to get another load to the trig point. It was a terrible day, heavy rain and mists. Then we had to give up owing to being wet to the skin. I thought it would clear up but it kept on all day.

Tues 18th   I went down 5 ft 6 ins and found O.S. Box, I made a wall of stones 3 ft square and covered O.S. Box with usual 11 × 2 wooden box. About 4 ft down I found a silver coin, George the third 1804, a five shilling piece. I filled in base to about 3 parts of the way up and left same owing to nasty mists and rain setting in.

Wed 19th   Weather to day is terrible, raining all day. Nothing can be done to day, fed up with it.

Thurs 20th   I left the digs at 8 am for the trig point. I have now constructed base 5 ft 8 ins deep, 3 ft square. Have inserted O.S. point on base in wooden box and also four supporting irons. I returned to digs at 8 pm, tired and ready for bed.

Fri 21st   To day I inserted flush bracket, put up shutterings, also centre pipe and beacon pipe, also four sighting tubes and outer tubes, inserted spider and three brass loops. I am staying tonight at the top of Cader Idris in an old hut for the night.

Sat 22nd   6 am. We took down shutterings and cut wire off flush bracket, removed centre pipe, filled sighting tubes and faced pillar, cleared site and had O.S. stores removed to farm. The above pillar had the new centre cap. This has been a tough job, but thank God it is up.

Aug 22 – 1936   PS: I have made a path around the pillar with spare materials. This is a bad time of the year to get pack horses, owing to hay making and they know it. The person who did the haulage with the pack horses was a coal merchant from Dolgelly.

Expenses
Re Triangulation pillar at Cader Idris
Aug 22nd 1936

	£	s.	d.
Constructors			
pay 3 at 10/–			
4 at 9/–			
6 at 6/–	5	2	0
Constructors			
allowance 11 at 7/6	4	2	6
Two Labourers			
50 hours each	5	0	0
Pack Horses from farm to			
trig point and men (3)	26	0	0
Haulage of material and			
stores to farm etc.	2	10	0
25 Cwt Chippings	–	10	0
10 Cwt Sand	–	5	6
7 Cwt Cement	1	8	0
Bus fares seeing about			
stores and materials			
cycle had not arrived,			
also taxi on arrival at			
station 10 pm		4	6
	£43	2	6

Despite the pillar builder's efforts, Captain Hotine showed his displeasure with the work, making the following comments on the report

CS [Chief Surveyor]
We should show (on the bill?) the number of journeys and the distance or time. It is not enough simply to put in a bill for £26 with no details. This pillar costs more than Ben Lomond where horses had to be transported by lorry.

The pillar was repaired at intervals but in 1983 it was found to have fallen over. In 1985 the remains of the old pillar and the cairn were demolished to find the original 1804 mark. Materials for a new pillar, weighing around 1½ tonnes, were transported to the summit, by helicopter this time, and the trig. pillar was finally restored to full operation on 21 June 1985.

mountains all around were clear. In June a fourth observing party was temporarily formed to occupy Ben Macdhui and, with a lightkeeping party to bring food and fuel to them, they camped on the snowy summit, until, after ten days, the clouds had cleared long enough to allow them to complete the observations.

Bilby towers

East Anglia is renowned for having 'a lot of sky', but this also means that it has few hills or natural vantage points. The man-made landscape did provide some compensations for the surveyors, with magnificent church towers and prominent water towers. Where neither of these was available, and points were needed to maintain a well-balanced triangulation, an alternative was to use a portable observing platform. Nine were purchased from America, and two more of a similar design were borrowed from the Geodetic Survey of Denmark.

The steel observing tower, called a Bilby tower, had been developed in America for surveying its vast flatlands and prairies. Each tower was in fact two independent structures. The instrument was supported on the inner tower and the observer and his assistant stood on the outer one. They needed careful erecting, including the laying of concrete footings for the legs. It was found to be easier for a trig. pillar to be built under the Bilby tower, once it was in position. At full height the towers rose to 103 feet and took about ten hours to erect.

Post-war retriangulation

After the outbreak of war no more primary work for the retriangulation was done until 1949, mainly because of the war itself, but later due to the urgent need for secondary and tertiary triangulation for the post-war mapping expansion. After this ten-year lull the Scottish work, which included the Highlands and the Shetland and Orkney Islands, was resumed.

Two parties, each of twenty-two men, were formed with two observers, two bookers and nine two-man lightkeeping sections. Each section was granted the use of an official van, the lighter-weight models being allocated to sections that had the largest number of sea-crossings to make.

Observations started in May, with the by-now familiar ritual of the senior observer falling waist-deep into a bog, accidentally, of course. Ben Nevis managed to exhaust the observers, who clambered up each, or every other, night to freezing conditions, through deep snow for twenty-two days until the observations were complete. They later discovered, when the subzero temperatures had driven them to huddle around the primus stove in their small tent, that their camp

Erecting a Bilby Tower in East Anglia. Notice the lack of hard hats and safety harnesses.

had been pitched on an overhanging snow cornice, under which was nothing – but a long drop!

The observer on Fair Isle, in the process of fighting off some Arctic skuas who had taken objection to the presence of the men, dislocated his shoulder and, with great courage, not only carried on observing with one hand, but also managed, with the help of his booker, to put the shoulder back. Regardless of the conditions work continued, and by the end of July the season's work was complete.

Disappointingly, computations revealed that the average error of the triangles observed through the season was outside the acceptable tolerance. It was speculated that these errors occurred where observations had been made across water, and in July 1950 a small party was despatched to reobserve the faulty work. After a total of fifty mostly foul-weather days, the party returned with observations that now gave satisfactory results.

Climbing Conachair, St Kilda, in 1957. The ruins of the abandoned settlement are clearly visible below. Photo: Tom Weir

For 1951 a huge task was set, covering approximately 3500 square miles of land and sea, from North Wales across to the Isle of Man, up the west coasts of England and Scotland and out to the Inner and Outer Hebrides. The last party eventually returned to headquarters at the end of November after seven months, having experienced some of the worst weather in the whole seventeen years that the retriangulation had taken. Remaining observations were completed in April and May of 1952.

Over the next eleven years, the retriangulation was refined. Astronomical observations were made and both the Herstmonceux and Greenwich Royal Observatories were connected to the primary network. It was at this time that a most unusual error was discovered. The Greenwich Meridian had been defined by the Bradley transit instrument circle until 1850, when the Astronomer Royal, Sir George Airy, had a new transit instrument built and placed in an adjoining room. The position of this instrument was accepted as the zero meridian in 1884 by the Washington Conference, but the Ordnance Survey continued to use the old position as the zero meridian. There is no explanation why Clarke, in his *Account of the Principal Triangulation*, failed to act on this change, especially as it was known to him. The difference between the two sites was found to be 5.79 metres (19 feet), and the Greenwich Meridian, as shown on Ordnance Survey maps is this distance west of its true position. Apart from its scientific value, this difference has little effect on current maps.

Assistance was given, in 1957, to the Air Ministry with the establishment of a primary triangulation station on St Kilda, 41 miles off the Outer Hebrides in the North Atlantic Ocean. Evacuated of its few remaining islanders some years before, St Kilda lay barren and deserted until the establishment of a guided weapons range and other Ministry of Defence projects. The observing party were transported to the island, by courtesy of the Royal Navy, in a tank landing-craft from South Uist, itself a six-hour ferry journey from Oban on the mainland. The triangulation station, near the summit of Conachair, was one of the steepest climbs encountered, rising for more than 1200 feet and giving a clear view of the deserted village far below. Observations were taken to five primary stations on the Outer Hebrides, and St Kilda was, after computation, added to the primary network.

The observations for the retriangulation were all taken at night, between dusk and about 3 o'clock in the morning. Climbs and descents were often made in the dark. The achievements of the staff, when tired through lack of sleep and physically weary from stumbling over hummocky ground and climbing up and down mountains, cannot be overemphasised. When the men eventually left the Highlands and Islands it was with mixed feelings. They knew that they had been experiencing one of the most exciting periods of the department's history, but were pleased to put the physical effort behind them. Some left reluctantly taking with them memories of the beauty of the country and the warmth of its people. There were quite a few broken hearts at the end, both those of the local lasses and some of the surveyors!

Although Hotine had left the department at the beginning of the Second World War, his plans were followed nearly to the letter. His unorthodox solution had proved to be effective, given the exceptional circumstances that prevailed.

Some of the staff employed to undertake computations, 1962.

Post-war plans

The expansion of the Ordnance Survey that resulted from the 1935 Davidson Interim Report, led to the post of Director General being upgraded in rank from Brigadier to Major General. MacLeod was duly promoted in early 1939 and should have retired shortly afterwards in May of the same year, at the age of fifty-seven, but in the run-up to war it was considered sensible to retain his services. This was beneficial to the department, who retained his extensive military expertise.

MacLeod was finally succeeded by Major General Geoffrey Cheetham in June 1943, but even then seemed to be reluctant to leave, expressing doubts about his successor. However, Hotine, in his legendary blunt manner, set him to rights.

> It is, of course, a common human failing to suppose that our deputies and successors can never achieve our own level. The last four Directors General of the Ordnance Survey seem to have been particularly afflicted that way. If they were all right, the job must be due to be held by a cumulative mental defective. It is simpler to assume they are all wrong; including, if I may say so yourself . . . Geoff will do the job perfectly well.

MacLeod won the admiration of his junior officers. His formidable intellect, First World War service record and sporting achievements all served to cast him in a heroic mould. He had a calm approach to the wartime difficulties of the department and never appeared indecisive or at a loss.

Through his skilful dealings with the Davidson Committee and his contributions to the post-war plan, he had defined the role of the department for future decades, giving both purpose and direction. MacLeod was once accused by Hotine of always being 'coldly logical', but he could be generous too. He married but had no children and bequeathed his substantial property, on the edge of the New Forest, to an organisation which cared for local elderly people.

Cheetham, with advice from MacLeod and Hotine (from his position as Director of Military Surveys) began to draw up plans for the further expansion of the department, in order to implement the recommendations of the 1938 Davidson Committee Final Report. Cheetham continued to include both men in these discussions even though MacLeod was supposedly fully retired. These three 'wise men' were, between them, the architects of the Ordnance Survey's post-war organisation.

They had originally envisaged that Ordnance Survey and the Geographical Section General Staff (GSGS) should merge into one organisation. Hotine, first as Head of GSGS and then as the Director of Military Survey, and MacLeod, at Ordnance Survey, had worked in harmony for most of the war, although relations between the two departments had not always been so cordial. At the beginning of the war, Hotine's predecessor at GSGS, Brigadier P K Boulnois, had felt that some functions carried out by Ordnance Survey should be done by GSGS and there followed argument as to where certain responsibilities lay. The result was a complete lack of direction in some operations and duplication of effort in others. MacLeod was uneasy and suspicious that a rival

Writing

While surveyors found that the introduction of tachy and air survey released them from some of the drudgery of their work, draughtsmen sometimes found that new technology stole away some of their more interesting tasks.

During the war the names for maps began to be produced by photonymograph, a photographic process which produced names on clear waxed film, ready to be stuck down in position on the draughtsman's fair-drawing of the map.

However, the writing for small-scale maps was still done by hand, and in 1945 Ordnance Survey found itself short of skilled writers. A training course was set up and, even though aspirants were 'compelled to do a substantial amount of practice in their own time', it proved immensely popular and soon consisted of fifty eager novices.

Beginners were taught, first using pencil, how to form the essential strokes of construction of a number of Ordnance Survey house-style alphabets, most of which were relics of the age of copperplate writing, and how to proportionally space the letters. Not until the learner was proficient with this would he or she progress to practice with a pen or brush, whichever they found the easier to use.

For comparatively large writing, bottled waterproof ink was used, but for the most fine and beautiful writing best results were invariably obtained by the use of Chinese stick ink mixed carefully to a consistency of thin cream. A sable-haired brush (size 2 or 3), carefully trimmed to a point of only one or two bristles, was generally used for the finest small-scale work. An expert writer was capable of producing work equal in every way to engraving.

Many found that this gentle art was more difficult than it looked. As one expert warned, 'Let no aspirant be deceived by imagining that small-scale writing – as it appears on a published map – is a gift. To achieve such perfection much hard work is absolutely essential.'

Phototypeset writing was fully introduced in 1953, and although twenty-two of the Seventh Series 1-inch maps had already been completed with hand lettering, the remainder were produced by the new, much quicker, phototypeset methods.

Lt-Col (later Major General) G Cheetham, Director General 1943–49.

survey organisation was being set up by Boulnois which he claimed was 'rather like saying that because the War Office used to run a few miles of railway between Longmoor Camp and Bordon, they should extend this for war purposes over the whole country'. These problems were only overcome with Hotine's arrival at GSGS.

With this experience behind him, MacLeod was concerned that the smooth running of a survey operation during war depended too much on the personalities of the two heads of department. The War Office and the Ministry of Agriculture and Fisheries both disagreed.

The War Office wanted to retain their own small military survey on the accepted logic that they needed to be able to command limited quantities of mapping, at very short notice. Sometimes this might be of a highly secretive nature, such as for planning a commando raid. They were, however, alarmed at the prospect of having to open their doors to the multifarious civil uses of mapping that were totally non-military in nature and of which they had no experience. Equally the Ministry of Agriculture were concerned that if the War Office took control of Ordnance Survey, then civil mapping would become the poor relation to military mapping.

The decision not to unite War Office mapping with Ordnance Survey was therefore consciously taken, and Ordnance Survey moved one step further towards becoming a fully civilian department. Additionally, after the war sufficient Royal Engineer officers could not be found to fill all the higher-grade technical positions and for the first time these were filled by promotion, or direct appointment, of civilians.

As well as GSGS and the Ordnance Survey, the need for a third survey organisation was raised by the Colonial Office, who decided that they now wanted to control their own Survey Branch for overseas deployment. Cheetham was opposed to the idea, believing that other departments might also try to do the same and 'The country might find itself with half-a-dozen Ordnance Surveys all trying to do different parts of the same job.' To Cheetham's disappointment the 'Central Organisation for Survey in the Colonial Empire', later called the Overseas Surveys Directorate, came into being in 1946.

From 1943, Cheetham sought to provide for the possibility of 'when a few draughtsmen might become surplus from war work for a few hours' and he developed what was termed the 'shadow programme'. This allocated to each section work that could be picked up at any slack time and put down when urgent war-work came through. He also obtained special authority to increase the establishment of men working on the retriangulation, as without the trig. control the planned post-war resurvey work could not begin. A detailed post-war plan was agreed by the Ministry of Agriculture and Fisheries which included both short-term measures for immediate needs at the end of the war and a longer-term plan based on the Davidson Committee recommendations.

The Cheetham plan advocated a vast expansion of staff from 2300 in 1939 to 6000 within two years of demobilisation and at the end of the war large numbers of men were sent to Ordnance Survey via the Ministry of Labour and National Service. These staff were taken on temporary appointments purely on the basis of their application forms, without an interview or even any enquiries being made. It was scarcely an ideal system because large numbers soon left on finding better-paid work elsewhere and some of those who stayed were not specially suited to the work.

The Chessington years

The move to the new Chessington accommodation began in 1943 but although purpose-built for Ordnance Survey these offices were only planned to be a temporary home. The blitz-damaged premises at London Road in Southampton were finally fully evacuated of all sections and stores in May 1944 and repair work began there soon afterwards. It was understood that the headquarters would remain at Chessington until at least the end of the war.

Staff gradually settled into the Chessington premises becoming accustomed to the noises that occasionally emanated from the zoo just down the road. Less welcome were the V1 and V2 'buzz' bombs at the latter end of the war which caused occasional damage but resulted in no injuries to staff.

In 1944, work on the runways of the future Heathrow Airport resulted in one of the terminals of the Hounslow Heath base having to be removed. This terminal, a 32-pounder cannon, had been emplaced there in 1791, when the base was remeasured. Ordnance Survey was pleased to receive it back and, to give a historical dimension to the drab and utilitarian new offices, it was mounted with due care on a plinth in front of the Chessington headquarters. Here it remained, as a kind of talisman, until the new headquarters were built at Southampton. In 1972, the cannon was restored to its original position at Heathrow.

Cheetham retired in 1949 having, as Hotine rightly predicted, done 'the job perfectly well'. He continued to influence the world of map-making through the *Textbook of Topographical Surveying*, a standard reference work which he updated and rewrote. This book was used during the training of surveyors in military and civilian centres in many countries.

Hotine, with his expertise in trig. and air photography, and his involvement in drawing up the post-war plans for the Ordnance Survey, would perhaps have been a natural successor to Cheetham, but in 1946 he retired early from the army to be appointed the first Director of Overseas Surveys by the Colonial Office.

The position of Director General at Ordnance Survey was taken by Major General Reginald Llewellyn Brown (universally known as Bruno). As a young man Brown had lost his right arm in a shooting accident whilst surveying in Ghana. His injury caused him considerable pain for the rest of his life but, with echoes of Colby more than a century before, he refused to allow this to affect either his career or his personal life.

Wellingborough

The grounds at Crabwood house in Southampton had, since 1938, been earmarked as the future site of a new purpose-built office for Ordnance Survey, but the extensive blitz damage to the city made the Ministry of Agriculture, Fisheries and Food (MAFF) think again. The conclusion they came to in 1950 was itself a bombshell to the staff. It was proposed, on security considerations, to move the office to Wellingborough, an expanding town near Northampton. The opposition from the staff was immediate and vocal, but for five years little happened and then, in 1955, a date for building work to commence at Wellingborough was announced. The staff were asked to accept this decision because 'as a principal port, Southampton was a city of strategic importance as a target to any enemy, and it was in the country's interest that this vital department should not remain located there.'

There was widespread disagreement with this reasoning, not only from the staff, but also from the people of Southampton who had grown fond of the 'map factory' which had given employment to so many local families since it came to the town in 1841. The view was expressed that Wellingborough, near the industrial heartland of Britain, was likely to be no safer from an attack than Southampton. The debate was taken to the House of Commons by local Members of Parliament but the Government were adamant that the move would take place.

The announcement by MAFF in 1956 that the 'strategic circumstances now did not make it worthwhile moving the Ordnance Survey office from its traditional home in Southampton' came suddenly and unexpectedly. Possibly economic circumstances made the move undesirable, and it was a further eight years before building work for the headquarters at the Crabwood House site finally started.

Field offices

New surveyors, on joining Ordnance Survey, had to agree that they would accept a posting anywhere in Great Britain (this still applies today). To the young, single man, this was a two-edged sword, the promise of adventure and a chance to see the country being weighted against the possibility of ending up where he least of all wanted to be.

The country was divided up into areas under the control of 'field division offices'. By 1949 there were six of these at London, Edinburgh, Bristol, Kidderminster, Nottingham and Harrogate. From 1953 they were known as region offices. Each region had under its control a number of smaller 'group' offices. The 1:1250 survey was originally carried out by 'town groups' and the 1:2500 survey by 'rural groups', but an overlap between the two types of work led, in 1952, to the creation of field survey groups which could cope with work at both scales.

Each group office in turn had a number of self-contained 'section' offices under its command which were responsible for the survey of a defined area of the country. These smallest and sometimes temporary offices were based in the areas where the surveying work was being carried out. New surveyors were allocated to a section and could be moved around to different offices within a region as the work demanded. On promotion they could, once again, be sent to an office anywhere in the country.

This box was used to store threads of web from the female Epeira-Diademate, or land spider (easily recognised by a white cross on its back). After capture, the spiders were gently encouraged to fall from a pencil, the thread produced being wound on a lacquered frame. The thread could be split with a sharp needle into two and then again to give four threads of about 1/3000 of an inch. Fixed under tension these were used to provide the cross-lines in theodolite diaphragms. Vacuum depositing of metal on glass eventually superseded this process.

After each area had been either resurveyed at 1:1250 or overhauled at 1:2500, a core of surveyors were left behind, to be responsible for its revision in the future. At first the balance of work was such that most surveyors had to move their work area quite quickly, but as the resurvey and overhaul progressed across the country more and more plans came under the care of continuous revision (CR) sections. In addition to being efficient, the CR principle was popular with the staff, as a posting to this type of work gave those who were married with a family the real possibility of settling down in one area.

Finding buildings suitable as offices for the field staff was always a problem and the ideal of well-lit modern rooms was often impossible to obtain, especially in towns where bombing had been heavy during the war. One surveyor recalled. 'As I drew nearer I found, to my consternation, that the Ordnance Survey Office was not the light and airy building that I had expected but was, in fact, a very dilapidated church hall.'

Balancing acts

In terms of production the continuous revision system took some years to put in balance. When surveyors were diverted away from overhaul and resurvey to CR, their work was added to the master drawings held at each field office. It was only economical to send these for fair-drawing when a certain amount of change had accumulated, and for this and other reasons there resulted a net drop of plans reaching the drawing office. The draughtsmen were in danger of running out of work, so it was decided to 'bypass' some of the 1:2500 plans in the field. This meant that in rural areas, where a quick reconnaissance revealed only a very small amount of change, the plans were passed for direct production on national grid sheetlines, without any revision being made. This expedient was regretted in later years as the amount of change in these bypassed areas had been largely underestimated.

In 1953, after a difficult term of office, struggling to impose order on the vast programme of work, Major General Brown retired. He had consistently refused to compromise the system of continuous revision, despite pressure to do so for the sake of completing the resurvey and overhaul more quickly. In his farewell speech to the staff, Brown threatened that if the Ordnance Survey management should ever abandon the policy of continuous revision, he would return from the grave to haunt them. Brown was a founder member of the Photogrammetric Society and also, on a more personal front, founded a workshop for the disabled at his home village of Yateley in Hampshire. He was married with one son.

Brown was succeeded by Major General John Christopher Temple Willis, whose first experience of Ordnance Survey had been a short tour of duty in charge of the Edinburgh Division in the 1930s. During this time he painted a number of water-colours which were chosen to adorn the covers of some of the Tourist and District maps. Now on his return to the department as Director General he found more serious matters to occupy his mind.

To put into effect all the recommendations of the Davidson Committee it had been calculated that a staff of about 6000 people would be needed. Large numbers of new recruits were taken on, but the size of government departments was closely regulated after the war and this number was never achieved. When Willis took over, the staff numbers stood at 4962 and retaining even this number was a problem as surveyors, particularly, resigned faster than they could be replaced. Willis reacted by examining areas of the department

Last base

To determine the scale of the retriangulation in international metres, the accepted standard of length, Hotine decided to remeasure the 7.2 kilometre Lossiemouth base, originally measured in 1909, and to measure a new base in southern England (the existing Salisbury Plain base failing to meet the criteria of intervisibility of its terminals).

The ancient Ridge Way was chosen as a site for the new base, with terminals at Liddington Castle, overlooking Swindon in Wiltshire, and Uffington Castle, also known as White Horse Hill. Between these two ancient hill forts the base line, measured in 1937, traversed its way through thirty hedges and fences, crossed three roads and a ravine, passed through a barn and, memorably, had to negotiate a large, very ripe, manure heap, 'with a rare stroke of luck on a windless day'!

Measurements were made with 24-metre invar tapes held in catenary. On an exposed section, crossing a ditch, the tape fluttered in the wind but with typical ingenuity a screen, which would normally have been used at ground level, was flown like a kite, allowing a satisfactory measurement to be made. On reaching the ravine, Hotine attempted to measure across the gap with a 300 foot steel tape but this method failed and it was successfully measured by triangulation. The Ridge Way base was remeasured in 1951, its length differing by just 6.6 mm.

In 1938, the Lossiemouth base had been successfully remeasured but attempts to connect it with the triangulation framework ran into difficulties because of the awkward siting of a single large memorial cairn. Two essential observing rays passed close by this which, as it heated up during the day, altered the humidity of the air in its vicinity, slightly bending or deflecting the observing rays. After careful thought Hotine decided to reject the base altogether.

A site near Caithness, in the far north east of mainland Scotland, was chosen to replace Lossiemouth, but part of its 15-mile route ran straight through a bog and there were fears that this would make the measurement impossible. However, once again the ingenuity of the surveyors found a way around the problem and a star-rating system was devised. The soggiest ground was awarded the highest number of stars and the more stars an area was given, the fewer personnel were allowed within a specified distance of the tape and measuring heads. This prevented undue disturbance of the carefully placed pickets supporting the measuring equipment and a satisfactory result was achieved for the base in 1952.

The results of the Ridge Way and Caithness base measurements gave conclusive evidence that the scale of the triangulation was a fraction too large, with an error of about 20 metres over the whole 1.2 million metre length of the country, but this had little or no bearing on the overall accuracy of any published map, only affecting exceedingly accurate measurements made over very long distances.

Odson's Barn. This obstructed the line of the Ridgeway base, and it was necessary to remove the sides to measure through it.

Crossing the River Lossie during the Lossiemouth base measurement in 1938.

where savings in time could be made. One of his conclusions was that new editions of maps were being made too frequently. He stipulated that at least five years must pass between new editions at the 1:1250 scale, justifying his decision with the argument that Advance Revision Information (ARI) was always available to the public from the master survey drawing at the appropriate field office. But the ARI system itself soon fell victim to cuts and the service was neither publicised nor encouraged on the grounds that it diverted resources away from regular production.

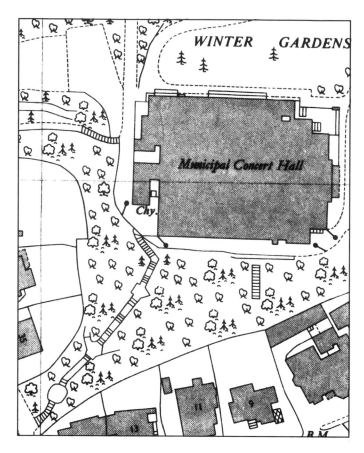

Part of a first edition 1:1250 plan of Bournemouth surveyed in 1947.

Willis felt that the programme was still achievable if only the Treasury would authorise 'the once-for-all expenditure of a capital sum' to pay for new equipment to speed up production. He pointed out that Ordnance Survey now found itself carrying on the work 'by methods which are completely out of date and which have long been abandoned by all major overseas organisations'. He felt embarrassed that the department had been 'held up to public ridicule before an informed International audience for this very reason'. Willis provided figures which showed that for example, in terms of increased production, it only took eight months to recover the cost of a new tacheometer. His arguments were persuasive and a programme of re-equiping the department was agreed.

By the time Major General Laurence Francis de Vic Carey took over in June 1957, the recruitment problem had also been solved. A marked increase in salary for cartographic draughtsmen and surveyors had been awarded by the Civil Service Arbitration Tribunal but the increased wage costs had to be met by savings in total manpower. The result was a staff cut of 200 employees. Meanwhile, as a result of improved

techniques and equipment, field output began to improve substantially and by the end of the decade plans were piling up so fast at the drawing office that surveyors were transferred to drawing duties to help redress the balance.

1:1250

Whenever men could be spared during the war, MacLeod had put them to exploring ways in which the Davidson Committee recommendations could be achieved. He knew it could be some years before any full-scale expansion of the department could take place, but he wanted, when the time came, to be prepared to move immediately. So in 1941 MacLeod, with an optimistic view that Britain would one day win the war, started a small project in Bournemouth to explore how old urban 1:2500 County Series plans could be made to fit a network of new control points within the framework of the National Grid. The answer was that they couldn't, at any rate not with satisfactory reliability. The only solution was to bring forward the suggestion made by the Davidson Committee that urban survey should be at 1:1250, and to resurvey the towns at this scale on the new Transverse Mercator projection. This added up to a task estimated at over 30 000 plans. The size of the workforce at Bournemouth was tiny, but by the end of the war the methods to be used for 1:1250 resurvey were largely agreed.

Tried and tested methods, which existing staff were familiar with, were favoured. With a vast intake of new recruits planned, the priority was to train them as quickly as possible and send them out to make maps. Little, if any, consideration was given to providing them with sound all-round training in surveying, and in this respect they were treated in much the same way as the sappers had been a hundred years before. The work was divided up into manageable tasks, with plenty of checks built in to the system, and by using this 'craft' approach staff became competent very quickly. Large numbers of men were needed and by simplifying the operations it was agreed that recruits, both surveyors and draughtsmen, generally needed to be educated only to school certificate level. As pay was still comparatively low, the department were in any case unlikely to attract those with additional qualifications.

Trainee surveyors were usually sent, in the first place, to a field office where they were employed on various labouring duties, while awaiting a vacancy on one of the six-month long basic training courses. Separate courses were held for those selected for trig. or levelling duties. National service was compulsory and young trainee juniors were taken on at age sixteen and a half, passing their time before national

The popular Ruggles comic-strip of the Daily Mirror ran a series about Ordnance Survey in 1952.
Daily Mirror

service at field division offices where they learnt a number of basic skills including drawing.

The order of surveying was dictated by the Director General who chose the priority towns in consultation with the planning authorities. In general, towns with a population greater than 10 000 people were all eventually destined for resurvey at 1:1250 scale. Before each town could be resurveyed, the trig. control down to tertiary level and the main traverse framework had to be complete. These were laid out by the trig. and levelling division, and 'broke up' the town into areas which enabled the surveying work to be carried on by the local field surveyor. The next task was to add 'minor control', shorter traverses which were usually under a kilometre in length. These were used to fix the coordinates of points known as revision points (RPs) on which the main lines of the detail survey depended. Revision points were sited as required, single RPs or groups of two, three or four at places such as the corners of houses. They were sometimes marked by a pipe nail at the actual point.

Sketches of the revision points were made and later photography was used to provide a record for future surveyors. For each photograph a man stood holding a slotted black board, nicknamed the hymn board, into which the plan number, reference number of the point of detail, date and so on were slotted. Carrying this heavy and cumbersome device around the streets was not a popular job! A large wooden arrow was used to indicate the revision point itself. The photographs were stuck into small albums, each page carrying the picture and a detailed sketch of the revision point. Years

later, surveyors referred to these albums to seek out those points that still existed, guided to them by their predecessors, immortalised in the photographs.

For the first few years after the war, survey was carried out almost entirely by chaining. The chains were made of steel with links every 2 decimetres along their 20-metre length. They weighed about 7 lbs and compared to a modern steel tape (which, if kinked, could break) they were rugged but quite difficult to handle; that was until the surveyor mastered the expert 'flick' that sent the chain off in the required direction without entanglement.

After some years, air photographs enlarged to map scale were used to build up a complex pattern of intersections from which the map could be constructed. Detail invisible from the air was later added by the surveyor. With care, the results of this graphical air survey were as accurate as chain surveying.

In 1955, the department went a stage further and committed itself to air survey by stereoplotting machine, as the preferred initial survey stage. The machine operator produced a plan directly from the air photograph, and the technique was particularly successful for surveying new housing estates where properties were divided by fences, and trees were not yet fully established. Some experienced surveyors claimed that this reduced the interest of their work which, as an elaborate 'join the dots' exercise, made it almost too easy.

However, there were plenty of areas where air photography was not available or feasible and here a tacheometer (tachy) was used instead. This instrument was an optical measuring device which measured distance and angles used

Minor control traverse in the 1950s using a Watts microptic theodolite.

in conjunction with a graduated 'stadia rod', and proved itself superior in both speed and accuracy to chain survey. Whereas chain survey was plotted on to the plan by the surveyor, tachy information needed computation and then plotting, using a polar coordinatograph. This was done either in the regional office by a dedicated section, or at headquarters. It took some years for the department to build up sets of tachy equipment and to train the staff in its use. In 1960 over 42 per cent of plans were surveyed using tachy, 20 per cent by air-survey plotting and 11 per cent by graphical air survey; the remaining 27 per cent were still chain surveyed.

For the newly trained surveyors the moment of truth came when they found themselves out, alone, for the first time. One such post-war recruit recalled:

> The great day came when I took up my first plan. On an adjoining plan was a colleague who had been on the same course as myself. With the course instructor's do's and don't's running through my mind, I spent about an hour looking for the magical shot that would start the work on my masterpiece. The near panic that assailed me on realising that the theory and practice of surveying are two different things, was somewhat alleviated by the arrival of my friend. He too had spent the whole morning wandering around in ever decreasing circles and had decided that two heads would be better than one. Together we went to his plan and looked for a suitable

> way of starting him off . . . but on our return to the office, neither of us had made a mark on our virgin plates.

In fact both surveyors had thought of several suitable ways of starting but these differed from the ideal methods taught at the survey school and they had lacked the experience to know whether they were acceptable.

Resurvey work was carried out on enamelled aluminium plates, 40 centimetres square, an innovation designed by a surveyor, Mr Charles Emery, in 1944 to prevent the slight distortions previously experienced with paper, as it expanded or shrank depending on the weather conditions. In due course, these were replaced with four 20-centimetre square aluminium plates that could be 'butt-jointed' together, and so became known as 'BJ' plates. Each 1:1250 plan was covered by four plates held securely in a sketching case. This system practically eliminated the difficulties of working across edges, as the surveyor could rearrange the plates so that the edge he was working on could be moved to the centre of his sketching case. The BJ plates were unpleasant to use in wintry weather, being very cold to the touch and liable, in extreme conditions, to freeze on to an unwary surveyor's hand. 'Huffing' warm breath onto the frozen area quickly freed the hand, but then caused the plate to ice over. Field work was noted on the plates using a sharp, hard pencil or a 'silver' point and later the information was 'penned in' using cerric ink. This was a viscous, enamel paint-like liquid that was notoriously difficult to use as it etched itself into the surface enamel. Control work was shown in red ink and the surveyor used black ink to add surveyed information. The supervisor, on checking the work, made any alterations in greek ink, and if seen by the chief surveyor the plan could even gain some brown ink.

In time, the size of the 1:1250 task grew, as more urban and developing areas were included. By 1961 the total number of plans for the scale was set at 44 300, of which three-quarters had been fully surveyed.

Overhaul

'Overhaul' was the term given to the process of revising the old 1:2500 County Series sheets and fitting them to the new National Grid sheetlines, eliminating some of the defects of the old map at the same time. Experiments to do this in urban areas had failed, leading to the decision to resurvey towns at 1:1250 scale, but in rural areas overhaul was deemed accurate enough and provided the quickest and most economical method of recasting the national plans on the new national projection.

The first stage of the overhaul took place in the field, where the new retriangulation control was surveyed on to the old County Series sheet so that they were in sympathy with local detail. Vector diagrams were produced in headquarters to show the magnitude and direction of the shift necessary to bring each control point to its true National Grid position, and the differences in coordinates were listed. The control points now had to be made to fall into their correct positions relative to the national grid. This was not done by moving the control points, but by distorting the grid.

Maps overlaid with the distorted grid were supplied to draughtsmen who had to alter the map so that its grid lines matched a perfect grid on glass plate. Using their skill and judgement they did this by cutting the sheet into pieces, leaving small gaps and overlaps in the detail. As few cuts as possible were made and these were carefully planned to cause least disruption to areas of close map detail, so, for example, an attempt would be made to keep the centre of a village or small town as one unit, with the adjustment achieved at more open ground on the outskirts. Having made the cuts, the draughtsman had to put the plan back together, like some obscure jigsaw puzzle, sticking it all in place. The recompiled map was then copied on to a stable translucent plastic sheet which became the surveyor's working document.

The surveyor revised the map adding new detail, but only checking the old where discrepancies occurred. There was an ever-present danger that in moving old detail to correct an error, that a series of consequential shifts would result in a cumulative error worse than the original one. As the surveyors gained experience they learnt to resist the temptation to try and achieve the impossible, of making the overhaul more exact than the original survey. There is no doubt that despite its frustrations, experienced draughtsmen and surveyors enjoyed the mental agility required by the overhaul task and found its dependence on their individual skill satisfying.

Like all long-term survey tasks the system evolved through the years as new technology became available. In the 1960s field surveyors began to be entrusted with stereoscopic air photograph cover of the overhaul areas at contact print scale, and single rectified enlargements at 1:2500 scale. Using these, dramatic improvements in output were achieved which justified the expense of the photographs and the training of surveyors in what was termed 'air–ground revision'. Previously almost all interpretation of air photographs had been done at headquarters, but the surveyor's knowledge of his local area gave him a head start in interpreting the detail shown on them. Air–ground was taken to with enthusiasm by the surveyors and was found to be economic, enabling them to spend wet days on interpretation of the photographs and dry days out on the ground.

Accuracy testing carried out on the overhauled sheets established that the plans generally remained within or close to a predetermined acceptable tolerance, the standard, however, remaining well below that obtainable by a 'first class' 1:2500 resurvey. Some areas, particularly those in the 'replotted counties' where the mapping had originally been based on the enlarged 6-inch survey, were found impossible to overhaul to an acceptable accuracy tolerance, and had to be resurveyed. The size of the overhaul task shrank as more plans were upgraded to be resurveyed at 1:1250, but by 1961 the scale was still only about 14 per cent complete.

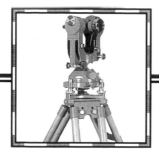

12 WORKING TO PLAN

After the Second World War draughtsmen were recruited in the same way as surveyors, with the same academic qualifications expected and an identical level of pay. However, the work could hardly be more different. The surveyor's working day, which often began with the cry of 'everybody out', was spent mainly out of doors. For the draughtsman and other headquarters staff, everybody had to be in by the designated time. A red line was then drawn across the attendance register book and those who were repeatedly late ran the risk of having their pay docked.

Draughtsmen began their careers with a fifteen-week basic training course during which they were instructed in line-drawing, ornament and general map knowledge. Most junior draughtsmen were then sent to the large-scales drawing offices where they learnt to apply their new-found skills to the simpler forms of drawing. Accuracy and neatness were essential for this work and only slowly could their skill be built up, bolstered by a second, more advanced drawing course. An understanding of the everyday problems of the surveyors was found to improve a draughtsman's interpretation of the plans submitted to the drawing office and selected draughtsmen were also given six weeks instruction in large-scale survey methods.

Gradually, as the years went by, the draughtsmen progressed to more complex and detailed work. The most demanding, in terms of artistry, was the 1-inch scale drawing and the senior draughtsmen who created these visual masterpieces won world-wide respect.

The war brought many changes to the draughtsmen's work, not least of which was the introduction for the first time of draughtswomen. This was such a novelty that efforts were at first made to keep them completely separate, with the women being accommodated in Crabwood House. After the war many women left Ordnance Survey, but those who wanted to stay were made welcome as the department needed an increased number of draughtsmen, the women's work was of a high standard – and they were paid less than the men.

The duration of the war was perhaps the only time when standards of penmanship were lowered. Speed was all and, provided that the maps accurately showed the detail required, then perfection was less of a priority. In the early peacetime years some difficulty was experienced in trying to raise the standards once again to pre-war levels.

Before work could begin on a 1:1250 map, it first had to pass through three other sections. Firstly, examination was made of the plan by the security section who prepared a trace showing items in red which the draughtsman had to delete and in green those which had been declassified and could be added. Just after the war there were large numbers of military sites such as anti-aircraft defences which it was felt desirable to omit, but security also applied in a slightly different sense to civil establishments such as prisons. The outer walls of these were defined but the positions of buildings inside the compound were not. The plans then passed through the Archaeology Branch who added any relevant antiquity information.

Finally, Ordnance Survey had, and still has, a duty to ascertain, 'mere' and keep a full record of public boundaries by depicting them on large-scale mapping. The position of the boundaries, their name and title being agreed with local authorities. 'Mereing' is the term given to relating the boundary to its correct position in relation to topographical detail. Changes to boundaries were incorporated on the maps at the first revision opportunity, with the record of the boundaries being open for public inspection. All maps passed through the boundary department for a check that the position of existing boundaries and their administrative names were correct.

The draughtsman was supplied with a varnished glass positive of the plan to which all new detail found by continuous revision had to be added. It was expected that any minor imperfections in the plan, such as broken lines, would also be corrected at the same time. All work was checked by the examination section and, if necessary, it was returned to the draughtsman for correction. Once satisfied that the plan was correct, the examiner sent it to be sprayed with varnish to preserve the new work from accidental damage.

In 1956 the department began to experiment with a new process, invented in America, called 'scribing'. This replaced the use of pen and ink with a process of cutting away, with a sharp-pointed tool, a translucent coating given to the glass. It was found to be quicker than drawing, with the added benefit that more consistent results were attainable. The principle was easily established but many experiments were necessary before the ideal combination of scribing instrument and base material was found.

The original Ordnance Survey scribing instruments were designed and made by one of the draughtsmen, Mr R A 'Reg' Jerrard BEM, whose common-sense approach contributed greatly to the success of the system. Copies of the instruments for general use were made by the Ordnance Survey's own workshops. The scribing points were made of hardened steel which the glass tended to blunt, but they were easily sharpened by the user. Gramophone needles were also used. These were readily available and could be sharpened to chisel points and to the required gauges on the honing jig. Once the principle of scribing was established, new scribing instruments were invented to do particular drawing tasks. For instance, double cutters were produced which would 'draw' two parallel lines a fixed distance apart with a consistent precision unobtainable by pen and ink. Contours were particularly suitable candidates for scribing methods. New recruits found scribing easier to master than pen and ink and by 1958 it was the favoured method for all 1:2500 plan production, giving a saving of over 25 per cent in time over the old methods. Within four years it was extended to include all revised 1:2500 and most 1:1250 plans.

Trials were concluded successfully to allow stable coated plastic sheets to be used instead of glass. Plastic was more suitable than coated glass for scribing, with the added advantage of being less fragile. Later cutters were commercially produced with steel shanks on which synthetic ruby tips were mounted. These were ground and polished to precise Ordnance Survey line gauges.

The draughtsman's work has, for the sake of conformity of mapping over the whole country, to be anonymous, although in the days before standard stick-down lettering it was possible for experienced draughtsmen to tell which of their colleagues had written the lettering on a particular map from the handwriting. In the very early days of the Ordnance Survey, names of the principle invididuals who worked on the maps were included in the map margins of the published sheets but in later years no such credit was given. Part of the argument was that contributors to the map, from the surveyor to the printer, were too numerous to mention. The draughtsman, however, was responsible for the final drawing and, human nature being what it is, they sometimes tried to disguise their signature amongst the rock depiction, vegetation or other close detail. Usually the sharp eyes of the examiner would easily find the extraneous information, but occasionally the more subtle signings appeared on the published map. However, culprits were severely reprimanded.

Photowriter working on a negative of a large-scale map.

All maps and plans had at some stage to pass through the photodrawing section where negatives of the maps were examined, minor imperfections touched up and last-minute corrections made. The negatives were supported on angled light tables in front of the draughtsman who worked using a jeweller's eyeglass to magnify the map. Touching up was done with a fine metal point and corrections to the writing called for particular skill as the lettering was reversed on the negative. The work was exacting, and tiring to the eyes, the whole room being in complete darkness to allow for clear visibility of the negative.

Sometimes, by way of relief from the close concentration, the draughtsman would doodle, usually in the margins of the map and would simply paint over or 'duff out' the doodle before passing the map on to the next production stage. It was in this way that one of the most celebrated 'errors' in the Ordnance Survey's history came about. One draughtsman, presented with a plan showing part of the Manchester Ship Canal, couldn't resist adding ships to the broad swathe of water cutting across the sheet. He drew them in simple plan view from above, duffed them out when his work was complete, sent the plan forward and thought no more about it. Unfortunately he had missed one and it was printed on the finished map, unnoticed until an observant member of the public wrote in to enquire what it was. To the draughtsmen this was a huge joke and the 'culprit' received many congratulations from his fellows on his achievement, but the department was not amused, especially as the sheet had to be

Application of lettering to a large-scale map.

Scribing on plastic.

Peeling out sections of a plastic sheet to expose building detail on the scribed underlay.

withdrawn from sale and corrected. Such errors were potentially damaging to the department's reputation for accuracy and steps were taken to try to ensure that it should never happen again.

══════ Consultation ══════

By the time Carey was appointed Director General he was already an 'old hand', having previously carried out three tours of duty with the department, starting in Norwich in 1929. Carey, from a prominent Guernsey family, was a man of great personal charm who, on taking over, seemed to release Ordnance Survey from its post-war preoccupation with production, allowing the department to 'come up for air'.

The battle with the Treasury for new equipment was won, the move to a new headquarters seemed unlikely to happen for a few years and men and women were once again applying for appointment with the department. A measure of stability at last seemed possible and the Ordnance Survey came out of its shell to meet its customers.

Since the end of the war, six-monthly advisory committee meetings had been held with other government departments, national bodies and the nationalised industries. In 1958 three extra meetings were held, particularly to discuss the 1:2500 scale maps and to see if, in fact, what was being produced was what was required by potential map users. It was found that there were some aspects of the map that they were unhappy with, especially the small 1 km × 1 km sheet size. The department agreed to publish future sheets at double the size showing 2 × 1 km, and took on board several other suggestions made for improvement.

Carey also encouraged the officers in charge of each region to liaise more closely with local authorities, and each council was personally visited over a couple of years. This approach was generally welcomed and three further channels of long-term liaison resulted. Firstly, a regular series of meetings was held with local authorities. These were hosted by Ordnance Survey at Chessington and Edinburgh. Secondly, in response to demand, the department began to hold courses to which councils could send officers to learn about Ordnance Survey maps. Such courses are held to this day. Lastly, the local authorities themselves suggested that they should each nominate one person to be the Ordnance Survey liaison officer, to which the department readily agreed. This custom also still exists.

The Maybush headquarters

On 1 May 1969 the new headquarters building of the Ordnance Survey was opened by Her Majesty Queen Elizabeth II, accompanied by Prince Philip, the Duke of Edinburgh.

For almost thirty years, the Ordnance Survey administrative offices had been scattered in Chessington, at Crabwood, at the reoccupied London Road and at other temporary accommodation. Finally, all could be housed on one site. Major General R C A Edge, the Director General, summed up the relief and sense of homecoming that was felt by the staff with his words: 'Today, the opening of these premises marks the end of our refugee status.'

The senior architect, Mr L P Murphy of the Ministry of Public Building and Works, was assisted in its construction by Mr R E Hall, the senior Clerk of Works, who confessed that it had been his lifetime's ambition, to build the new Southampton home for the department. He achieved this just before his retirement.

Architecturally the building is typical of its era, constructed in concrete and glass, dominant to its surroundings, with no attempt to disguise its functionality. As befitted a government department it was designed without grandeur or pretension but this did not preclude innovation. The restaurant, for instance, boasted an unusual single-span elliptically domed roof and the exterior concrete of the main buildings was protected by 23 million mosaic squares which were 'guaranteed to preserve the walls for many years ahead'. More than twenty years on, the building still seems

Ordnance Survey headquarters at Maybush, Southampton.

breathtakingly large, and few staff can claim to have seen inside every room.

A covered way links two blocks of the building to provide a frame for 'The Mural', an abstract concrete work, by Mr K I McCarter DA (Edin), MSIA, AIBD, intended to suggest the relationship of astronomy and cartography, but which has perplexed staff and visitors alike since the building opened. Crabwood House was preserved together with some of its parkland setting. As the 3000-strong headquarters staff settled in and the 9 million individual maps

were tucked away into their purpose-designed store, all seemed ideal compared to the inconveniences of many of the old buildings.

With the new headquarters came a new image provided for the department by the Central Office of Information. Moss green was selected to be the new house colour and a simple but effective logo, still in use today, was created to replace the intricate royal arms.

The new headquarters was referred to as Maybush, named after the parish in which it stood, to distinguish it from Crabwood House.

In 1961 Carey was succeeded by Major General Arthur Henley Dowson who continued the consultative initiative and added a further dimension the following year with the founding of the Map Users Conference to which any interested group of map users, from farmers to hikers, could send a representative. The diversity of people and interests represented around the table ensured that a lively, but not always constructive, debate ensued. In 1970 this conference was divided into two groups, one for users of mainly large-scale and the other for users of mainly small-scale maps.

Dowson found that the continuous revision sections were fighting a losing battle against an ever-rising backlog of unsurveyed detail and, to counteract this, he transferred more surveyors to continuous revision duties from overhaul and resurvey work. This had the added benefit of reducing pressure on the drawing office, who had been unable to keep

up with the flow of plans from the field offices. The loser in this solution was the resurvey and overhaul programme, and the estimated date for completion quietly slipped a further decade into the future.

Winter weather usually had little effect on production, but the weeks of freezing weather and snow, in the winter of 1962/63, made surveying impossible in some areas, and difficult in many others. The men were used to working out of doors but found their work hampered by the difficult travelling conditions and by hard-packed snow covering the control points and features they had come to survey. This caused consternation in the drawing office, who had cleared their backlog and were now beginning to run out of work. Dowson began to lobby the Minister of Agriculture for more survey staff, rejecting the suggestion that the continuous revision programme should be put to one side for ten years to release staff for overhaul and revision.

The Joint Survey Service

In 1963 the department came under pressure from the Estimates Committee of the House of Commons, which examined the structure of the Ordnance Survey and looked for ways of making economies and increasing revenue. They recommended a gradual reduction of the numbers of military staff, and proposed the sharing of a new professional staff between the three survey organisations in existence. The result was the Joint Survey Service (JSS) whose members' careers could span the Directorates of Military and Overseas Survey as well as Ordnance Survey.

To join this elite, from which it was intended that Ordnance Survey should draw its senior management, it was usually necessary to be either an associate member of the Royal Institute of Chartered Surveyors (RICS) or to be recruited into one of the three departments at graduate level. The net effect on the department was that graduate surveyors would spend their early years with the Overseas Surveys, before arriving, after promotion, to a more senior grade at Ordnance Survey. The first appointments were made under this system in 1969.

This created problems, not least of which was the damage to the moral of the 'home grown' staff who had hoped that, once the military began to leave the department, there would be an enhanced career structure for themselves. The JSS staff, arriving from overseas, sometimes found their own difficulties in adapting from working with a fair degree of autonomy in undeveloped countries, to being a manager in a large and somewhat more claustrophobic civil service department. There still remained a layer of lower management to be filled by promotion from technical grades, but here Ordnance Survey fell into a trap of its own making. In the post-war years staff had only been trained in particular narrow specialisms, and this had led to a generation of staff being given no opportunity to broaden their knowledge. As a result they lacked the more general experience considered necessary for promotion.

Belatedly, in 1966, the department set up a new training division to provide opportunities for promising staff to gain wider experience through further survey-related education.

Two ministries

In 1965 the Director Generalship of the department was taken over by Major General Raymond Cyril Alexander Edge, and shortly afterwards Ordnance Survey's seventy-five year association with the Ministry of Agriculture, Fisheries and Food came to an end, when responsibility for the department was passed to the newly created Ministry of Land and Natural Resources. This change of 'owner' gave the department a fresh opportunity to put its case for extra staff to clear the backlog of large-scale mapping. The estimated completion dates of the resurvey and overhaul had, by this time, moved to the year 2000 a clearly unacceptable state of affairs. Approval was given to increase the staff by 20 per cent over the next ten years to bring the estimated completion date back down to 1980. This was an important decision because it recognised that the continuous revision programme was an inviolable necessity, despite the existence of other high priorities. Nothing, however, comes free of charge, and the expansion was agreed on condition that the extra cost of the staff would be covered by increased revenue from the plans – in other words the price of the large-scale plans had to rise substantially. 'The 1980 Plan', as it became known, gave a focus to the large-scale work and it became almost a point of honour that the department must achieve that date. Close interest was paid to production rates and anxiety resulted from any slippage on yearly estimates of production.

In 1966 Edge decided that the terminology used to describe Ordnance Survey maps was misleading. His concern centred around the use of the word 'plan' which had two meanings, firstly, in the mapping sense of a 'large-scale plan', and secondly, as, for example, in a 'plan of action'. Ordnance Survey *plans* were often used for *planning* and though staff were seldom confused, customers sometimes were. The scales of maps had been divided into: large-scale plans – up to 1:2500 scale; medium-scale maps – the 6-inch and 1:25 000; and small-scale maps – anything smaller scale than 1:25 000.

Edge declared that from 1966 there would only be large-scale *maps* or small-scale maps. The large-scale maps included the 6-inch and the small-scale the 1:25 000.

In his policy statement of 1967, Edge included the aim of securing 'the maximum return from sales, royalties' and so on, provided that this was 'appropriate for the department and does not lead to undue dispersion of effort.' It was also agreed that the department should not 'engage in additional activities for the sake of profit nor compete with other organisations offering satisfactory service in similar fields'. The emphasis here was on co-operation with other companies provided that this did not compromise the department's own commercial position. With hindsight this policy seems almost half-hearted but the general view at the time was that if commercial considerations were allowed to become dominant, then the result would be a degradation of the national mapping service provided. Edge also had to tread carefully to avoid criticism from commercial companies who, if the department was too aggressive in its policies, might claim that the vast Ordnance Survey, with its heavy government subsidy, was trying to map them out of existence.

The Bloggoscope

Throughout its history Ordnance Survey has benefited from the inventiveness and ingenuity of its employees, but only one staff invention has earned itself a place in the Science Museum. For this, the accolade goes to William Blogg.

In the 1950s, when Bill Blogg, a surveyor, was working in the Air Survey Branch, Ordnance Survey was still only making moderate progress towards full-scale map production using air photographs. One of the most stubborn problems was how to eliminate distortion in the photographs caused by tilting of the camera in the aircraft, when, for instance, it was affected by air turbulence.

Bill knew that the position of the camera at the moment of exposure had to be found. Once the tilt angles were known they could be set into a rectifying enlarger, the easel of which would be angled at a compensatory tilt. The photographic image could then be projected on to the tilted surface and, in much the same way as projecting photographic slides on to a screen, the operator knew that, when a perfect square was obtained, then the picture was free from distortion.

At home, in his garage, Bill designed and then made a wooden model of his 'Blogg Tilt Finder'. This replicated the position of the camera in the aircraft flying over the land. The perspective centre of the camera was represented by a small filament bulb, mounted above the base board (datum plane). Nine holes allowed light rays to shine through nine control points on a contact print suspended in a carrier under the light. The light passed through the print and on down to the same points marked on the 1:2500 plan of the area, laid on the base board. The different heights of the ground, calculated from contours on the 1-inch map of the same area, were represented by adjustable blocks placed on the plan and over the control points. These created, in effect, a three-dimensional model of the ground.

The carrier holding the print could be moved up and down and tilted in all directions. When the nine rays of light coincided exactly with the nine height blocks, the angle of the camera as it was at the moment it took the photograph had been found and could be read from scales on the carrier.

Trials proved that enlargements made using the angles found by the Bloggoscope, as it became called, were free from distortion and tilt. Bill Blogg's suggestion earned him a mere £10, but it became clear over the next few years how important this invention had been for the department and on his retirement in 1972, after 47 year's service, he was presented with a cheque for £1500, which still stands as a record payment for a staff suggestion. He was also awarded the British Empire Medal in 1967, and the ISM in 1971. Of his invention, Bill Blogg said he enjoyed making things and that 'I felt I just had to find an easier way of doing the job.'

In 1989, having finally been superseded by computerised rectification techniques, a quarter-scale model of the Bloggoscope was placed on display in the Science Museum in London.

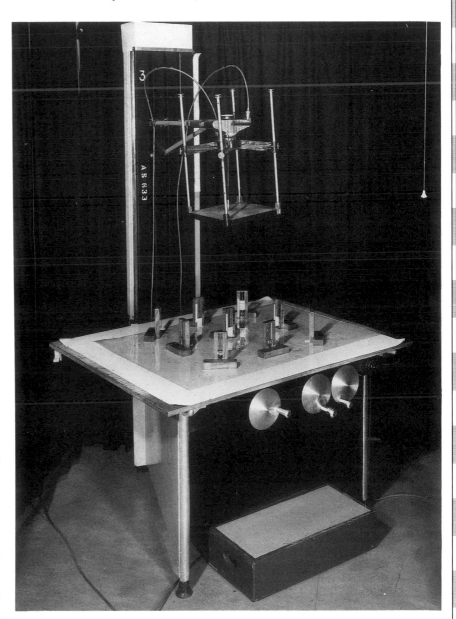

Bloggoscope rectifying machine.

In 1967 the Ministry of Land was abolished and Ordnance Survey passed into the care of the Ministry of Housing and Local Government. Some concern surrounded the question of which ministry should be responsible for the department as it had previously been felt that there was a danger that any ministry might place pressure to ensure that their own mapping needs were given priority. As a result Ordnance Survey acquired a measure of independence in its day-to-day operation whilst remaining subject to general Civil Service constraints on manpower and other resources.

The quickening pace of surveying in the 1960s was not matched by an equally fast rise in output in the drawing offices and this problem was compounded by difficulties in recruiting new draughtsmen. Overtime in the drawing office and transferring surveyors to continuous revision work rather than overhaul was not the answer as this put the 1980 Plan at risk. In 1968 the department took the drastic step of compulsorily transferring surveyors to drawing duties for periods of six months at a time in an effort to put the surveying and draughting output in balance. In 1969 a much better solution was found and an agreement was made with Ordnance Survey of Northern Ireland for a scribing unit to be specially recruited and trained in Belfast to undertake 1:2500 work. Once operational the system worked well and was retained until the early 1970s.

Air photography

Throughout the war, maps had been updated using air photography. First of all Ordnance Survey had used the 'Arundel method' which was named after a trial air survey in 1926. This assumed that photographs were vertical and free of tilt, and consisted of identification of common points on overlapping photographs to draw a minor control plot for each photographic sortie. The accuracy of these plots was dependent to a large extent on the skill of the individual and the whole process was very slow. Later in the war an American 'slotted template' method was adopted for fixing minor control, which improved both the accuracy and the speed of plotting.

At the end of the war attention turned once more to the consideration of air photography as a quick method of survey for civilian maps, and in the autumn of 1945 the newly created Air Photo Division took up the investigation. The Davidson Committee had recommended that a special air survey unit should be created under the control of Ordnance Survey but, as there was a surplus of both pilots and planes in the Royal Air Force, their facilities were used instead.

The RAF made great efforts to supply the photographs required but were beset with difficulties caused by constantly changing aircrew, unsuitable aircraft and problems with clumsy and outdated camera equipment. The quality of the photographs was often poor and the outlook for extensive use of air photography for a while appeared gloomy. Everyone agreed that survey from air photographs should logically be economical, but somehow it never was. This was a disappointment to Major General Brown, the Director General, who was a convert to the merits of air survey, even learning to fly himself. He had been keen to further the use of air photography but was severely hampered by lack of funds for equipment. However, progress was made by applying graphical ground survey techniques to air photographs and for some areas where ground survey was difficult, such as docks and railway sidings, it was particularly valuable.

In 1951 the arrangement with the RAF was terminated and flying was undertaken instead by the Ministry of Transport and Civil Aviation (MTCA). Under this agreement, Ordnance Survey purchased its own cameras and provided its own air camera operators.

Surveys by air photography of the line of low water continued to be carried out by the RAF at suitable tide states for some years. Here the use of infra-red film showed clearly the distinction between water, wet sand or mud, and dry land.

Air Survey Branch in the 1980s with Wild 8 stereoplotting machines.

The quality of air photographs began to improve and an experiment carried out using photographs of Oxford, in 1954/5, made it clear that savings would result from plotting map detail directly from the air photographs. Substantial economies were promised, convincing the new Director General, Willis, that investment in stereoplotting equipment would be repaid by savings in surveying time. In the 1950s, the department was facing a phased reduction in non-industrial manpower from 4800 to 3800 staff by the end of the decade, and the race was on to develop air survey techniques to compensate for reduced staff levels.

Most of the expensive equipment was made in Switzerland, and it was difficult for Willis to persuade his Minister that such large sums of money should be sent abroad. Fortunately, Professor E H Thompson, formally a Captain in the Royal Engineers, who had spent some years with Ordnance Survey, had perfected a new design for a stereoplotting machine. A prototype was produced and sent to Ordnance Survey for trials, which proved successful. The machine was produced by a British firm, Hilger and Watts, and five were purchased by the department, and a further seven by 1958. Over the next three years the number of plotting machines rose to twenty-five. A new era of sophisticated photogrammetry had begun.

Air photography was taken in strips, with each photograph overlapping the next by 60 per cent and adjacent strips having an overlap of 25 per cent. These large overlaps are necessary to produce the stereo effect. With the new equipment and its successors a number of defined uses could be made of the air photography.

Air triangulation, for producing survey control from air photographs, was an early success and methods were developed which remain broadly the same today. One essential requirement for its success was the marking of trig. pillars so that they could be clearly seen from the air, done in the simplest manner by sending a person to the trig. pillar with a pot of white paint. The unfortunate individual had not only to paint the pillar itself but also a broad circle, usually made up of large stones around it, to form a distinctive bull's-eye appearance from the air. Other control points, such as church towers, were also used.

A stereocomparator, which compared and adjusted the coordinates of pillars and other points observed, was used to extract the control information. The complex calculations involved were at first adjusted by the computer at the National Physical Laboratory but later by the department's own mainframe computer.

Stereoplotters provided, from air photographs, the position of actual map detail, such as fences, on to plots used by surveyors as a working document, on which ground survey information was added. A big saving in time was also made when the stereoplotters were first used to provide map contours. The operator's 'floating mark' within the machine could be set at the height of any contour and, by chasing the mark over the surface of the image at that level, the operator could plot the contours much more quickly and easily than a surveyor on the ground. The laborious ground survey techniques were soon abandoned except, for a time, in very flat areas, like the Fens. Here the required accuracy was only attainable by ground survey until 1972 when an acceptable technique was worked out for applying air survey methods.

Air photography continued to make significant contributions to archaeology. A number of operators became adept at spotting sites on photographs and hundreds of new, often major, sites were found. Since 1966 all flying for air survey work has been carried out by contract with civil companies. The camera operators, as before, are supplied by Ordnance Survey with staff ready to fly at a moment's notice of suitable weather. Some aerial photography (Ordnance Survey has now adopted the term 'aerial photography') is supplied under contract from commercial companies.

Levelling off

In 1950 it was decided that a third geodetic levelling was necessary to resolve increasing inconsistencies within the existing levelling network.

Work in England and Wales started in late 1951 and took until 1956 to complete, incorporating 115 fundamental bench-marks (FBMs). Some of these had already been built, but not used for the second geodetic levelling. Additional lines of levelling, to incorporate tide gauges and new FBMs and to resolve levelling anomalies, were also added. Geodetic lines were kept away from subsidence areas, but efforts were made to establish lower-order stable bench-marks in these areas at a careful selection of sites. In Scotland the third geodetic levelling was started in 1956, and was completed in 1958.

The results of the geodetic computations were disappointing, showing for example a rise at Dunbar of almost 6 inches. A systematic error was thought to have affected the results and for this reason the FBM values of the second geodetic levelling for England and Wales were retained and the new levelling adjusted to these for control of lower-order work. In Scotland, where the second geodetic levelling was in any case more recent, it was retained without adjustment. The results of the third geodetic levelling were held for scientific purposes only.

From 1956, secondary levelling lines were run from the geodetic lines to break down the polygons into manageable tertiary levelling blocks of between 150 and 400 square miles, depending on the type of area covered. The larger tertiary blocks covered mountain and moorland areas and it was intended, at the time, that these would be relevelled on a cyclic basis, every forty years; smaller blocks covering urban and rural areas were to be levelled every twenty years; mining subsidence and fenland areas every five or ten years. Tertiary levelling was to a lower standard of accuracy than secondary work and placed cut bench-marks at a density of about four per linear mile, or eight in towns. All types of bench-marks were shown on the plans.

The levellers moved along the lines of their levelling blocks at the rate of, on average, 1 mile a day, varying with the terrain. The section offices tended to be situated in the middle of a number of levelling blocks, and the levellers very rarely visited them, so they were mostly small and little more than a storeroom and office for the section supervisor. Occasionally the levellers would make use of a corner of a convenient field section office, but, for a majority of them, 'the office' was their digs or the back seat of their car. The leveller's assistant, the staffholder, was often employed on a casual basis, although many stayed with the department for years, moving around with the work. Supervisors, mainly ex-levellers, saw their staff once or twice a week and always at the end of the week to pay the casual staffholder and to collect the week's work for checking and despatch to headquarters for computation. Computation of tertiary blocks was made as the work progressed so that the need for any relevelling was quickly discovered while the leveller was still in the area.

The workhorse levelling instrument of the period was the spirit bubble, Cooke, Troughton and Simms S401. Similar in design to its larger brother, the S500 used for geodetic work, the S401 had originally been used for secondary levelling but was now a 'hand-me-down' for tertiary work. This instrument, like many theodolites, gave an upside-down view of the stave, which had in consequence its numbers printed upside-down so that they read correctly through the instrument. It was finally superseded by the semi-automatic Wild Na2 in the 1970s, a level that used a clever method of a 'suspended' prism held within the optical line of the instrument. As the prism responded to gravity it made the instrument self-levelling within a narrow tolerance. It also gave a right-way-up view and inexperienced levellers found them quicker to use, but typically the more experienced 'craftsmen' levellers preferred their old, but now obviously worn, 401s.

In 1962, the five-year cycle for levelling of subsidence areas was abandoned. Further economies followed six years later with a decision to reduce the density of tertiary bench-marks. This left some of the old, but still extant, marks from

the second geodetic levelling unlevelled. These were termed bypassed marks, and although their heights were retained for publication on plans and bench-mark lists, they could not be compared directly with any of the newly levelled marks as they were based on two different parent levellings.

In 1973 the Janes Committee report on the Ordnance Survey recommended that tertiary levelling should cease altogether, except as a repayment service, but opposition to this from the Royal Society and other professional organisations led to the suggestion being withdrawn. However, in 1975, cyclic levelling was abandoned and became sporadic, only being undertaken in areas that had suffered high bench-mark losses or where major building development had taken place. In 1987 a five-year moratorium on tertiary levelling was called, although new levelling continued to be available on a repayment basis for customers who wanted it. The decision on 'What comes next?' may hinge on experience gained with height surveying from satellite information.

Six-inch mapping

As a result of the adoption of the 1:2500 scale as the largest scale of national mapping, the 6-inch map began to decline in importance. It tended to bear the brunt of economy cuts and delays and was usually far more out of date than was considered desirable. Where 1:2500 mapping was introduced, the 6-inch maps were derived in its wake, but the delay between publication of mapping at 1:2500 scale and its appearance at 6-inch scale grew as the years passed. The Davidson Committee recommended that the scale should be retained, noting that it had been in existence for over a hundred years and was extensively used for keeping records of all kinds, such as the positions of boundaries.

Many of the 6-inch maps were hurriedly updated just before the Second World War to provide a Special Emergency (Air Raid Precaution) map for local authorities. The series had to be recast on the new national projection and brought into the National Grid system, and from 1943 any maps revised remained published on their old sheetlines but had the national grid added. This policy was later abandoned when it was decided to directly produce them on the new National Grid sheetlines, each map covering 5 km × 5 km. This series was termed the Provisional Edition as it was undertaken with minimum redrawing, although it did incorporate some revision.

The Regular Series gradually replaced the Provisional Edition. Within this series there were derived Regular maps, whose source was the 1:1250 or 1:2500 scale map, and basic Regular maps which were surveyed at 6-inch scale and covered moorland and mountains. In 1956 the basic scale of

Close encounters

In 1964, seven years after the launch of the first artificial satellite, Sputnik 1, Ordnance Survey began experiments in satellite triangulation in the form of simultaneously photographing a satellite against a background of stars from two known positions some distance apart.

A camera capable of taking such pictures had been designed by Mr Joe Hewitt of The Royal Radar Establishment at Malvern in Worcestershire. Two were built and sited nearly 300 miles apart – at Sheriffs Lench near Evesham and at Earlyburn near Edinburgh.

The advantage of satellite triangulation was that a complete framework could quickly be built up, with the sides of triangles being several hundred miles in length. Observations were co-ordinated by the International Association of Geodesy.

In July 1967 the cameras were transferred to Ordnance Survey ownership and a permanent eight-man team was set up to operate the Sheriffs Lench camera. The Earlyburn system was operated by The Scottish Royal Observatory. Mr Hewitt, the camera designer, stayed as consultant to the project until his sudden death in 1975.

Staff worked in pairs on a three-week shift system. The first week making camera observations, the second on photographic processing and assessment and the third on photographic plate reading, data processing and making orbital predictions of the satellites.

Long winter nights with temperatures as low as −10°C could be very tiring, but there was a certain romance in observing the night sky, waiting for satellites to pass through the 'bible black' of the Worcestershire countryside. However, the down-to-earth camera operators working at Sheriffs Lench had some mysterious tales to tell. Some reported locked doors being opened, with the only key in full sight. Others told of books, boxes, cups and trays being noisily moved, or a sensation of being watched, but with no one else apparently in the room. Try as they might, they found it impossible to reason away these strange occurrences.

Each satellite pass is a unique event, which may result in a simultaneous observation from two or more tracking stations and over the years many hundreds of simultaneous observations were captured, one of the most remarkable being with a tracking station in Brazil. Others were made with the USA and USSR despite it being during the depths of the Cold War.

Satellites such as Echos 1 and 2 and Pageos were silvered balloons originally conceived as

The Hewitt camera at Sheriffs Lench, in its day 'the most accurate camera in the world'.

passive telecommunications satellites and they made ideal targets for the camera. As well as observing for the Western European Satellite Triangulation Network, work was also carried out for Mr D G King-Hele from the Royal Aircraft Establishment at Farnborough. This consisted of photographing and measuring low-orbiting bodies, from which upper atmosphere conditions were studied. Some interesting photographs were also taken for NASA of the Apollo spacecraft 'fuel dumps', made as the module journeyed towards the Moon.

Ordnance Survey staff working on these satellite tracking operations were moved on to other tasks after a three-year tour and replaced by other willing volunteers; but by the mid 1970s, improved technology was overtaking optical camera systems. A flashing light carried by the Geos satellite was observable by the camera, but the same satellite also carried laser reflectors which were observed by more accurate laser ranging systems.

In 1978 Ordnance Survey observations ceased because, 'With the development of other satellite systems . . . and the general decline in the requirement for optical satellite data for geodetic purposes', the department could no longer justify the expense of operating the camera. Responsibility for it was handed over to the Satellite Research Unit of Aston University in Birmingham.

The value to the scientific community of the Ordnance Survey's work may best be explained by quoting from a letter written by Mr King-Hele to the Director General in 1978:

The contributions made by this magnificent camera, which is still the most accurate camera in the world, have been vital in providing the high quality observations needed to make advances at the frontiers of research by means of orbital analysis.

survey for the Highlands and Islands of Scotland was confirmed as the 6-inch. Areas of mountain and moorland in England and Wales could be overhauled and revised, but in Scotland, where a large proportion of the maps were not contoured, resurvey was the only answer.

The methods used for the resurvey were a mixture of ultra-modern and age-old surveying techniques. Air photography was used to supply some of the control and an outline plot for the surveyor. A special team of surveyors was dedicated to the 6-inch task and had to be prepared to work intensively, often for seven days a week in summer, to maximise use of the good weather.

Air-photo plotting was not an ideal solution to the problem of the sparse Highland landscape and the machine operators found it difficult to pick out the wire fences which were a major surveyable feature in these areas. The surveyors found that much of their day was spent walking long distances across rough ground before they could reach their area of work, and eventually it was found to be economical to airlift them by helicopter to and from their location. The actual surveying was mainly done by plane tabling, a rapid mapping technique which is used by Ordnance Survey for work at this scale only, generally being considered too inaccurate for larger-scale work.

The 6-inch map is the largest scale on which contour information is shown, and from 1943 the contour interval was surveyed at 25 feet plotted mainly from air photography.

===================== **1:25 000** =====================

The concept of national mapping at 1:25 000 scale was approved in 1938 by the Davidson Committee who recommended that a number of trial sheets should be put on sale to gauge public reaction. In fact, after the outbreak of war, cover

of the whole country was quickly produced for the War Office by photographic reduction of the 6-inch maps, making a practical, if difficult to read, map. This edition was soon in demand for post-war planning and was made generally available at the end of hostilities.

A high priority was given to replacing the War Office map with a civil, more cartographically acceptable, version on National Grid sheetlines. This was produced by derived reduction of the 1:10 560 scale, the War Office edition, and from revision collected for the 1-inch maps. The first 10 km × 10 km map of this 'Provisional Edition' was issued in November 1945 and the remainder was intended to follow within two years, but in fact it took until 1956 to complete England, Wales and the industrial areas and east coast of Scotland. By this time the planning authorities were complaining that it was out of date and the usefulness of the series for post-war reconstruction was diminishing.

Revision of the Provisional Edition was started in 1950 and shortly afterwards a start was made on replacing this with the Regular Edition. However, other higher priorities led to this being abandoned and only eleven sheets of the Regular Edition, of the area around Plymouth, were published.

The revision of the Provisional Edition was continued instead and its name changed to the 'First Series'. Scotland was never completed as, although it had been suggested that the 1:25 000 scale should be adopted as the basic scale of survey for Highland areas, the 1:10 560 was preferred by the Scottish authorities.

In the early 1960s, work began on the Second Series 1:25 000. Criticism had been levelled at the small size of the First Series sheets and, in response to this, a new 20 km × 15 km format was chosen. Despite the production advantages of a map of this size, the numbering system, which used the national grid coordinates of the south-west corner of every

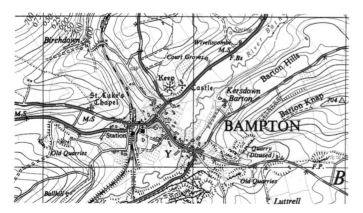

Part of 1:25 000, sheet SS60, Provisional Edition, published in 1964.

Part of 1:25 000 Pathfinder 1256 (SS82/92), revised to 1989.

sheet, became cumbersome and difficult to use unless the corners fell on regular 10 km grid-lines and the size was therefore reduced to its current 20 km × 10 km format.

The Second Series was produced primarily by reduction of the 1:10 560 sheets and showed public rights of way for England and Wales in green. This colour, which had not been used for the First Series, was now also applied to woodland. The map was printed in five colours, and the carefully drawn-up specification ensured that no one colour or feature unduly dominated another. The result was a cartographically superb map, arguably the most beautiful of the modern Ordnance Survey maps.

Pressure on resources to complete the overhaul and resurvey meant that progress was slower than intended for the 1:25 000 Second Series, for it could never be designated a priority. By 1970 only seventy-eight sheets out of a national total of about 1400 had been published. To fill the gap, First Series sheets continued to be updated with major changes until Second Series sheets covering the area became available.

=== **The Half-inch and One-inch maps** ===

The Half-inch

A new edition of the ½-inch map on national grid sheetlines was begun in 1938. Termed the 'Second Series', it immediately fell victim to the war, during which all work on it was put to one side. It fared little better when peace came as pressure on resources meant that by 1959 only one sheet, Birmingham, out of the series of fifty-seven was published.

Others were 'at an advanced stage', but no more were ever printed, and in 1961 the department 'reluctantly decided to abandon the Half-inch map as a national scale'. Apart from a few Tourist and District Maps, such as that produced for Snowdonia in 1966, this sector of the market was left to commercial map makers.

The One-inch

The Fifth Edition 1-inch map series failed to realise the high hopes that were held out for it in the early 1930s. It was perhaps ahead of its time, being highly acclaimed by reviewers but rejected by the map-buying public. Its appearance, with the emphasis on relief, represented quite a departure from the hugely successful Fourth and 'Popular' Editions and,

Part of the Fifth (Relief) Edition, sheet 106, NW London and Watford, published in 1935.

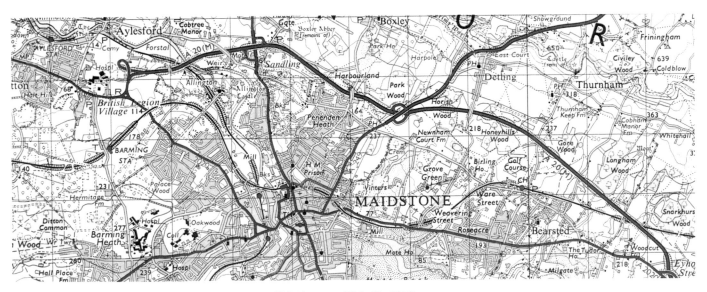

Part of the 1-inch Seventh Series, sheet 172, Chatham and Maidstone, published in 1970.

although it was printed in full colour and in much larger sheets, the public appeared unconvinced that at its higher price it represented value for money. In 1934 a simpler edition, minus the relief, was published, but fared little better. In all just over thirty of the complete set of 146 maps of the Fifth Edition had been published by the time work was stopped in 1939.

Somewhat chastened, the department immediately began work on the Sixth Edition, which as a reflection of its content was termed the 'New Popular', but publication of the first sheets was suspended for the duration of the war. A military edition of the whole country was produced during the war and, in 1943, permission was granted for this War Office edition to be released for general sale.

This was no more than a stopgap and a high priority was given to the Sixth Edition which was completed by 1947, helped partly by the fact that a number of sheets were merely reconstituted Fifth Edition material. The quality of these maps generally did not reach the standard of the old Popular and Fourth Editions and on examination it was decided to press ahead with a Seventh Edition rather than try to improve the Sixth. Part of the problem was that blitz damage had destroyed 1-inch reproduction material and, although security copies had been made, once reconstituted there remained a degradation in quality that was generally unacceptable.

Design work for the Seventh Edition was started in 1948 and the first two sheets were published in 1952. Initially printed in ten colours, and called the Seventh Series, the maps were well received and praised for their clarity. Their design had taken into account all the lessons learned from previous mistakes, except perhaps that their art deco covers were rather dull in comparison with scenic covers from earlier decades. The entire series was complete by the end of 1961. It was immediately popular with the map-buying public and between 1959 and 1966 annual sales of the 1-inch maps doubled to reach nearly 1½ million copies. At the same time production costs were reduced by printing the map in six colours instead of the original ten, with only a minimal reduction in quality.

The Seventh Series was to be the last of the 1-inch national series and in it was embodied the accumulation of all the skills and expertise gained by Ordnance Survey since it had first begun publishing its own maps at 1 inch to 1 mile in 1805.

An air photo view of Ranworth Broad and Marshes, Norfolk, flown at 7600 feet.

13 CHANGING DIRECTION

By the time Major General Brian St G Irwin took over from Edge as Director General in 1969, the staff were fully settled into their new accommodation. The inevitable reorganisation of directorates and divisions had taken place and benefits were beginning to be felt from the new resources that the building had to offer.

Irwin came to the department from his post as Director of Military Survey at the Ministry of Defence and had previously served two tours of duty with Ordnance Survey. His military career was distinguished and he was mentioned in despatches no less than three times, whilst on active service during the war and later in Cyprus. He took on the role of Director General wholeheartedly and encouraged staff to think of Ordnance Survey as a family firm in which they had an important part to play. He made particular efforts to meet members of staff and introduced a more open style of management than was usually to be expected from a man of his military background.

The installation into the new headquarters building of the department's own mainframe computer was an advantage soon exploited with the introduction of a purpose-designed computerised planning model. This enabled better predictions to be made of potential bottlenecks and slack times in the complex map production flow-lines. The computer also allowed the department to resume direct supply of maps to the trade in January 1971, after a thirty-year break in this service. Stanford's in London had performed the task in the meantime but now Ordnance Survey was keen to build 'a closer relationship with its customers' and a computerised order processing system was developed. However, it had been forgotten just how onerous and difficult wholesaling maps was. Overoptimism and the unlucky coincidence of a national postal strike resulted in some time passing before the goal of processing orders within forty-eight hours of their receipt was achieved.

Measures to improve sales revenue had been introduced to satisfy recommendations made by the Estimates Committee of 1963. These met with some success, but the cost of running the department rose in proportion to the gain in income, and in 1969 the rate of cost recovery, at 30 per cent, was only a marginal improvement from that achieved in

Major General B St G Irwin CB, military Director General 1969–74 and civilian Director General 1974–77.

1962. Without waiting to see if recent improvements would have any effect, an inquiry was ordered and the Janes Interdepartmental Committee sat in 1970 with the special aim of examining the extent to which the department might be expected to increase its revenue in the future.

The Committee reported to the Department of the Environment who, after their absorption of the Ministry of Housing and Local Government in 1970, were Ordnance Survey's new masters. The recommendations relating to the continuance of large-scale maps were no surprise; otherwise a far more commercial approach was advocated, with a view to reducing exchequer support.

One of the most controversial proposals was the abandonment of the 1:25 000 scale of mapping, as a national series. It was recommended that this series should only be published for areas where the sheets were likely to be profitable. The department itself had worried about the viability of the 1:25 000 series and map users had been warned at the consultative meetings of 1969 and 1970 that its future was in doubt, because of the expense of its production and low sales (an average annual sale of less than 200 copies of each sheet). The Janes Committee consultations were restricted to public bodies who had only limited use for the 1:25 000 maps and, as most of these maps were actually bought by individuals rather than corporations, the Committee's perception of the potential sales of the series could really be no more than an informed guess. The outcry which followed news of the plans for the abolition of the 1:25 000 from the Ramblers' Association and other public interest groups was unexpectedly sustained and vociferous and the controversy became the subject of debate in the House of Commons. As a result, a reprieve was granted for the series, the Minister, in his reply, pointing out that it was not the Government's intention that 'products and services should be abandoned altogether, if it is in the public interest that they should continue to be available'. Exchequer support had only previously been promised for basic scales of survey, but now a precedent was set that the interests of the general public would be taken into account when considering maps and services provided by Ordnance Survey.

The Civil Service as a whole had come under scrutiny in the Fulton Report of 1968 which recommended consideration of 'hiving-off' certain parts of the Service into autonomous boards or corporations. With its independent attitude and commercial potential, Ordnance Survey looked a likely candidate, and the Janes investigations, together with the fact that their report, once made, was kept unpublished for some time, fuelled speculation over the department's fate. Rumours continued until questions raised in Parliament forced a statement to be made. To the relief of both staff and customers, it was confirmed that the department would not be 'hived-off' and would continue to function as the central survey and mapping organisation in the public sector. However, it seemed that one of the barriers against the Ordnance Survey leaving the Civil Service was its lack of proper commercial accounts. It was recommended that these should be introduced as soon as possible, after which the question of privatisation would be reviewed.

Whilst as relieved as anyone that the department would remain intact, Irwin welcomed the encouragement to be more enterprising and could 'see no reason why this change of direction should lead to any reduction on the value of the contribution which the Ordnance Survey makes'. In his 1971/2 Annual Report the heading 'Map Marketing' made its first modest appearance and although progress was slow to start with, steady gains were made as experience and confidence were acquired by management.

Everything but acres

Ordnance Survey had been in favour of metrication for some years before the government announced its support for the metric system in 1965. The National Grid, in use since the war, was based on metres, which were also used for all linear measurements made by surveyors. Earlier requests by the department for further metrication had been rejected, but the subject had received much consideration. When the go-ahead was finally given for Britain to 'go decimal', the Director General was able to immediately put forward the department's proposals to the Joint Standing Committee set up by the Ministry of Technology to oversee the metrication of Britain.

Conversion of mapping to metric values and scales began with the large-scale maps which needed to conform to metric standards coming into force within the construction industry. The scales of 1:1250 and 1:2500 needed no conversion and there was little problem with the Imperial 6-inch (1:10 560) scale which was to be replaced with a metric 1:10 000 scale. However, argument did occur when converting imperial values on the maps to their new metric equivalents was discussed. It was finally agreed that all measurements would be shown in metres, except for land parcels where a powerful agricultural lobby won agreement that the British acre would be retained. Hectares were introduced alongside acres to give consistency with the rest of the metric information (1 hectare is equal to 2.471 acres).

From 1969 large-scale maps began to be produced in fully metric form and imperial values were changed when sheets came forward for revision. Heights were given in metres, bench-mark values to two decimal places and spot heights to one decimal place. Metric contouring of the country at 5-metre vertical intervals in lowland, and 10-metre vertical intervals in hilly and highland areas, was completed in 1987 and introduced on to the maps as the information became available. Conversion of the 6-inch (1:10 560) scale to 1:10 000 took until 1990 to complete, marking the end of Ordnance Survey's 150-year association with the 6-inch scale.

1:50 000

The need to replace the immensely popular 1-inch scale with a 'natural' or metric scale was a cause for some nervousness.

The department was satisfied in its own mind that the 1:50 000 scale would be the best option, but undertook an extensive research exercise to confirm that this view was shared by its customers. Having found that it was, planning for the new series could begin in earnest. It was decided to produce a 1:50 000 provisional or First Series by photographic enlargement of the existing 1-inch material, revised where necessary and recompiled on new sheetlines, each sheet to cover an area of 40 km × 40 km. Very careful thought was put into the arrangement of new sheetlines with several sometimes contradictory aims having to be borne in mind. Customers naturally disliked buying sheets containing a lot of sea so this had to be kept to a minimum; excessive overlaps between sheets increased the number of maps needed to cover the country so this was also to be avoided; and major conurbations needed to fall squarely on a sheet and not on the corner of several. Fifteen more sheets were needed to cover the country at 1:50 000 scale than had been required for the 1-inch Seventh Series, bringing the total number in the new series to 204.

The 1:50 000 was launched in two stages, the southern half of Britain, on a line approximately Lancaster to Bridlington in 1974 and the rest of the country in 1976. The map detail itself was of course the same as the 1-inch although

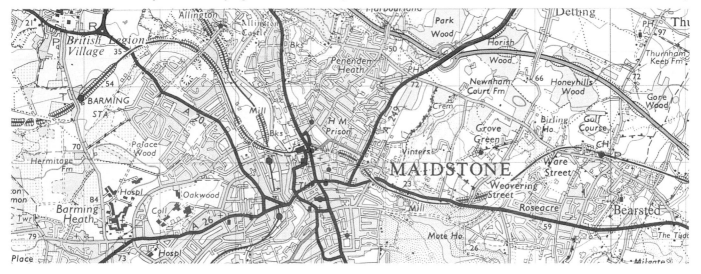

Part of the 1:50 000 First Series, sheet 172, Chatham and Maidstone, revised to 1969.

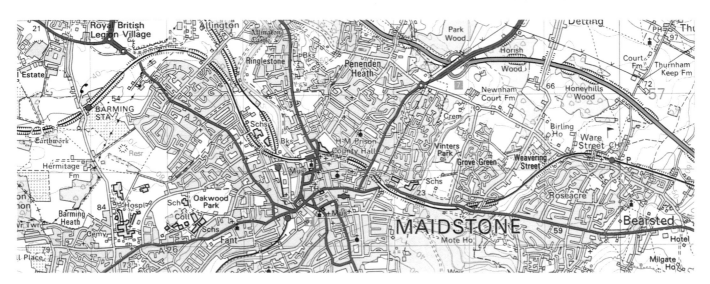

Part of the 1:50 000 Second Series (Landranger), sheet 188, Maidstone and the Weald of Kent, revised to 1989.

slightly magnified, but the opportunity was taken to look ahead to a 1:50 000 Second Series and colours were chosen with this in mind. Generally, less use was made of black, brown and grey in favour of lighter colours and these, combined with the larger scale, gave the map a more spacious feel than the 1-inch on which the kilometre National Grid lines had formed an almost overpowering effect.

A huge effort was made to publicise the new 1:50 000 map. A national advertising campaign brought in orders for ¾ million copies from retailers. Naturally there was criticism from some purchasers, but many of the complaints were emotive in nature and were directed against the passing of the familiar 1-inch scale and metrication in general. To the department's relief opinions of its new flagship map were mostly favourable.

The First Series was an interim edition, pending the introduction of a newly designed 1:50 000, the first sheets of which were published in 1974. At first glance there was not much discernible difference between the First and Second Series maps, but a closer look reveals a number of important design improvements.

The more modern typeface of the Second Series is called Univers, and replaced the Gill Sans and Roman type that had been used on the 1-inch since the 1920s. All hand-drawn symbols were phased out and replaced with annotated symbols or a textured effect using printing screens. Special attention was paid to the clarity of the road network and both the colours and methods of road depiction were altered slightly to improve the distinction between 'A' and 'B' class roads and to emphasise the difference between dual-carriageways and other roads.

Market research found that the public wanted more information for tourists on the maps and a range of distinctive sky-blue tourist information symbols was added. These showed the location of viewpoints, picnic, camping and caravanning sites, tourist information offices and parking availability. A translation of some items of the map legend in both French and German was also included.

There was a subtle difference between the metric content of the First and Second Series, with the First Series showing distances in miles, followed by kilometres and the Second Series placing the kilometres first, followed by miles.

In 1979 the 1:50 000 series was named 'Landranger', chosen after a competition amongst staff. By that time other maps had adopted popular names: the 1:250 000 series was known as 'Routemaster' and the 1:625 000 series called 'Routeplanner', and it was felt that the 1:50 000 map should also have a name that was easier to remember than just the map scale. In 1985 the covers of the maps were improved by the introduction of colourful photographs on the fronts of each. An increase in sales was noted after they were introduced.

Landranger maps are the smallest scale of Ordnance Survey mapping to be surveyed in the field, a small team of surveyors being dedicated to its revision. These men (so far no woman has ever been employed on these duties) can be asked to work anywhere in the country, from Land's End to the tip of Shetland, but urban areas are naturally revised more frequently than rural areas. The London maps being fully revised every five or so years, but mountain and moorland only every thirty.

In past years the 1-inch map revisers often travelled by bicycle, using a 'curved bicycle level' to measure road gradients on steep hills. More recently a combination of driving and walking is preferred, with four-wheel drive vehicles available for mountainous terrain areas and helicopters used for inaccessible areas and outlying islands.

The field revision document is compiled from the outline edition of the 1:50 000 map, enlarged to 1:25 000 and updated as far as possible from air photography and intelligence from other scales of mapping of the area. At 1:50 000 newly surveyed information is 'tied in' to existing map detail by eye by use of a prismatic compass. At headquarters experienced draughtsmen produce the familiar generalised map, skilfully balancing artistry and accuracy in the Landranger's stylistic representation of ground features.

The whole of the Landranger series was completed by November 1987, two years ahead of schedule. With around 2 million copies sold each year, the Landrangers are Ordnance Survey's best-selling small-scale maps achieving the ideal of being a true general purpose map.

Double accounting

As a government department, Ordnance Survey accounting procedures naturally differed substantially from those of commercial companies. Often work, information and services were exchanged with other government departments free of payment. This saved unnecessary accounting and billing between departments, but as soon as questions began to be asked about the cost of the Survey to the taxpayer, then the system was shown to be inadequate.

A major initiative to pin down costs to their source had been made in the late 1920s when the concept of 'cost accounting' was introduced. This had set out to determine the actual cost of each map production stage. It was concluded that the prices charged for maps were adequate to cover the costs incurred in printing, storing and selling the maps. Surveying and drawing costs, however, were held to be chargeable to the Treasury.

Computers at Ordnance Survey

The mathematical nature of Survey work has always meant using the most advanced aids to calculation available. For many years these were eight-figure and then twelve-figure logarithmic tables and slide-rules, including beautifully crafted brass spirals two or three times the length of a conventional rule to provide greater accuracy.

In the 1930s, trigonometrical computations were made using hand-cranked analogue calculators, superseded by more sophisticated machines such as the Brunsviga, with its double-banking facility, and the Facit which boasted a keyboard. A team of around fifty staff were constantly employed on these computations. In the early 1950s computations were automated using IBM punched-card machines.

Ordnance Survey became one of the very early computer users when in 1952 experimental work began on the pilot ACE computer (now in the Science Museum) developed by the National Physical Laboratory (NPL) at Teddington. In early 1953 Ordnance Survey began to use the ACE, and then its successor the DEUCE, for air survey calculations. Initially the programming was done by NPL staff but in 1956 this was taken over by the Ordnance Survey.

These early pioneer programmers would cram the punched cards into saddlebags and cycle from Chessington to Teddington to wrestle personally with the huge machines. However, in response to the challenge of new technology, the workshop designed and built special card transporting boxes which could be made to fasten on to a programmer's bicycle! The use of NPL computers continued until 1968 with one of the final applications being to compute the UK section of the European triangulation.

In 1965, Survey decided to invest in a computer for pay as well as technical computations and selected the ICT (later to become ICL) 1902, installed in 1968 in the new headquarters building.

The 1902 had a 16K word main memory unit, large for the time! To operate at its best advantage no program was allowed to be larger than 8K words. In 1972 a second-hand ICL 1904 was installed, but was replaced in 1975 by a 'real' mainframe – an ICL 1906S with 192K words of memory, a sophisticated operating system and exchangeable discs. This was said to be 'so powerful that there would be little for it to do from Monday afternoon onwards of each week'.

The dawning of the computer age: the department's first punched-card machine with its proud operators in the 1950s. Les Auckland

In 1983 a 'new range' ICL 2966 computer was purchased but computing demand continued to increase and in 1988 a more powerful replacement was installed, upgraded to support over 31 gigabytes of on-line disc storage. Although this ICL 39/80 was fourteen times more powerful than the old 1906S, in 1991 the Digital Mapping Archive System was given its own 'mini' computer with 64 gigabytes of disc storage.

The first computerised management system successfully handled the calculation and payment of all monthly pay from 1968 until superseded by the Chessington Bureau central payroll system in November 1973.

Ordnance Survey also decided to computerise map sales, accounting and statistics but, with approaching a ¼ million product lines, the requirements were greater than any commercially available system could support and development of the on-line Publication Division System (PDS) took until 1978 to complete. By the mid 1980s a new system was needed which proved just as difficult to develop and PDS was not totally superseded until 1991. In 1983 the department introduced what was certainly one of the first implementations of combined vote and commercial accounting in a single general ledger.

From 1972 onwards a 'work recording' system was introduced to monitor all headquarters production areas. Later microcomputers installed in region offices supplied information via telephone links to headquarters. Both systems were superseded in 1989 by the Production Information and Monitoring System (PIMS) which provided a production control, work recording and costing system linking headquarters and field offices.

Although most systems were function orientated, several areas were often interested in the data held. The first designated 'corporate' system was the Map Information Database (MID), introduced in 1985, which defined the ownership (the area enabled to alter the data) of different items. All users were permitted to view the data but only some to change it.

To facilitate transfer of data between disparate machines, a broadband local area network was installed between 1986 and 1988 to cover most of the headquarters offices. At about the same time the requirements of the Digital Field Update System (DFUS) resulted in the development of wide-area network communications using telephone facilities.

The personal computer (PC) came to Ordnance Survey in the mid 1980s. The largest single application was the Section Management System which was introduced into all field survey offices in early 1988. PCs quickly became widespread throughout the department and benefits of new developments include the use of desktop publishing and computer graphic programmes for design and publishing work.

Just after the Second World War the department was recovering 12.5 per cent of its total cost from sales and receipts which was gradually raised to approaching 30 per cent by the mid 1960s. This figure was boosted further by a policy decision in 1968 that government departments for whom Ordnance Survey carried out work would be billed for its full cost and by 1973/4 some 47 per cent of expenditure was being recovered in receipts from sales and services. These heights were not sustained as other departments who had not previously charged Ordnance Survey for their services now began to do so. For the first time rent, furniture, stationery and other items had to be directly paid for, resulting in a drastic reduction in the recovery rate to 34 per cent.

The funding of Ordnance Survey as a government department was (and still is) by way of the 'vote' system, under which a sum of money is voted to it by Parliament each year to cover its cost. The accounting system reflected the need to explain where this money was spent, but gave no indication of how well the department was performing in commercial terms. No regard was paid to the capital value of assets, and no breakdown was made of costs or receipts from products or value given to work in progress. At the end of each financial year 'we close the books and start all over again'.

The first professional accountant was appointed to the department in 1971 and before long a budgeting system was introduced. This allowed managers to calculate the amount of money needed for their area of work at the beginning of a year, and to monitor actual expenditure against it. By this method managers were made aware of the actual cost of the work under their control, information they had lacked before.

In 1973, the Government Trading Funds Bill was published which mentioned Ordnance Survey as a candidate for funding by Trading Fund rather than by voted money. The Fund would be financed by loan from the government which, like any commercial loan, would accrue interest and have eventually to be repaid. Losses on large-scale maps would be accounted for by making a 'notional sale' to the Department of the Environment. However, after debate in both Houses of Parliament, Ordnance Survey's name was deleted from the Bill, concern being centred on the 'serious danger that the necessity to show a proper return would lead to neglect of the public service activities'.

The Trading Fund idea was shelved, but in compliance with the Janes Committee recommendation a system of 'Trading Accounts' had been introduced in 1972 to run alongside the vote accounts. These more closely followed commercial practice and were designed to give a detailed accurate picture of trading operations to management, government and Parliament. Providing these comprehensive

accounts took some years, as all existing accounting systems had to be scrutinised for suitability and additional systems introduced. The accounts were rigorously examined by the National Audit Office and it was not until 1987/8 that Ordnance Survey was permitted to begin annual publication of these accounts.

Meanwhile financial targets were set for the department to attain. Activities were divided into large-scales (up to and including 1:25 000) for which 25 per cent of the cost had to be recovered and small-scale maps and repayment services for which 100 per cent of costs had to be recovered. These targets were introduced in 1980 by which time the total recovery rate of the department was around 40 per cent.

A second proposal that Ordnance Survey should be financed by a trading fund rather than under the vote account system was again rejected in 1984 in favour of increasing the financial targets for the department. Three categories of work were identified. Large-scale work was to recover 35 per cent (later 40 per cent), repayment work to recover 100 per cent and small-scale mapping to achieve 110 per cent. For the first time in its history Ordnance Survey was instructed to make a profit on its small-scale maps and by 1985 the department was recovering 56 per cent of its total cost to the nation.

Progress towards achieving full cost recovery continues but no target date has been set by which this must be reached. In 1989/90 some 66 per cent of the department's costs were recovered by receipts from sales and services provided.

Last chance

In 1947 Mr C W Phillips, was appointed to the position of Archaeology Officer at Ordnance Survey.

Like other archaeologists, Phillips was worried by the accelerating destruction of archaeological sites in Britain. Having survived for centuries there was a real danger that many of them would be lost within the span of a single lifetime, a casualty of rapid modern progress. In farming, for instance, the advent of mechanised equipment made it very easy to 'plough in' ancient barrows, and farmers were being encouraged by a grant system to actively farm marginal lands, previously left undisturbed. Forestry was increasing and new conifer plantations disguised, perhaps for ever, the traces of earlier settlement beneath them. New houses, factories and even whole new towns were being built on what had been open countryside. Although legislation protected the most important ancient sites, the archaeologists were concerned that large numbers of less individually significant but collectively important sites were being destroyed. Their loss could not, in many cases, be prevented but a 'last chance to make an accurate field survey of most of the field antiquities' before they disappeared still existed. The Ordnance Survey's teams of surveyors, travelling the length and breadth of the country, were the ideal vehicle to undertake such a survey of the antiquities. These were set up under Phillips' control, moving independently and ahead of the main survey work. The surveyors were selected from amongst interested applicants of the department's own staff.

Archaeological survey was organised on a county basis, partly because local societies and published sources usually followed county lines. The priority given to 1:1250 mapping of urban areas, where numbers of antiquities were limited, allowed the archaeological survey to gain a head start and to ensure that the information was ready and waiting for the topographical surveyors to include, when they reached each area.

Before archaeological field survey could be undertaken, all the literature on each subject, published later than the seventeenth century, was examined and an extensive library of expensive, but necessary, reference books was gradually built up. Air photographs were studied where available and contact made with local archaeological societies and museums. The system of 'honorary correspondents' was also maintained and details of sites supplied were checked by the surveyors.

A briefing about the possibilities of an area was given to the archaeological field surveyor, who then made a reconnaissance and survey of the sites, talking with local informants and assimilating new information as it came to light.

For archaeological purposes the country is naturally divided into highland and lowland zones, the dividing line stretching from the Humber to the mouth of the River Severn. The highland zone displays a larger number of visible archaeological features, mainly because of the wider use of stone for construction and because of less damage due to later habitation. In the lowland zone settlement was, like today, much heavier, but more construction was of wood, and stone from earlier buildings tended to be recycled in later structures. In the rural lowland areas air photographs were a tremendous help as they revealed the outline of field systems and settlement not visible from the ground.

Each Ordnance Survey region of the country eventually had its own small specialist team of archaeological surveyors. Scotland posed a particularly difficult task because of the many villages ruined during 'the clearances', when whole populations were forcibly moved by landowners to clear the land for sheep farming. All these ruins, which dated from around 1750, were recorded. To deal with the complexities of Scottish archaeology, a special office was created in Edinburgh and two teams of surveyors operated from this base.

A record card was completed for each monument or site found, noting the condition of the site and national grid

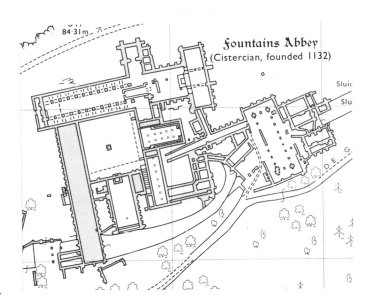

Extract from SE2768 1:2500 map showing the remains of Fountains Abbey in North Yorkshire.

reference and enhancing the record with sketches and photographs. A note was also included of literary sources and the names of any informants. Thousands of record cards were completed every year and by 1974 the archive contained some 290 000 cards, open for viewing by appointment to all interested persons. These cards were sold to County Councils and now form the basis of local records. A complete set of 6-inch maps provided a visual index for recording the position of each feature and, in areas where many sites existed, a larger-scale map was used for the same purpose.

To avoid overwhelming the modern detail with antiquity information, a selection was made according to the scale of the map and the relative importance of each feature. Particularly important monuments were shown on all scales of maps, but lesser antiquities were included where they did not interfere with other map detail, and some sites were only shown on the largest-scale map. Miscellaneous finds of little general interest were kept on record but not shown on the maps at all. To ensure that professional archaeologists were happy with the Ordnance Survey work, an Advisory Committee was set up in 1968 on which all principal organisations concerned with archaeology were represented.

The definition of an antiquity was accepted, from about 1950, to be a feature dating from before 1714, the date of accession of George I. An antiquity could be a monument or building, a portable object, a battlefield, caves once used as dwelling places, burial sites and so on. Some pre-1714 features were omitted, such as post-Norman Conquest domestic buildings, unless they were outstanding examples of their type. Conversely, features dating from 1714 to about 1850 were recorded where they were felt to be of interest, such as good examples of industrial archaeology.

A number of important finds were made, including large numbers of previously unknown prehistoric settlements. It was concluded that the 'Ordnance Survey surveyor, ranging indiscriminately over highland and lowland alike as the topographic survey of the country has progressed, had thus entered what is, archaeologically, virtually unexplored ground and had reaped a rich harvest.'

Continuing in the tradition of Crawford's period maps, a number of archaeological and historical maps were published from 1950. These included revised editions of Crawford's 'Roman Britain' and 'Britain in the Dark Ages', but also included the new titles of 'Monastic Britain', 'Ancient Britain', 'Southern Britain in the Iron Age', 'Hadrian's Wall' and the 'Antonine Wall'. The publication of new titles came to an end after the Janes Committee recommendation of 1972 that the cost of archaeological and historical maps should be covered by the income from their sales; and if this could not be achieved, then they should be withdrawn. Between then and 1983 only one new map, 'Britain before the Norman Conquest', which was already in preparation was published.

By 1980, archaeological revision of the basic map scales was complete, except for parts of Scotland. Following the review of Ordnance Survey in 1979, it was agreed that further archaeological work should not be carried out by Ordnance Survey but by the three Royal Commissions (of England, Scotland and Wales) on Historical Monuments. The record system, now called the National Archaeological Record (NAR) was transferred to their keeping in 1983 with twenty-two Ordnance Survey staff. The three Royal Commissions continue to supply Ordnance Survey with archaeological information for both standard maps and a new series of special interest historical and archaeological maps.

═══ Advance Revision Information ═══

Continuous revision of maps and the availability of 'Advance Revision Information' (ARI) were concepts that went hand in hand. There was no point in having marvellously up-to-date maps at field offices if they were kept hidden away from public view. However, the idea of supplying copies of working documents directly to customers was considered, at first, to be almost heretical. It was also time-consuming for surveyors to be involved with customers and prevented them from putting their full effort into productive revision work. Consequently the service was not widely advertised and customers, apart from certain privileged bodies such as local authorities, were not encouraged.

It wasn't until 1964 that a real effort was made to 'unlock this survey for users' benefit in advance of formal publication' by the installation of reproduction equipment in the London survey offices. This allowed staff to produce copies from the master survey drawings (MSDs) on demand. The main hope for an efficient nationwide service rested on the use of microfilm to copy all MSDs, but first trials were disappointing as the electrophotographic paper on which the copies were printed marked easily and was susceptible to damp, making it unsuitable for use out of doors. However, in 1971 further experiment took place and 35 mm negative microfilms of published large-scale maps were made available. The original glass negatives of the maps were accurately photographed resulting in microfilms of exceptionally high quality which were mounted in 'aperture cards'. One Ordnance Survey agent was given stock of these microfilmed maps covering the whole of his area and customers were given the choice of either purchasing the large-scale printed map or, at a reduced price, a print-out made from the microfilm. Most chose to pay less and accepted the lower quality print-outs.

Encouraged by this, the department began to microfilm the MSDs held at field survey offices, every time a specified number of 'house units' of change had accumulated upon it. (A house unit being the amount of change equivalent to, for example, the addition of one house to the map.) The microfilms were supplied to Ordnance Survey agents who provided copies from them to customers.

This was an improvement but some customers needed still more up-to-date information, and for this reason SUSI (Supply of Unpublished Survey Information) was introduced. The service was made possible once the old opaque butt-joint survey documents had given way to a transparent media which could be laid directly on to diazo copiers housed at local Ordnance Survey offices. This process was ammonia based, a strong flavour of which became common in the offices lucky (or unlucky) enough to possess one of these machines until ventilation systems were installed to remove the fumes. SUSI first made its appearance in 1973, and the 35 mm microfilm service was formalised and named SIM in 1977.

Field-penning was originally a method of unambiguous communication between Ordnance Survey surveyors and draughtsmen and was never intended for interpretation by the public. The advent of the SIM and SUSI services therefore prompted the launch of a major training programme to secure a significant improvement in the clarity of surveyor's penning. However, to some the successful use of viscous etching ink in a bladed pen on the durable polyester surfaces of the survey document was still regarded as something of a black art.

Straight line in a small space

High-precision surveying under difficult circumstances has long been the Ordnance Survey geodetic surveyor's forte and this ingenuity was put to the test in 1969 by a most unusual request. The Atomic Energy Authority (AEA) approached the department on behalf of the Science Research Council, to ask for help with the construction of a new radio telescope for the Mullard Radio Observatory near Cambridge. (A radio telescope is used for detecting radio waves from the Universe, using a number of fixed and movable aerials.)

The ten receiving dishes, each about 14 metres in diameter, had to be placed on a precise line with one another. The AEA specification required a 5-km line to be measured dead straight, deviating by no more than 10 mm, at a height of 8 metres above ground. There was no time for testing and development of laser systems, so an optical method using a high-powered telescope of 100 times magnification was perfected instead. This was placed on a concrete tower and aimed at the distant target. At the specified distances along the line, ground marks representing the future position of the dishes were aligned from Bilby towers. Observations, in the bitter cold of midwinter, were made at night, during which the position of each Bilby tower was continuously checked using an optical plummet capable of detecting movements of 1 millimetre. Both the curvature of the Earth and problems with refraction had to be taken into account, putting further demands on the surveyor's abilities. The survey was successful and the spatial coordinates of the ten ground marks were calculated and found to be well within the tolerance specified.

Outdoor Leisure Maps and Pathfinders

Ordnance Survey had for many years produced Tourist Maps and Special District maps for popular holiday areas of the country, usually at 1-inch scale. These sold in large numbers but, although ideal for touring, the maps were at too small a scale to be considered an ideal walker's map.

Outdoor Leisure Maps (OLMs) were conceived to satisfy the need for a walker's map of tourist areas and the 1:25 000 mapping on which they were based was particularly suitable for climbing, hillwalking and other leisure pursuits requiring a detailed topographic map. The first to be published, 'The Dark Peak' in 1972, won wide praise in press and radio reviews. Betty Drewitt, who established the series, regarded it as one of her main achievements and 'also invented the title "Outdoor Leisure" . . . although I had great difficulty in persuading my colleagues to accept the title – the term "Special" map having hitherto been used to distinguish maps outside standard series'.

In its first year 'The Dark Peak' sold 15 000 copies and further OLMs were soon planned for the Lake District, Cairngorms, the 'Three Peaks' and several other areas. At first the maps were based on First Series 1:25 000 mapping but as soon as it was available the Second Series specification was introduced. In 1975 the seven OLMs then published accounted for one-quarter of the revenue from mapping at 1:25 000.

Outdoor use of maps in wet conditions is a problem. Unless kept dry they will, like any other paper product, fall apart. To address this problem, Ordnance Survey in 1979 produced the OLM of the New Forest on a waterproof plasticised paper and sold it with a questionnaire asking for comments. The experiment was initially very successful, and at exhibitions the map was placed in a tank of water – complete with goldfish – to prove its durability. Unfortunately, although very popular, the paper had to be withdrawn from use due to unsolvable production problems. New OLMs on ordinary paper continued to be published and by 1989 most national parks and other areas of natural beauty were covered. The 'Mountainmaster of Ben Nevis' published in 1989 returned once again to the problem of waterproofing. This map was specially designed for mountaineers and hillwalkers. The expensive, imported paper on which it is printed is 'stronger when wet' and the cost of this is reflected in the price of the map.

Meanwhile the 1:25 000 Second Series maps continued to be extended across the whole country, but in contrast to the OLMs their sales remained stubbornly low. To make matters worse, whenever an OLM was published, the Pathfinders or First Series sheets of the same area sold barely at all. The financial losses on these 'underlying' sheets were unacceptable and some were withdrawn from publication. Other ways of cutting costs included the introduction of 'integral' paper covers, rather than the traditional glossy card covers. In 1979 the Second Series 1:25 000 series was given the more convenient and apt name 'Pathfinder'.

Market research showed that the National Grid numbering system of the series was a subject of great confusion to ordinary members of the public. Consequently a simple numbering system was introduced starting in Shetland with sheet No. 1 and working sequentially down to the south. National grid sheet numbers were retained at the request of the map trade and maps may be ordered by either number. The Pathfinder series was completed in 1990 with the publication of sheet 1362 (SX 54/64); covering Newton Ferrers and Thurlestone.

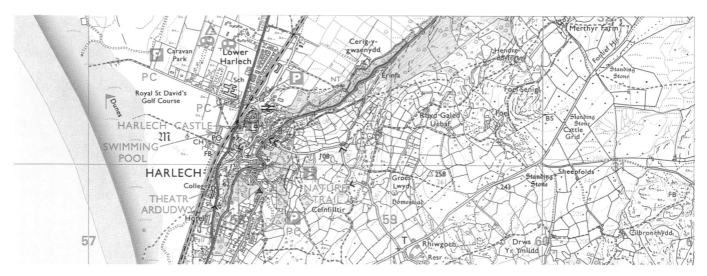

Part of Outdoor Leisure Map sheet 18, Snowdonia (Harlech and Bala), revised to 1989.

1:250 000

First introduced in the 1950s, this scale of mapping replaced the ¼-inch scale (1:253 440) in a move which brought Ordnance Survey maps into line with other European maps. As the actual change in scale was so small, it was decided to keep the name that the public were familiar with and to designate this the Fifth Series. It was published in seventeen sheets, and produced by generalising 1-inch Seventh Series material. The maps were always considered to be primarily for motorists, and as such were updated at regular intervals with road networks revised annually on the most popular sheets. Information included gradient symbols, tolls, airports and ferry routes for vehicles. Physical features were added using a combination of contours, layer colouring and hill-shading, this last depicted as if a light was shining over the landscape at an angle of 45° from the north-west corner. The maps folded to a compact 13 cm × 19 cm and the series was a commercial success with demand exceeding expectations.

In 1969 a separate gazetteer of all the names on the maps was completed and published as a booklet. This was also combined with all seventeen maps and published as a loose-leaf reference atlas. The maps were left full size, but were folded and hole-punched to fit in the folder. At 18 × 26 inches (45 × 66 cm) this was no pocket atlas!

Production started on a completely redesigned 1:250 000 series in 1978 and by this time, as it was no longer appropriate to continue to name the series ¼-inch, the name 'Routemaster' was created for the series emphasising its motoring purpose. This time there were only nine sheets in the series, a feat achieved by printing on both sides of the paper. However, it transpired that the public preferred, for motoring maps at least, to have the map all printed on one side of the paper, so this was put in hand, producing the largest maps of any Ordnance Survey national series. Needless to say, complaints were then received about their unwieldiness, especially when used in a car!

As a motoring map the Fifth Series exhibited a number of design faults. Its colour layer-tints became progressively more orange the higher the ground, making minor roads difficult to distinguish against the background, and major towns, shown by a too-regressive grey shading, also suffered by being named in too small a type. The Routemaster design corrected these and other problems, highlighting towns with a rather positive yellow, and using a green shade box to emphasise the more prominently lettered names of 'primary destinations'. The map also began to acquire additional 'useful information' such as telephone numbers of regional weather centres, a distance chart and tourist information. Once again the legend was translated into French and German and, as a result, substantial sales were made for some years to a Swiss map publisher who added their own cover and successfully sold them throughout Europe.

1:625 000 Route Planning Map

Planning maps first made their appearance during the Second World War, initiated by the Advisory Map Committee of the Ministry of Works and Planning. At this scale Great Britain conveniently fitted on to two sheets, north and south, and

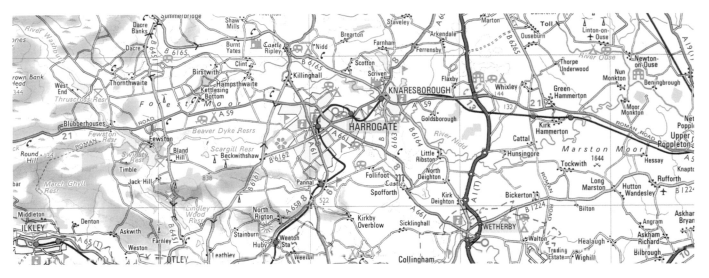

Part of the 1:250 000 Routemaster, sheet 6, East Midlands and Yorkshire, revised to 1989.

formed a base for maps sponsored by government departments and public bodies. The thematic maps included population change, land utilisation, geology and distribution of coal and iron ore, as well as a number of more general interest maps. In 1955 the specialised maps all became the direct responsibility of the sponsoring bodies and eventually only four topics were deemed to be of sufficient general interest for Ordnance Survey to maintain. These were the road map, a monochrome outline map, a physical map, and one showing the administrative areas of local government.

In 1964, a redesigned road map was published to provide an annually revised map of main road routes. Called the Route Planning Map, it sold 25 000 copies in just three months, proving that there was considerable demand for this type of map. Its design was frequently changed, to adapt to customers' changing needs, to reduce production costs and to improve its appearance.

In 1983 the name was changed slightly to match other maps, such as Routemaster and Landranger, and it became the Routeplanner.

Electronic Distance Measuring

At the end of a hard day, taping through hedges, down muddy tracks and paths, through building sites and across railway lines, roads and ploughed fields, about the last thing a traverse surveyor wanted to do was wipe his steel tape clean of mud and muck, oil it and carefully reel it up. But that was his lot – before EDM.

Electronic Distance Measuring (EDM) first came into the eager hands of Ordnance Survey surveyors in 1953. Made by the AGA company in Sweden to a design by its inventor Dr E Bergstrand, of the Swedish Geographical Survey, the geodimeter (as it was known) used a pulsed light beam to measure the distance to a reflector. It was trialed in co-operation with the United States Army Map Service on the Ridge Way base, considered the most accurate long base line in the world, and the Caithness base, which was less accurate but longer. The measurements confirmed that the lengths of the bases were correct within millimetres. Partly as a result of these trials, the accepted value of the velocity of light *in vacuo* was brought into question. The geodimeter was established as

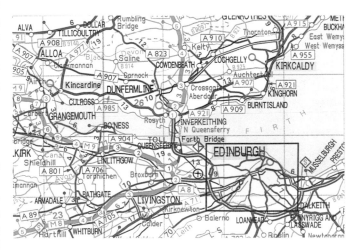

Part of the 1:625 000 Routeplanner Map, revised to 1990. Produced using selected features from the database of the same scale.

a very accurate instrument, but as it was bulky and laborious to use, and this early version could only be used at night, its adaptation to general survey techniques was not followed up until such problems had been overcome.

Four years later, in 1957, Ordnance Survey was once again involved in the trials and demonstration of new EDM equipment. The tellurometer, from the South African Council for Scientific and Industrial Research, had already been investigated by the International Association of Geodesy who recommended its use for measuring to geodetic standards. This measured distance with radio microwave pulses and could be used day or night. The tellurometer was used to measure the Ridge Way base and its extension triangles, proving much more convenient than the geodimeter. Again a revised figure for the velocity of light and electromagnetic waves was found and, after being independently proved by the National Physical Laboratory and other organisations, the new figure was internationally agreed.

A set of tellurometer equipment was obtained and used to measure a total of sixty-eight primary triangle sides and the base at Caithness. The measurements served to show that the scale of the retriangulation was slightly too large. This had been expected, although the size and variations across the country were larger than anticipated. The scale errors had been caused by the need to fit the new retriangulation to the old Principal Triangulation and thus to avoid significant changes in graticules on maps and charts. Ordnance Survey began to regularly use both improved geodimeters and tellurometers for testing existing triangulation and the provision of new triangulation stations and control.

By the early 1970s, surveying instrument manufacturers were vying with each other to promote their EDM surveying equipment and Ordnance Survey had the opportunity to test many new sets. The department purchased the Distomat DI 10T, which operated on a pulsed light-beam principle and

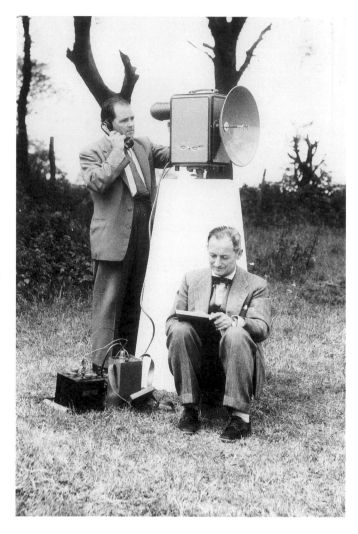

Dr T L Wadley (booking) taking part in the British trials of his invention, the Tellurometer, in the 1950s.

Anyone for table tennis?

The Great Glen, which cuts through Scotland from Fort William to Inverness marks the location of a crustal fault-line and was considered by the Earth's Strains Studies Working Group of the Royal Society in 1971, to be a suitable site for measuring crustal movement. Ordnance Survey was asked to co-operate with the Geophysics Department of the Imperial College of Science and Technology to establish a number of stable terminals in the Fort Augustus area, so that regular check measurements could be taken.

After reconnaissance, thirteen triangulation pillars were built along the Glen and angular measurements to geodetic standards began in the autumn of 1972. To reduce the effect of refraction, it was necessary to work at night, but it was discovered that the normal geodetic observing beacon lights were too powerful on the short 3-kilometre distances involved, even with the lowest wattage bulbs available.

As it was also desirable to be able to observe to the pillars from different angles without having to revolve the beacon light, the search began for some sort of weak but precise light that could be seen from any position. Trials

with illuminated glass and perspex rods failed to provide an answer but a simple solution was then discovered. By placing a 3.5 watt torchlight bulb inside a table-tennis ball, a beacon with all round visibility, of perfect strength for the distances required, was produced. With a suitable brass pillar-fitting, observations went ahead giving results which were found to marginally improve on the work of the retriangulation.

Work was completed in 1972, leaving the Geophysics Department to continue their long-term studies.

was used for minor control traverses and Wild T2 theodolites were modified to take the Distomat detachable 'head', which had the appearance of a stubby pair of orange-coloured binoculars. Although by modern standards the control box with its black rubber dial viewing hood and mass of cables was very heavy and cumbersome, it was a boon for the surveyors involved, being capable of measuring up to 2.4 kilometres in suitable weather conditions. Steel tapes were rarely, if ever, used again.

Following closely behind the Distomat came the AGA 12, with a range of 1.2 kilometres. This had a positive read-out of the distance, a major advance on the Distomat with its whirling green-lit drum display. The AGA 12 heralded a revolution in surveying in the Ordnance Survey as this was the first EDM equipment to become widely available to most field surveying groups. This allowed the surveyor to send an assistant with a prism to the detail to be surveyed. The surveyor then recorded the angle and distance to that point before signalling the assistant to move on to the next point. Angles and distances given by the instrument rapidly built up on the booking sheet and surveying was completed faster than ever before. From 1983 data recorders, into which surveyors keyed the survey information, were brought into use and effectively ended the laborious process of filling out booking sheets. The information from the data recorder was held on cassette tape and computed at headquarters.

New instruments that followed featured built-in recording facilities which memorised distance and angle as the surveyors entered on to the keypad the various commands. The surveyor, because of the extended range of the measuring equipment, now had to keep in contact with the assistant by personal radio, directing them from point to point as the work proceeded. The data could be given additional codes to differentiate between the different types of detail surveyed (fence, road, etc.), and in 1982 automated plotting facilities were introduced at headquarters. Connected to a Vax 11/750 computer, a Kongsberg flatbed plotter automatically transferred the computed instrumental surveys on to the surveyor's master survey drawing. The MSD was then returned to the field for detail survey to be added.

Meanwhile EDM work to geodetic standards was continued and, in 1969, tellurometer measurements were taken on seven lines across the Irish Sea, strengthening the geodetic connection made 17 years earlier. The longest line measured was 137 kilometres, which would have been considered science fiction when the connection was originally observed.

The accuracy limits of the retriangulation were accepted and for day-to-day survey work the errors were too small to make much difference to the published maps, but for scientific purposes it was decided to remeasure the Primary Triangulation framework using EDM. Measurements were taken on 180 primary triangle sides, spanning the country and fifteen Laplace azimuths (astronomical observations of direction) were also observed. An adjustment of the whole triangulation as a single unit was then made and the results of this, known as the Ordnance Survey Scientific Network 1970, provided accurate scientific positions of the primary triangulation stations. A further refinement from additional measurements and observations led to the publication of an updated version in 1977. This gave a better fit to the World Geodetic System (WGS 72) World Datum used in the calculation of navigation satellite orbits.

This activity has led to the development of Global Positioning Systems (GPS) using satellite orbit technology, but EDM continues to be used as one of the detail surveyor's main working tools.

Large-scale digital mapping

The department's first adventure into the digitisation of maps was made in 1966 when Ordnance Survey, which at that time did not have its own digitisation equipment, entered into an investigation of the automation of cartography with the Experimental Cartography Unit (ECU) of the Royal College of Art. By 1969 ECU had digitised an area around Bideford in Devon at 1:2500 scale and plotted this at derived scales of 1:10 000, 1:25 000, 1:63 360 and 1:250 000, demonstrating that accuracy and line quality were adequately obtainable at those scales. The experiment highlighted faults and problems with the digital data which required hand-finishing by draughtsmen. The new techniques were not therefore cost effective, but valuable information had been gathered about the technique of transferring map information into a digital cartographic data bank.

Experimental work was also concentrated on digitising contours directly from the encoded movement of the output shafts of a Wild A8 stereoplotting machine, the object being to compile a contour databank from which contours at 1:25 000 and possibly smaller scale maps could be automatically plotted using a Calcomp drum plotter. Other mapping organisations were embarking on similar experiments by this time and some were more advanced than Ordnance Survey, using newly available linear encoders on the stereoplotters.

By 1971, the first Ordnance Survey digitised map product, of the coastline of Great Britain at 1:125 000, was available for sale on magnetic tape, and development continued with the intention of providing large-scale mapping for sale on the same medium. A pilot scheme began to digitise areas in South Hampshire and Herefordshire and Worcestershire, using Ferranti freescan digitisers and a Ferranti master

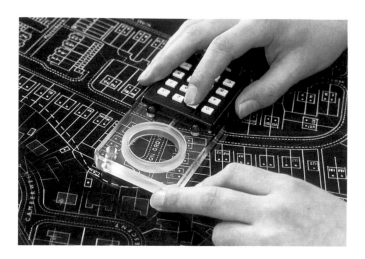

Digitising a large-scale map in the 1980s.

plotter purchased in 1972. 'Digital maps', as the output plots from the new flatbed plotter were called, were far superior to those from the superseded drum plotter and were produced by a computer controlled light-spot projector drawing on to photographic film under darkroom conditions.

Digitising entailed a draughtsman tracing, with a hand-held cursor, along each line of a twice-size copy of the surveyor's working field document, creating, by pressing a button on the cursor at selected points on the line, a record of their coordinates. As the draughtsman worked slowly over the document a map was formed, being held as a list of coordinates in the computer's memory. Different types of detail, such as fences, houses and road information, were identified with codes, registered by placing the cursor over the appropriate feature code on a 'menu' at the side of the working document and then pressing the cursor button. The feature codes were memorised by the computer, so that each feature was depicted by the correct symbol, line width and style when output to the plotting machine.

The equipment used by the draughtsman was 'blind', which meant that the linework traced by the draughtsman could not be viewed until a plot or copy of the digitised and stored work was produced. As equipment reliability was at first poor, information was sometimes lost or plots were output with additional lines drawn on them which were wholly unrelated to the input work. Usually errors could be corrected by further digitising, but all too frequently the draughtsman had to take a deep breath, and start all over again. At the end of the first year of the pilot digital mapping production project, fifty-three 1:1250 plans had been fully digitised.

The Director General B St G Irwin was in no doubt as to the potential of the digital system and, after the first map was produced covering 2 square kilometres in Herefordshire at 1:2500 scale, he said that he believed 'this to be an event of the greatest possible importance in the mapping of Great Britain'. Even at this early stage, Irwin envisaged 'a vast data bank comprising all significant topographic information in the country, continually updated and capable of producing an almost limitless variety of outputs to suit the needs of users'. It was also hoped that digital production methods would prove to be cheaper than conventional drawing methods, and easier to update.

Large-scale maps plotted from the digital mapping pilot scheme were in most respects similar in appearance to conventionally produced maps, but the additional cost of capturing the information on magnetic tape made them more expensive to produce – without taking into account the cost of the equipment needed. Customers showed considerable interest in the project and purchased maps with which to conduct their own experiments. By 1978 some 4500 digital maps were available for a wide variety of areas around the country and about a hundred staff were employed on digitising.

Piecemeal digitisation, while spreading the word about digital mapping, did not provide enough contiguous map cover to prompt customers into investing in the expensive equipment needed to take advantage of the digital data. At this time, when economy was a watchword in most Ordnance Survey work areas, some regarded the arrival of yet more fabulously expensive plotting machines and dedication of staff to the project to be a waste of precious resources. 'Digital Mapping is an ingenious development, but having proved we can do it, what next? Does it serve any real purpose?,' asked one member of staff in the departmental newsletter.

Certainly too little data was spread too widely across the country and the department decided to concentrate resources on producing one complete county (West Midlands). The fact that this was initially scheduled to take five years to complete served to highlight the enormity of the task of digitising the whole of the country's large-scale maps.

Maps at 1:10 000, 1:25 000 and 1:50 000 scale were also experimentally digitised, or derived from large-scale digital data, but production resources were firmly concentrated on refining digital techniques on large-scale maps.

A major breakthrough came in 1982 with the introduction of interactive digital workstations. These allowed captured data to be drawn up on a visual display unit and corrections to be verified on the screen. This innovation broke the loop that when corrections were made on the blind digital workstations new errors tended to be introduced. Output increased and the morale of digitising staff improved as they felt more in control of their work.

The Royal Engineers beat their retreat from Ordnance Survey in 1983.

In 1982 a major study of the needs of potential digital data customers was carried out which conclusively laid to rest any remaining doubts that no one would buy the data. More than half of the respondents claimed that they would be ready to start receiving their large-scale maps in digital form before 1990. A need was also identified for an efficient update system – a digital equivalent to the SUSI service.

Marching out

In January 1974 it was announced that the post of Director General would no longer be filled by a Major General on the active list but Irwin was invited to continue in post and became a civil servant in April of the same year. The decision therefore had little initial impact on the department.

Much more of a preoccupation was the achievement of the 1980 Plan, which was in danger of being affected by government spending cuts across the Civil Service. Staff numbers at Ordnance Survey were reduced from a peak of 4577 in 1974 to 3638 by the end of the decade as the department's 'contribution to current savings in national expenditure'. Irwin was determined that the 1980 plan would not be jeopardised but was equally adamant that 'no attrition of the programme of continuous revision' would be made. He warned that continuous revision had to be preserved 'at whatever cost to other operations' to avoid storing up problems for the future. Cuts and economies were therefore made in other areas, causing the 1:10 000 map production to fall behind schedule. The programme of upgrading developing areas to 1:1250 scale was also cut back in an attempt to cut costs. Despite the spending cuts, the 1980 Plan was achieved on time (except for a few sheets) and all large-scale mapping

'Being market-oriented means that an organisation takes its principal guidance from the present and future needs of users and not from what it has always done in the past, what it likes doing or even what it does best.' Mr W P Smith CB, OBE, Director General 1977–85.

of the country had been either resurveyed or overhauled between 1946 and 1981. Publication of the maps was completed by March 1982.

To succeed Irwin on his retirement in 1977, the post of Director General was advertised both within and outside the Civil Service. Applicants were expected to be 'professional land surveyors, whether a servant of the crown or not, who possess the appropriate qualifications and expertise'. The successful applicant was Walter Smith, previously Managing Director of a private survey company, but also a man whose experience included war service with the Royal Engineers, a spell with the Directorate of Overseas Survey and service with the United Nations in New York.

Smith took over just as discussions as to what new aims should be set for the department after the completion of the 1980 Plan began to gain momentum. It was clear that a smaller workforce would be sufficient to keep the maps continuously revised and, with the success of digital mapping techniques and the possibility of privatisation, a number of questions about the future strategies of the department needed to be addressed.

Shortly after taking office, Smith became closely involved with the formal discussions of a newly appointed Review Committee under the chairmanship of Sir David Serpell which set out to clarify the post-1980 policies of the department. Where all parties were in agreement, there was no controversy and it was logical to do so, extracts were made from the review for immediate action by the department. As a result, interim financial objectives were set for the department to increase its recovery from one fifth to one quarter on large-scale maps and a change of senior management structure was implemented to ensure the department was organised to meet customer needs.

The post-Serpell years were an unsettled time for the department. The report was published in 1979, but for five long years a cloud of uncertainty hung over the department's future status. Further cuts in staff numbers were gradually implemented by a policy of not replacing staff who left and numbers crept down to 2815 by March 1984. This ban on recruitment created an imbalance in the ratio of draughtsmen to surveyors and a number of draughtsmen were retrained to take field posts. The continued debate over privatisation and lack of new staff created a feeling of stagnation and sapped morale, which was further undermined by disaffection with government pay policies that led to Civil Service industrial action.

The remaining military personnel, whose position within the Ordnance Survey had begun to appear incongruous, left the department in 1983. It had been planned to phase out the military posts over a slightly longer period but the Ministry of Defence accepted that there was no military need for them to remain, and Ordnance Survey finally became a completely civilian organisation, after a formal ceremony at which the Royal Engineers Beat Retreat, in October of that year.

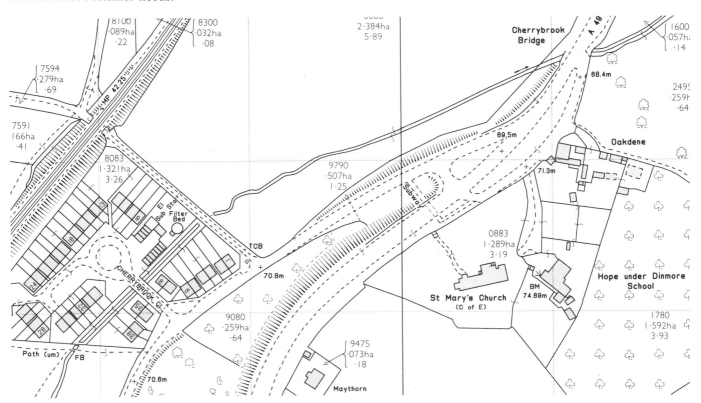

Part of the first 1:2500 digital map, SO 5052–5152, published in 1973.

14 MARKET LED

Serpell

The Serpell Review set out to consider the tasks facing the department in the twenty years from 1980 to 2000. Just as Sir Charles Close had decided, in 1911, that there were four main reasons for Ordnance Survey's existence, the Serpell Committee in 1980 concluded that there were four major tasks facing the department. However, only one aim, the maintenance of the archive of national mapping, was common to both; all the others had changed. The three other modern aims were the prompt supply of mapping to customers 'in forms acceptable to them', the expansion of digital mapping and the transformation of the department 'from being a rather inward-looking and conservatively run organisation into one that looks to the future and is responsive to change and developments elsewhere'. The inclusion of this last item as a 'major task' acknowledged that this was not something which could be achieved easily or within a short space of time, the ingrained attitudes and working practices of nearly two centuries being difficult to overcome.

One of the Serpell recommendations, intended to help the department become more outward looking, was the setting up of an Advisory Board whose members could provide 'broad management and financial advice'. The first Board was formed in 1982 with seven members, including the Director General. The other six advisors were drawn from senior individuals from various public and private companies and organisations. However, for a variety of reasons the arrangement did not work well, and in 1986 the Advisory Board was replaced by the Management Board, which consisted of four Ordnance Survey executive directors and three non-executive directors with commercial and marketing experience from outside companies.

The old consultative committee system was also reorganised to separate sections of map users with contradictory interests. The seven (later eight) committees, with the exception of the Public Services Committee, were sponsored by independent authorities. Customer groups represented included outdoor sports interests, sponsored by the Central Council of Physical Recreation, the gas, water, electricity and telecommunications industries, sponsored by the National Joint Utilities Group (NJUG), and the scientific community sponsored by the Royal Society.

The years of speculation which had created continued unease amongst staff over whether or not Ordnance Survey would be privatised finally ended in December 1984 when it was announced by William Waldegrave, the Under-Secretary of State for the Environment, that 'Ordnance Survey should remain a vote-funded Civil Service Department'. This cleared the way for a detailed response to be formally given by the government to the Serpell report. Many of the recommendations had already been implemented in the intervening years, but it was apparent that some, such as the acceleration of the digital mapping programme would be impossible to adopt without an increase in resources. This was granted, and in 1985 surveyors and cartographic support staff began once again to fill up the training school, boosting numbers towards the new authorised complement of 2979 non-industrial staff. Clear objectives, the lively and refreshing input of new recruits and, above all, the lifting of the stress of uncertainty over its future led to renewed optimism within the department.

Overseas and over here

The Royal Engineer Survey Companies were raised for the express purpose of carrying out the national survey, but sections were always held in readiness for service with the armies in the field. The Survey Companies were also responsible for Colonial Surveying, and officers and men were regularly sent to all corners of the British Empire. In addition Ordnance Survey supplied men for various Boundary Commissions which delineated the boundaries between countries, such as the United States and Canada in the 1840s. Ordnance Survey also trained limited numbers of surveyors from overseas at its headquarters. The cost of the overseas work and training was paid for by either the governments concerned or the Colonial Office.

At the end of the Second World War the Colonial Office decided to set up its own independent surveying organisation, appointing, as its first Director in 1946, Brigadier M Hotine, who had been so instrumental in planning the post-war structure of Ordnance Survey. He held the directorship for a remarkable seventeen years.

Part of the 1:125 000 Tourist Map of Kenya.
Survey of Kenya

The initial task of the Directorate of Colonial (later Overseas) Surveys (DOS), was to map the colonies at 1:125 000 or 1:50 000 scale, whichever was most appropriate, and to follow this with larger-scale mapping of townships and development areas. The Colonial Office and its successors, eventually the Overseas Development Administration (ODA), allocated a proportion of British aid money to DOS, which in turn decided where the money should be spent. Mapping programmes generally continued in countries following independence from British rule. Many of the maps produced – and all those with complex specifications – were printed at Southampton. Perhaps the finest of these was the 1974 map of Mount Kenya at 1:125 000, printed in ten colours, for which Ordnance Survey won the Thremmy Trophy, the top award in an Excellence in Lithography competition.

In 1981 the aid system was changed to give the beneficiary countries more control over the money allocated, and, understandably, the priorities were food, roads, hospitals and schools. Funds available for overseas mapping were dramatically reduced and a question mark hung over the future of DOS and its 300 or so staff. The solution to merge DOS with Ordnance Survey was, given their close relationship, obvious, if unpalatable to them both.

DOS was based in Tolworth, Surrey, and the staff were faced with the prospect of either a transfer to Southampton, with all its attendant personal upheaval, or of leaving their department. For the surveyors, who were used to crossing the world, the move to Southampton was a small matter, but for administrative personnel and cartographers it proved to be a powerful barrier. In the event only eighty-four DOS staff joined Ordnance Survey from Tolworth. This was still too many for the liking of many Ordnance Survey personnel, who gloomily calculated the effect on their own promotion prospects with the influx of younger staff at higher grades than themselves.

By the time DOS finally merged with the department in 1984, all of Ordnance Survey's senior technical staff, and the Director General, had some experience with DOS field surveying parties. This was usually as a result of exchanges under the Joint Survey Service scheme; similarly, all DOS senior staff had spent some time at Ordnance Survey. After the merger, DOS staff were gradually absorbed into Ordnance Survey activities, mainly at middle and higher management levels.

ODA now funds a core of thirteen people at Southampton, known as 'OS International', acting as survey and mapping advisors to ODA, whose services are available to all developing countries. Work is normally in progress for fifteen or so countries at any one time and embraces all aspects of land surveying, including the supply of consultants and field surveyors. Ordnance Survey now offers a wider range of surveying, cartographic and reprographic expertise to developing countries than DOS, before the merger, could have done by itself.

The tradition of training nationals from developing countries in practical cartography and photogrammetric techniques, printing and, more recently, digital mapping methods still continues, with a constant class of around twelve trainees attending personally tailored courses at the Southampton headquarters. OS International also boasts a huge library of about 100 000 maps, 2 million air photographs and records of survey data from all the countries where work has been undertaken. This has been built up since 1946 and provides a unique information resource for use by ODA and British consultants as well as by overseas countries.

A recent development is the selection of maps from countries where there is an established tourist trade, for revision and republication in a new series of Ordnance Survey "Worldmaps". These maps were originally produced for the country concerned, so permission for the venture is negotiated with the individual country. By 1991 Worldmaps were available for a growing number of Caribbean islands as well as for Seychelles and Kilimanjaro. The magnificent Mount Kenya map was also republished and a map of the world produced at 1:40 000 000 scale.

The merger of DOS with Ordnance Survey created, in the words of Walter Smith, 'a breadth of talent that is hard to equal in any other national mapping organisation'.

then published as a new edition. All large-scale maps were to be swept at least once every fifty years. This allowed the department to keep abreast of the change essential for its customers, but also gave an opportunity for complete resurvey at regular intervals. New editions were also published for sheets under continuous revision, whenever the amount of change on a map exceeded preset limits, which prevented the maps from becoming too untidy in appearance.

At first, resources for periodic survey were limited and progress was slow, and it was this type of work and the upgrading of maps from 1:2500 to 1:1250 scale in areas of urban growth that was contracted out to private survey companies. The first survey contracts were let in 1983 for Crowborough and Honiton. However, the cost of quality assurance made these surveys no cheaper than using Ordnance Survey's own staff. After 1988/89 no more survey contracts were awarded, but by this time forty-eight towns had been surveyed by private contract.

From 1988, new techniques and use of up-to-date air photography led to dramatic increases in production and even without the input from contracts the department was able to reduce the interval between full revision of maps to a maximum of forty years.

Sweeping on

Trials for contracting out survey work had never been successful in past times, and suggestions made in the early 1980s that Ordnance Survey should once more entrust part of its survey operation to private companies was met with scepticism. Not only was it doubted whether the contractors could meet the department's exacting specification, but Ordnance Survey was reluctant to lose direct contact with its customers, just at a time when it was being urged to make more effort to understand their needs.

Up until 1981 the map archive was updated by continuous revision methods, but an increasing balance of unsurveyed map detail led to a change in this long-established working practice. A distinction was now drawn between 'primary' change, of first importance in maintaining the archive, such as demolition or new houses, and 'secondary' covering change of lesser importance. Primary revision continued to be surveyed on a continuous basis with the aim of collecting new detail within six months of its appearance on the ground, but the secondary change was deliberately bypassed. This was however surveyed by a 'sweep' of the area at regular intervals, at which time all changes in primary and secondary detail, names, boundaries and vertical control were collected to provide a completely updated map. The map was

A prototype Portable Interactive Edit Station (PIES).

Following equal opportunities legislation in 1976 the department reluctantly admitted women to its ranks of surveyors. Most other Ordnance Survey jobs were by then open to both sexes but the department had avoided appointing female surveyors in this traditionally male occupation, expressing fears about their personal safety. A small but steady stream of female applicants has since been maintained and in 1991 just over 3 per cent of all surveyors were women.

In the 1990s GPS, and dramatically improved photogrammatic techniques, look set to change surveying practices. Advances in air-plotting machines had made the work ever more efficient but basic techniques remained the same for many years. However, the application of sophisticated computer technology to photogrammetry since the late 1980s led to renewed innovation and speculation that machines which could recognise the air-photographic images might soon be able to produce maps almost automatically from photographs. Even the time-honoured surveyor's sketching case is threatened with extinction as research into lightweight computer terminals with high resolution 'touch screens' holds promise for the future. The Portable Interactive Edit Station (PIES) will completely remove the need for paper output, pens, pencils, scales and set-squares, and the art of good penmanship amongst surveyors will eventually become as redundant as engraving on copper plate has amongst draughtsmen.

══════ Satellites above the horizon ══════

In the last twenty years, the technology associated with satellites has advanced sufficiently for their use as survey tools to become possible. The use of satellites removes the need for intervisibility between observing stations. The stations, therefore, no longer need to be on hilltops or high buildings and are usually placed conveniently by the roadside. Satellite system technology has also finally conquered the elements and surveyors can now make observations regardless of the weather.

Ordnance Survey's first major use of satellite positioning equipment was in 1984 when it took part in a scheme to provide a control network for the North Sea. This used a satellite system known as TRANSIT Doppler to provide horizontal coordinates of the observed offshore oil and gas platforms to an accuracy of 1 metre.

The TRANSIT system has been superseded by the Global Positioning System (GPS), which provides very high accuracy relative positioning to a few millimetres over a few kilometres. This is at least as good as anything possible by terrestrial methods and is achieved in far less time. Ordnance Survey has been using GPS for the provision of control

stations for large-scale mapping since 1987 and has made more extensive use of the system than any other European organisation.

A decision was made in 1990 to replace the triangulation network with a control framework provided by GPS. This network will be several times more accurate than the Primary Triangulation. As GPS is a three-dimensional system, the new framework will provide heights as well as plan coordinates, when the shape of the geod has been more finely determined, making possible the integration of plan control and levelling networks for the first time.

GPS can also be used for the transfer of heights across water which is always a problem with spirit levelling. A scheme observed by Ordnance Survey and the *Institut Géographique National*, the national survey organisation of France, provided the plan and height control framework for the Channel Tunnel project.

In 1991 Ordnance Survey operated eight GPS receivers, giving the department the capability to provide control on an international as well as domestic level. Observations at six stations in Great Britain have allowed the determination of the shape and size of the country more precisely than ever before. These stations form part of the European Reference Frame (EUREF) which provides an homogeneous control framework for the whole of Europe.

However, GPS is not the only satellite system used in the EUREF campaign. Satellite Laser Ranging (SLR) stations, such as that at the Royal Greenwich Observatory, track a satellite covered in retro-reflectors and allow very accurate positioning. For the most accurate measurements of all, surveyors look beyond the stars to intergalactic bodies such as pulsars and quasars which emit electromagnetic energy. These are used in Very Long Base Interferometry (VLBI) which allows distances of 100 kilometres to be measured with an accuracy of 1 millimetre. Ordnance Survey participated in such measurements at a station at Buddon near Dundee in 1989. Man has also left reflectors on the moon, capitalising on the availability of this natural satellite for geodetic purposes.

Further applications of GPS continue to be developed, including its possible use in detail survey work. This is likely to complement rather than replace existing revision methods such as graphic survey.

The use of satellite systems for high-order control work results in substantial economies and removes much of the hard work – and with it aching limbs, sodden clothing, frozen fingers and chapped lips – but also some of the romance of the surveyors' work. No longer will climbing the mountains of Britain be a part of their job, no more will faint lights shone by colleagues on distant hilltops be sought through the mist.

Digital Field Update System (DFUS)

The Serpell Report spoke of the need to clarify 'the level of update required and the methods by which updates to the digital data will be collected and distributed' but two years later a 'serious delay' was reported in formulating such a policy for digital mapping.

In February 1983, it was concluded that customers were not purchasing Ordnance Survey digital map data because there was no efficient update service. The level of service for digital updates had to be at least as good as the SUSI service. This provided update of as little as twenty units of change, within three months of the completion of a new development. Clearly the digital update facilities then available for intervals of around fifty units of change were inadequate.

The Digital Field Update System (DFUS) aimed to take the updating service out to the field. This was a radical proposal which involved installing digitising equipment in field offices, the original concept being that surveyors would digitise their own revision from the master survey drawing (MSD) after each day's surveying. Digitising equipment was therefore installed in the field office at Birmingham for an extended field trial in November 1983. New work added to an MSD by the surveyor was digitised and then ink-plotted on to its reverse side using the precise back-digitising of the flat-bed plotter.

It was soon recognised that it was impracticable for all surveyors to compete for the use of the one DFUS system every day, so a full-time digitiser, a draughtsman, was transferred to Birmingham for the remainder of the trial which was a complete success.

The next ambitious step was to undertake a full production trial of the DFUS system to prove that MSDs could be efficiently updated in a field office, and the data supplied both to a customer's own digital library and to Ordnance Survey headquarters for update of the large-scale digital databank. This commenced in 1985 using three computer workstations to cope with the total output from fifteen surveyors. The DFUS equipment was staffed by a team of four draughtsmen, all of whom worked hard to overcome delays and problems, including the unreliability of transferring the data on cassette tape to and from databanks.

The trial was successful and DFUS began to be installed in other offices. The first was at Dudley and, during 1987, systems were installed at Ordnance Survey offices in Glasgow, Stockton-on-Tees, Oxford, London, Crawley, Hedge End (Southampton), Bristol and Milton Keynes. A DFUS section was also set up at headquarters to provide training and support, and to test new equipment. The cassette tape system was replaced with full data communication facilities using telephone links to transfer data to and from the ever-growing headquarters digital databank.

At Milton Keynes a trial took place (Project '88) which examined the possibility of replacing MSDs with temporary survey documents (TSDs). These could be produced from the locally stored digital data as and when required and, being free of sheet edges, the area to be updated could be plotted to fall conveniently in the centre of the TSD. The successful outcome of Project '88 led to the decision to commence a programme of disciplined removal of MSDs at some eleven more field locations during 1989 and to increase the number of DFUS equipped offices at a rate of about fifteen each year with the aim of providing a nation-wide service by 1996.

The benefit of DFUS to digital map data customers is that the data is updated immediately on completion of the survey. It can be supplied at any selected threshold, generally between twenty and fifty units of change. For non-digital customers, SUSI is still available where the MSDs have not been withdrawn, otherwise, plots from the updated digital data can be supplied.

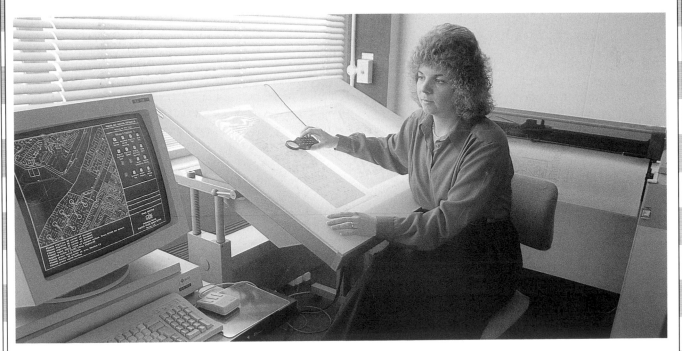

Digital Field Update System (DFUS).

Global Positioning System equipment in use near the Channel Tunnel workings.

Getting there

From the beginning, demand for digital mapping greatly exceeded the supply available, a problem which the department solved by inviting customers to declare a firm intention to buy the maps as soon as they were digitised. These 'commitments to buy' were then included, together with the department's own perceived priorities, in a rolling five-year digitisation plan. The more committed customers there were for an area, the higher the priority it received for digitising.

By 1985, conventional map production lines were being run down and all 1:1250 resurvey and revised maps were produced digitally. Extra funds for digital mapping were granted by the government that year and a target set for digitisation of the whole country by the year 2015.

To achieve this date, some of the digitising work had to be contracted out to private companies and by 1987 about half of the new digital work, to a value of over 6 million pounds, had been produced in this way. Some problems were initially encountered because of the exceptional quality and accuracy standards set by the department; in fact many contractors did not believe the standards were possible to achieve. Fortunately Ordnance Survey could show examples of its own work to prove otherwise and guidance was given to the contractors to help them raise their own standards to the same level. Contract work was initially quality checked at Ordnance Survey by direct overlay of the digital maps on to the original,

a costly and labour-intensive system. The department's research and development division later devised an automated quality sampling system using a series of nine tests which allowed contractors to pretest for quality before submitting their work. These tests were also applied to maps digitised at Ordnance Survey.

One factor which slowed down the capture of digital data was the large number of feature codes used for describing what each line or point represented. More than 170 codes, some used extremely rarely, were defined. However, after discussion with major customers the number was reduced to a lean specification of thirty-one codes, making the job of the digital draughtsman easier, if less interesting.

With fewer codes and an agreed system of quality control, it became easier for contractors to satisfactorily digitise maps, and by 1990 areas contract-digitised for utilities began to be accepted into the Ordnance Survey map databank. Digitisation of 1:1250 maps was completed in 1991 with all basic-scale mapping due for digitisation before the year 2000.

Research into the full automation of production continues and Ordnance Survey has enjoyed considerable success with its own software. The addition of ornament such as trees, sand and shingle, has now been automated on all 1:1250 and new edition maps, as well as the calculation of land area information, previously a skilled but slow task. Total automation will relieve the department of having to print small uneconomic numbers of large-scale maps on paper and, instead, paper maps will be plotted on demand from the digital database.

Following trials in selected areas from 1988, a new service called 'Superplan' became available for London and Birmingham. This provides site-centred maps on demand from constantly updated digital data, to the customer's own specification in terms of scale, size, content and even colour. Ordnance Survey is committed to extending this service in the future and, when available nationwide, not only will the Supply of Unpublished Survey Information (SUSI) no longer be required, but the concept of Advance Revision Information will itself be an anachronism.

Small-scale digital mapping

In 1984 a study of customer needs for small-scale digital data concluded that demand existed for fully structured data, particularly for 1:50 000, but predicted that the cost of production would, in most instances, be more than customers would be prepared to pay. By then the 1:625 000 scale map had been digitised and was already being used to produce the Ordnance Survey Routeplanner map. This first digitally produced small-scale map was criticised for its inelegance, especially for the computer-style typeface, but in later editions such problems were resolved and current productions are as cartographically pleasing as any conventionally produced map. The data itself was released for sale in 1986 and immediately found favour with customers involved in the development of road navigation and route-finding systems.

A draughtsman editing structured data.

The 1:250 000 structured data became available in 1990, and after consultation with customers it was initially decided to offer this for sale on a 'menu' basis of twenty-four feature groups, in 'tiles' of 50 km × 50 km. The 1991 Ordnance Survey/Hamlyn *Motoring Atlas* was produced directly from the digital data, giving an opportunity for a number of design changes to the mapping, and the ability to easily update the information in future years.

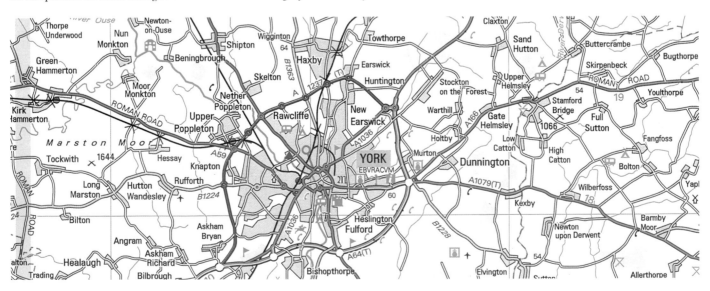

Extract from the 1991 Motoring Atlas. *Graphic output at 3 miles to 1 inch from 1:250 000 digital map data.*

1:50 000 digital data initially made a bad start with an experimental sheet (Landranger 111) attracting a disappointing reaction from customers in 1987. However, a new approach was made to the problem, and in 1990 customers were invited to view pilot structured data for a small area in Kent. This time a favourable response was given, and full production of digital data at this scale is under consideration. Digital height data, produced by the Directorate of Military Survey is already available for much of the country as either contours or as a 'terrain model', a three-dimensional matrix.

Towards GIS

It soon became clear that the unstructured nature of digital map data, aptly described as 'spaghetti', needed to be reorganised if customers were to be able to use the data as part of a Geographic Information System (GIS). The concept of such a system is to use mapping as a base for displaying other information, in particular linking databases to digital maps, rather than solely using the data to produce mapping. Such a system would attach data to features on the maps, but first the data has to be structured so that each feature can be identified.

Structured data has to be 'clean', that is points and lines meant to coincide do in fact do so. When a map is digitised by a draughtsman, every effort is made to make perfect the junctions that occur at such places as the corners of houses and fences, but sometimes a tiny gap or overshoot, invisible to the eye, but not to the computer, may remain. These are unimportant if the customer only wishes to output printed mapping from the database. However, in a GIS application, a customer may wish to add shading or colouring to a feature on the map, such as colouring all lakes and lochs in blue. It then becomes important that they form a geometrically complete polygon within the data. If just one gap occurs, adding colour to the polygon causes the colour to flood out to fill the adjoining polygon, staining all in its path until held by 'watertight' linework. To solve this problem the data can be cleaned by a computer program which searches for gaps and overshoots. These are deemed to be unintentional when smaller than a specified size and are purged by 'snapping' the points together so that they are described by a common co-ordinated point within the data.

Digital data is sold by the 'tile', as this is a more appropriate term than the description 'sheet'. For large-scale maps, however, the tiles do equate to existing conventional map sheetlines. Structured data allows the customer to make a choice and to buy only the features he or she wants, for example, the road network, as 'datasets' or, if they wish, customers may buy all datasets and have a complete set of

features. Small-scale digital maps are 'structured' in this way. The structured data itself contains more information than unstructured data and each link or node will 'know' what it represents, whether part of the M1 motorway or part of the River Severn. There is also intelligence between datasets allowing the data to 'know' whether it is perhaps a bridge crossing a road or a tunnel passing under a river.

Structuring of small-scale digital mapping is undertaken at initial digitising, the division of features into datasets being decided after market research with customers, and is immediately available for GIS applications.

However, for the vast large-scale database, structuring existing data will take much longer and this is being carried out where there is a demand for it. Many users simply want the flexibility of a map in digital form, perhaps on which to overlay their own digital information such as pipe or cable networks, and are uninterested in GIS. The first large-scale structured data product, Ordnance Survey Centre Alignment of Roads (OSCAR) already exists for much of the country. Each link carries information about itself such as its length, whether motorway, 'A' road, etc., and its Department of Transport route number. OSCAR data is used by customers developing in-vehicle navigation systems and for devising highway maintenance systems. Further structuring of large-scale digital data is under consideration. The provision of administrative area polygons is one suggestion as well as the placing of a 'seed' into each building giving a unique reference to which information about its size, type and occupants could be added. Typical GIS applications might be market research and local authority planning.

Printing

Ordnance Survey maps are renowned for the quality of their printing. This is carried out at the Southampton headquarters where reproduction floor staff work a two-shift day to make the most economical use of the costly printing machinery. The reproduction and print areas are geared primarily to the production, folding and casing of sheet mapping, as well as the production of all the intermediate maps, negatives, documents and proofs that the public never sees but which are essential to the eventual production of the finished map. Naturally use is also made of the facilities for printing publicity material and departmental documents of all kinds.

The photographic work is unusually precise, as reductions and enlargements of maps have to be exactly scaled. Huge computer-controlled cameras provide larger photography with a maximum single enlargement size of 1270 mm × 1066 mm, dictated by the largest size of the sheet of paper on which a map can be printed. By contrast the smallest size

Installed in 1990, this four-colour press is capable of printing 140 maps (1610 mm × 1120 mm) every minute.

regularly produced is a fifteen times reduction of large-scale maps to 35 mm microfilm. Since 1984, increasing use has been made of roomlight film which can be safely handled under normal fluorescent lighting without danger of fogging, exposures being made by high intensity ultraviolet light. This removed the need for staff to work under darkroom conditions.

Large-scale maps are usually printed in monochrome but most small-scale maps are now printed in the four process colours of magenta, cyan, yellow and black, from which a large number of colours can be derived by combining colours and using printing screens. In the past, each colour had to be individually printed using the correct colour ink and, as multi-colour maps entailed the use of up to twelve colours, the conversion to four-colour process printing, which was begun in the 1970s, resulted in major savings in time and cost. Comparison with some of the old Tourist Maps, such as the 'Lake District', which were printed in twelve colours, with the same sheets currently printed in process colours, shows just how successful this new printing technology has been.

Maps are mainly printed by lithographic offset proving and printing methods where the map image on an inked aluminium printing plate is transferred to a rubber blanket and then to the paper surface. The department continually updates its printing machinery, but for all the computer-aided controls now available the process still works on the basic principle that grease and water do not mix. Some work is still carried out by letterpress, such as overprinting on map covers, and as the name suggests this printing uses a traditional raised printing surface in the form of metal type and blocks to print directly on to the paper.

After printing, the maps are trimmed by programmable guillotine and passed to folding machines built in Switzerland to Ordnance Survey specification. Over the years the department has accumulated considerable expertise in methods of map folding, but the basic 'Bender' fold, named after the member of staff who invented it in the 1930s, is still most commonly used. This results in a concertina fold which allows any part of the map to be looked at without completely unfolding the map. From the folding machine the maps pass to the casing machine which aligns the map with its cover, activates the glue and completes the fold.

Testing, testing

Ordnance Survey's world-wide reputation for quality and accuracy is jealously guarded, the first line of defence being formed by the integrity of the mapping and charting officers (MCOs) who survey and draw, or digitise, the maps. It is the surveyor whose pride in the job ensures that change is recorded quickly and accurately and it is due to the draughtsmen's skill that this is correctly presented to the customer.

However, accuracy is not left solely to individual workers, as errors may occur due to circumstances beyond their control and, for this reason, a small team is permanently dedicated to accuracy testing. Their task is not concerned with checking the completeness of the map but with the accuracy of the map detail on the MSD or in the databank. Members of the team select a representative sample of detail points spread over an area of mapping. The positions, the plotted national grid coordinates of these test points, are compared with their 'true' national grid coordinates obtained from an independent and higher-order instrumental survey. The differences found can be expressed as an error statement which is evaluated against the accepted standard for the mapping. In this way a check is maintained of the accuracy of the survey and any degradation can be quickly identified and investigated. The team also test the accuracy of all surveying instruments and digitising tables, to ensure that these give results within specified tolerances, evaluate new survey instrumentation and assess new survey techniques and procedures.

Testing of a different sort is carried out by another specialist team, the map production test group (MPTG) who concern themselves with the quality of materials and equipment used in the production process. This group was originally formed in 1946 as the 'investigation section' to help solve problems experienced with materials of variable quality. In this role of 'facilitating production' they also undertook some research and development work, being responsible for the introduction of plastic for field documents and for scribing experiments.

Today's map production test group still carry out experimental production work and test new methods, as well as the quality of materials such as inks and papers, against predetermined standards. Take the example of paper, the durability of which is close to the customer's heart. Not only must the paper be a suitable weight and strength but it must be white enough for the finest details of the map to be clearly visible. Ordnance Survey measures both the colour and the opacity of the paper it receives as well as its dimensional stability. A test is made to see whether it will stand up to folding without cracking or breaking, which would result in loss of map detail on its folds. The machine used to do this is the Schopper Fold Endurance Testing machine which, though purchased in the 1930s, is just as accurate and efficient as any new machine of its type, giving it the distinction of being the oldest machine still in regular use by the department.

All new editions of Ordnance Survey maps are 'proved' before printing, by printing a limited number of copies on paper, or sometimes just one on plastic. These are returned to the sections who originated the work and are examined for errors. Proofs of 1:50 000 are seen by the small-scale surveyors who worked on the sheet and are checked by each,

Prototype in-car navigation system.

retracing his steps in a mental journey across the land surveyed months before. After proof corrections have been made, printing can proceed but even here sharp-eyed printers have been known to occasionally spot an error missed by everyone else and, if it is a serious mistake, the press is stopped while advice is sought on whether to continue printing.

The final arbiter of accuracy is of course the customer. By its very nature a map is only a snapshot of the landscape at a particular time and the older the map, the less accurate it will be. Any 'mistakes' due to the age of the map are corrected when it is revised but sometimes errors are discovered and, if reported, will be corrected at the earliest opportunity.

Research and development

After the Second World War the department sought a replacement for H Jolly, its scientific advisor, who had left to join the Commission on Germany. Eventually Thomas O'Bierne MA, F Inst P was appointed in 1947, but within two years he resigned complaining that no 'single qualified scientist can satisfactorily serve the purposes of the Ordnance Survey'. He found that he was expected to be a 'walking encyclopedia . . . in the interval between which he does something which may be called "research", so far as he can on his own'.

Made to measure

As well as providing its usual range of maps and services Ordnance Survey is often called upon to meet requests for mapping on a commercial contract basis. A rapid and accurate survey was, for instance, made in 1966 of the Welsh village of Aberfan where a colliery tip, made unstable by water building up within it after heavy rain, slid without warning to bury the village school in black sooty slag causing the deaths of 115 children and 28 adults. A priority was to assess how far the tip had moved and whether it was still unstable, and Ordnance Survey were called in to help. Air photographs were immediately taken from which an accurate, 2 km × 1 km, 1:1250 scale contoured map was completed in less than three weeks.

Occasionally Ordnance Survey surveyors have been called upon to accurately survey other incident sites for investigation. Such surveys include the plotting of items not normally found on large-scale maps but which may be of interest to an inquiry. So, for road traffic accidents for example, the position of street furniture, such as lampposts and street signs, may be included as well as manhole covers, kerbs and any other relevant details.

Ordnance Survey were naturally called upon to assist in the Falklands conflict of 1982 when large numbers of maps of the islands were printed at extremely short notice for use by the forces. Ordnance Survey again had to swing into production for the war which followed the invasion of Kuwait in 1990. The maps of the areas involved in the conflict were urgently required by the coalition forces and were compiled, produced and printed by the department under direction from the Ministry of Defence.

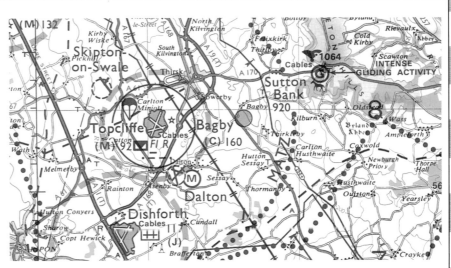

Part of Tactical Pilotage Chart, sheet 9, North East England, Edition 12. Civil Aviation Authority

Surveys have also been made of the States of Jersey which, as a separate state, does not benefit automatically from coverage by large-scale mapping. A similar task has been carried out for Alderney. Public utilities and the private sector are also major customers of Ordnance Survey technology and experience, and significant contributions were made to the Channel Tunnel Project and to the planning of the rail link connecting the Tunnel to London. Tailor-made mapping is regularly produced for local councils and for private customers, such as the Camping and Caravanning Club. Ordnance Survey is also contracted to produce aeronautical maps for the Civil Aviation Authority.

The UK shares a responsibility with other allied nations, to produce military maps of various series covering the world for use by air and ground forces. Some of these are produced on behalf of the Directorate of Military Survey.

A wide variety of other world mapping is produced, an example being four town plans of Muscat, Oman, produced to commemorate the Sultan's twenty-fifth anniversary of his succession to the throne. These drew acclaim for their presentation and timeliness.

At a rather less grand level, standard mapping can be adapted, and even personalised, to suit many customers' requirements by simple enlargement, reduction, production of composite maps, wall maps and even postcards.

Finally, the department sells the information it uses to produce the maps. Accurate bench-mark heights and trig. positions are available for purchase at a fraction of the cost that would be incurred by a company having to find the information afresh for themselves. Aerial photographs, mainly black and white, are available for the whole country.

O'Bierne did believe that research was a proper function of the department, doubting otherwise whether it would be done at all, but argued that a dedicated team should be set up for the purpose. Far from this happening, O'Bierne was not replaced, the department being content to leave investigation to individual sections, to intermittent interest from universities or to the investigation section. As O'Bierne predicted, the scientific reputation of Ordnance Survey suffered and in later years it was criticised for its inward-looking attitude in the post-war years.

Resources for research remained extremely limited and in 1960 the investigation section still only consisted of one

officer and three staff, conducting experiments very much related to production. During the 1970s resources were increased, mainly to assist with digital mapping experiments, but the Serpell Review severely criticised what it saw as a lack of commitment to research and development. They recommended that the department should 'greatly strengthen' its capability in this field and should appoint a chief scientist to 'command respect inside and outside OS', and that considerably more money should be devoted to research.

The call for a scientist to be appointed was 'noted' but not accepted, but increased funds were made available, not only for the department's own use, but also in support of collaborative projects at a number of universities. Ordnance Survey also began to take a more active role in international professional organisations such as the European Organisation for Experimental Photogrammetry, of which the Director General became the UK head and later President. The department already received advice from its Scientific Consultative Committee, but in 1987 this was strengthened by the setting up of the Ordnance Survey Science and Technology Advisory Committee, whose function is to alert the department to potentially fruitful areas of research and advise on how advances in science can be harnessed.

By 1991 the total number of staff employed, full-time, on research and development work was forty-eight and department policy set expenditure on research at 'not less than two per cent of the Department's total budget'. By these measures Ordnance Survey is regaining its scientific standing and winning respect for its development strategies.

Books

During the first 190 years of its history, Ordnance Survey published only the occasional atlases and a small number of scientific volumes, not considering that it was within its remit to enter the book publishing trade. However, following exhortations of the Janes Committee to the department to seek to maximise returns on products and services and the Serpell Committee to 'adopt a more aggressive and imaginative marketing policy', consideration was given to the possibility that books with a high mapping content might prove to be a suitable new market to explore. The department's lack of expertise in book publishing was resolved with the idea of pursuing such ventures on a joint basis with other publishers.

In 1981 the department was directed by the Secretary of State for the Environment to engage in such joint ventures and a general invitation was issued to publishing houses to

A selection of co-publications produced in 1990/91.

attend open days at Ordnance Survey to examine the range of maps available and to discuss publishing opportunities. From these well-attended events negotiations were opened with several publishers and within two years the first book, *Walker's Britain* published jointly with Pan, was in the shops, closely followed by the first of several atlases, based on Routemaster mapping, published jointly with Hamlyn.

The first hardback atlas was styled as a home reference book and, as well as mapping, contained essays and thematic maps covering Britain's physical, historical, economical and human geography. At £14.95 in 1983 it was expensive, but proved popular. Having addressed its traditional market with this book, the department progressed to producing a cheaper road atlas and, cheapest of all, a large 'floppy' motoring atlas. This last book was something of an innovation, its large format being unmissable on the bookshop shelf, but stubbornly too large to fit into the map pockets of most cars. Despite this drawback it became a best-seller, inspiring a host of imitations from other map publishers. This low-priced and prominently year-dated atlas changed the map-buying habits of the motoring public, who switched from mainly buying maps to mainly buying atlases within a few years. Sales of the Routeplanner map series suffered in consequence.

From atlases and walking guides it was only a small step to the travel market and a co-venture with the AA resulted in a series of *Leisure Guides* of popular holiday destinations. The volume covering the Lake District won the Hunter Davies award for best book of the area in 1984. Books covering canals and waterways, books for birdwatchers and naturalists, long distance or Sunday afternoon walkers, school text and activity books, gazetteer and reference books, and historical books all followed in quick succession. In 1991 Ordnance Survey had almost a hundred books in print, most of which were co-ventures with a wide variety of commercial publishers.

Agency

In 1985 Walter Smith retired from Ordnance Survey, but not from cartography. He remained intensely interested in the future of mapping, serving as Chairman of the National Committee for Photogrammetry and Remote Sensing and as Deputy Chairman to the Committee of Inquiry into Handling of Geographic Information, acquiring the status of elder statesman of the mapping world.

He was replaced at Ordnance Survey by Peter McMaster who was promoted from within the department after applying for the post, advertised both inside and outside the Civil Service. Service with the Royal Engineers, specialising in surveying, first led him to the department in 1966 as officer in charge of computing and investigations, but he left the army in 1970, training as a barrister with the intention of eventually obtaining a position as a company secretary.

A family concern

For twenty-five years I've known it
And seen its boys grow old
And train their sons to the service
And back to the Survey fold.

(Winterbotham, 1934)

Many Ordnance Survey employees complete a lifetime's loyal service to the department without it even being thought exceptional. In 1991 an analysis of the 2500 staff revealed that: the average length of service of all employees in post was over 17 years, and the average length of service of draughtsmen and surveyors was over 20 years. The longest recorded total service ever was that of William Morgan who joined straight from school and was kept on after normal retiring age during the war, to accumulate a staggering fifty-four years employment with the department.

With its diverse range of employees, from surveyors, draughtsmen and printers to computer programmers and administrative staff, Ordnance Survey has a slightly unusual ability to provide employment for several members of a family. Strict rules are applied to ensure that one family member never supervises another, to prevent favouritism – although in times gone by, having a relative in the business was a distinct advantage. As late as the 1930s, preference was given to job applicants from Survey families. 'The advantage of this principle is that it brings boys into what is properly a technical engineering occupation from a home in which those particular points had been discussed and had been, so to speak, the breath of life.' Many instances can be found of generation following generation and a survey revealed two staff members who could both claim lineage back through five generations to the same forefather, who had served with the Irish Survey in the 1830s.

At certain times of the year the visitor to headquarters can be forgiven for thinking that the department is still trying to 'start them young' as children are seen accompanying their parent(s) to work. In fact they are being brought to the highly successful holiday playscheme, which at the time of its founding in 1983 was one of the first such schemes to be operated by a government department in the country.

A thriving Sports and Social Club has existed for many years with many clubs and activities from aerobics to travel on offer. Perhaps the oddest club ever was the 'Pig Club' active during the days of war and post-war meat rationing. The pig, to whose fattening the members contributed, was kept in a pen at the Crabwood House premises. Today the emphasis is on encouraging staff to reflect the ideals of a leaner, fitter Civil Service by becoming so themselves and the Social Club and the Unions are working closely with the department to improve sports facilities and to support health initiatives.

Very Long Base Interferometry (VLBI) mobile receiver.

However, an opportunity arose to rejoin the Ordnance Survey as a civil servant and he never regretted his decision to return. By the time he became Director General, McMaster had served as Assistant Director of the cartographic division where he was closely involved with the design and production of the 1:50 000 Landranger series, and as Director of Marketing, Planning and Development.

One of McMaster's aims was to make Ordnance Survey a far more approachable organisation for its customers by providing as much information as it was possible economically to give. As part of this initiative the Ordnance Survey mission statement, which replaced the old unpublished policy statements, was published in 1987, setting out the department's six objectives for the next decade. To:

1 Operate within the framework of government policy
2 Keep the National Data Archive up to date
3 Provide for the needs of users from the National Data Archive
4 Maintain a position of leadership in use of technology
5 Maintain a high reputation for excellence
6 Expand the market for Ordnance Survey products

Each of these broad headings was subdivided into more specific aims which laid out policy for the future. For the first time the department publicly committed itself to a number of aims including the achievement of full cost recovery, reducing its running costs by 1.5 per cent per year and producing structured digital data of Great Britain as

quickly as possible. The mission statement encouraged discussion and certainly became a hot topic for debate within the department, where every member of staff received a copy. However, it was perceived as not going far enough by the Committee of Public Accounts which met in 1987 to discuss the Objectives and Management of the Ordnance Survey. While recognising the department's strengths and agreeing that the old policy statement system was not a good basis for effective strategic management, they concluded that business should be conducted in a sharper and more professional way, with greater emphasis on corporate planning, financial control, target setting and marketing. 'Vigorous action' was expected by the Committee for the future, and that was what they got.

Within a year a major review had been undertaken for improved marketing of large-scale and digital mapping leading to the appointment of account executives to directly look after the needs of the gas, water, telecommunications and electricity industries. Further initiatives included better use of marketing intelligence from field offices, with the appointment of region based marketing executives, and agreements with the utilities for third-party digitising of Ordnance Survey maps in order to complete the digital coverage of the country more quickly.

Digital mapping provided a new challenge to the copyright laws which had been drawn up in an era before computers. Digitisation made the copyright situation less clear-cut, as even the definition of what constituted a copy came under question. The same problems were facing software and data industries in general and, as a consequence, a new Act of Parliament was passed in 1988 setting out a number of 'restricted acts'. Under these, Ordnance Survey's copyright in its digital data is safeguarded and customers can only use it under licence from the department. Revenue from licences and copyright receipts from conventionally produced mapping are ploughed back into the production and maintenance of each product range. Income from copyright in 1990/91 was £12 million, one-quarter of the total revenue of the department.

As part of a financial review, the department literally 'took stock' of its situation and sold a large spare plot of land, never used by it, for private housing. A close look at the stores also revealed numerous out-of-date or surplus equipment which was sold off at a series of auctions. The list of items for sale revealed, in its own way, much of the recent history of the department and some staff purchased old survey instruments with which they had worked, out of pure nostalgia. At the same time, much greater emphasis was placed on controlling stocks of all kinds for the future and procurement procedures were considerably tightened.

In 1987 the technical staff of the department were 'restructured' to fall into line with the professional and technical officer grading structure of the Civil Service. This was seen as a major victory recognising at last the level of technical knowledge of the staff and helping to dispel the old craftsman image of the surveyors and draughtsmen, who were renamed mapping and charting officers (MCOs). A complete level of lower management was abolished in the process, the biggest losers of the change being those people who had perhaps served twenty years at a basic grade before their hard-won promotion only to find themselves, after restructuring, at the same grade as those they had recently been supervising. Pay was improved, but this was earned by higher levels of individual responsibility. A much smaller percentage of basic survey work was subjected to detailed examination leading to substantial cost savings, with no apparent degradation of accuracy.

Relations between Land Registry and Ordnance Survey gradually improved after the Second World War as the department was able to commit increasing resources to their mapping needs. In 1964 the Land Registry announced a programme to progressively cover all areas of England and Wales by compulsory registration. The consequential increase in work for Ordnance Survey led to the development of new methods of production and the maps were produced on plastic drawing film from which Land Registry could print all the copies they required. By 1990 the task was complete and Land Registry opened its archive of the details of 13 million properties to the public for enquiries. Details of the remaining estimated 9 million unregistered properties will be added when these change ownership. Ordnance Survey's task is now limited to casework but close co-operation is maintained between the two departments.

Under the government's Next Steps initiative of 1988, which aimed to improve the quality of public services, the opportunity arose for Civil Service departments to be granted Agency status. Ordnance Survey already possessed many of the hallmarks of an agency, such as having a management board, corporate plan, annual report, trading accounts and performance targets and, while little initial difference would be made to the day-to-day running of the department, the potential flexibility of agency status was perceived as a future benefit. Ordnance Survey's standing was formally confirmed as an independent government department with the Director General reporting directly to the Secretary of State for the Environment, and the switch to agency status progressed smoothly. The Serpell Committee had commented on the continued recurrence of the phrase 'trying to do business with one hand tied behind our back' that it had met within the department. Agency status offered the security of remaining

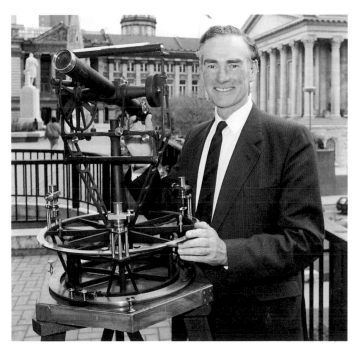

Peter McMaster CB, Director General 1985–91, with the 18-inch Ramsden theodolite.

within the Civil Service but with the possibility of loosening at least some of the bureaucratic knots which prevented the department from adopting perfectly sensible commercial practices.

Announcing the change of status at the official launch in London on 1 May 1990, Minister for the Environment and Countryside, David Trippier, said:

> Today Ordnance Survey becomes the 31st Executive Agency and the 5th largest so far. With almost 200 years of mapmaking behind it, the name of Ordnance Survey has become synonymous with accuracy, with high standards, and indeed with maps themselves. It now aims to add 'Customer Service' most positively to this list. In an increasingly competitive and entrepreneurial market place, quality of products coupled with quality of service will provide the key to the successful businesses of the 1990s. I am confident Ordnance Survey will be amongst them.

To round off two centuries of national mapping, the Director General and invited guests celebrated Ordnance Survey's bicentenary in the gracious presence of her Majesty Queen Elizabeth II and the Duke of Edinburgh on 26 June 1991 at the Tower of London, Ordnance Survey's first office. A set of commemorative stamps was issued by the Royal Mail in September of the same year.

The Landlady

The following account was written by Lieutenant Colonel J E Portlock whilst on the Trigonometrical Survey on the Isle of Man in 1825, and is dedicated to that venerable institution, the landlady, who has a special place in every surveyor's heart.

Landing at Douglas, his [Colonel Colby's] first object was to hasten towards North Baroole, and to locate himself at its base in a small public-house on the roadside, kept by Mrs Looney. The next morning, as the month was June, he started with a small party of men, about three o'clock, for the summit, and was soon hard at work preparing for and erecting the object [the 3-foot Ramsden theodolite]. A few hours thus employed, and the free breathing of the wholesome mountain air prepared the stomach also to do its duty; and welcome therefore was the sight of Mrs Looney, attended by her maidens as she scaled the summit, with kettle in hand, a store of burning fuel in an iron pot, and all the glorious appendages of a substantial breakfast. The repast was soon ready, appetite was boundless, and digestion sound, and yet the supply was inexhaustible. With new vigour the work was now resumed, and about eight o'clock, pm, the party descended, when Mrs Looney, whose heart was a generous one, served up a dinner, or supper, which, though it might not have suited the palates of a court of aldermen, was in quantity sufficient to gorge a company of giants. Day after day the same hours, the same labours, and the same feasting were repeated, when having completed North Baroole and Snea Fell, the author took his leave of Mrs Looney, and was somewhat astonished when, for several days' lodging, for roasting-pigs of some months old, for gooseberry-pies more than a yard in circumference, and custard-puddings in half gallon jugs, and for all her journeys to the mountain-top, that lady demanded the *exorbitant sum of nine shillings!* Peace be with Mrs Looney! and let us ask, where should the wanderer with, as our poorer brethren sometimes express it, a wolf in the stomach, go for comfort if not to the humble inn of Mrs Looney, at the foot of North Baroole.

APPENDIX: CHRONOLOGY

1726 4 May: Birth of William Roy at Miltonhead, Lanarkshire.

1746 Defeat of the Young Pretender, Charles Edward Stuart and Jacobite forces at the Battle of Culloden.

1747 Roy begins the military survey of the Highlands (prematurely stopped by the approach of the Seven Years War in 1755).

1763 Roy makes a first proposal for a National Survey of Great Britain. (Second proposal made in 1766).

1782 Charles Lennox, the 3rd Duke of Richmond, appointed Master General of the Board of Ordnance.

1783 Cassini de Thury proposes a triangulation to link the Greenwich and Paris observatories.

1784 Hounslow Heath base measured by Roy.

1784 Order placed with Jesse Ramsden for 3-foot theodolite (delivered 1787).

1787 Triangulation of south-east England. First cross-Channel connection made.

1787 Base of verification measured on Romney Marsh.

1790 1 July: Major General William Roy FRS FSA dies.

1791 21 June: Board of Ordnance purchases Ramsden's second 3-foot theodolite. This is the accepted Founding Act of the Ordnance Survey.

1791 22 June: Mr Isaac Dalby engaged by the Board of Ordnance for the Trigonometrical Survey.

1791 12 July: Major Williams and Lieutenant Mudge appointed to the Trigonometrical Survey.

1791 Remeasurement of the Hounslow Heath base. Commencement of Primary Triangulation (completed 1841).

1793 Britain is at war with France. 'Invasion coasts' receive priority for mapping.

1794 Salisbury Plain base measured.

1795 The 1-inch map of Sussex published under patronage of 3rd Duke of Richmond, based on the triangulation of Trigonometrical Survey, published by W H Faden.

1795 Survey for 1-inch map of Kent commenced.

1798 Death of Colonel E Williams. Colonel Mudge appointed Superintendent of Ordnance Survey.

1800 Royal Warrant creates Corps of Royal Military Draftsmen. (Amended to corps of Royal Military Draftsmen and Surveyors in 1805. Disbanded in 1817).

1801 1 January: 1-inch map of Kent published by W H Faden.

1801 Founding of Ordnance Survey engraving department.

1802 Ramsden's zenith sector delivered and used for measurement of Dunnose – Clifton arc of Meridian.

1802 Second Lieutenant T F Colby appointed to Trigonometrical Survey.

1805 18 April: Essex 1-inch map published by Trigonometrical Survey.

1810 First recorded use of name 'Ordnance Survey' on 1-inch sheet 10, the Isle of Wight and parts of Hampshire.

1811 Invasion scares cause Master General to prohibit sale of Ordnance maps. (prohibition lifted in 1816).

1816 First use of advertising for Ordnance Survey maps.

1816 Map sellers notified that copying Ordnance Survey maps is prohibited under the Copyright Acts.

1820 Death of Major General W Mudge LLD, FRS. Captain T F Colby appointed Superintendent.

1825 Survey of Ireland at 6-inch scale begins (completed 1846).

1827–8 Lough Foyle base line measured.

One-inch, 1:50 000 and 1:25 000
Main Map Series, 1800–1991

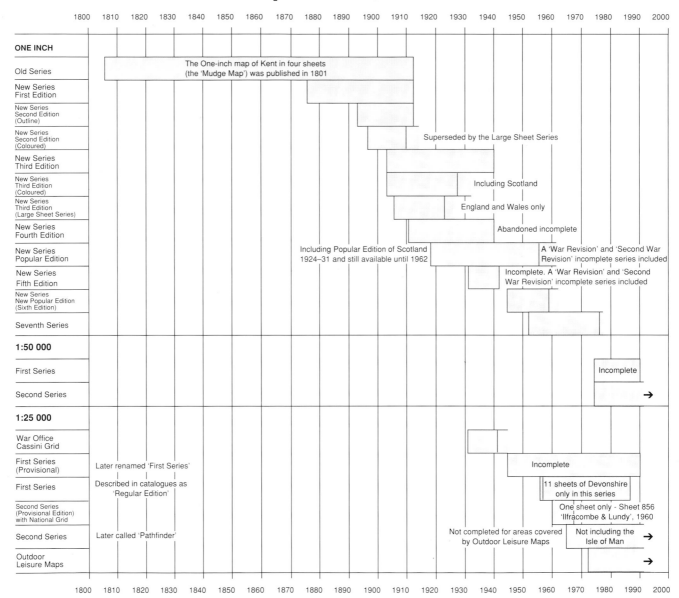

A Note on the Chart

Starting dates in the above chart indicate when a series became available to the public. Generally, starting dates are more precisely arrived at than end dates. The date (where known or arrived at by supposition) of the last printing of a map within a series is recorded by a vertical line within a shaded bar. In some cases maps within a series continued to be available until stocks ran out or were withdrawn, and this is shown by an open-ended extension of the bar. An arrow indicates that a particular series was still in print and available in 1991–2.

1833	Publication of first Irish Ordnance Survey 6-inch map (Londonderry).
1835	Geological Survey founded by Ordnance Survey under control of Sir Henry De la Beche.
1837	Primary levelling of Ireland commenced (completed 1843).
1840	Electrotyping introduced for copying engraved copper plates.
1839–40	First use of contours on Ordnance Survey maps.
1840	Six-inch scale approved for surveys of northern counties of England and Scotland.
1841	Survey Act passed which lists boundaries to be shown and gives right of access to private property by Ordnance Surveyors.
1841	Fire at the Tower of London. Ordnance Survey moves to Southampton.
1841	Mean sea-level at Liverpool accepted as levelling datum. Initial levelling of Great Britain commenced (completed 1860).
1845	Geological Survey passes to control of the Office of Woods and Forests.
1847	Major General T F Colby LLD, FRS retires. Lieutenant Colonel L A Hall RE appointed Superintendent.
1851	Charteris Committee recommends abandonment of the 6-inch scale and a return to 1-inch mapping. The beginning of the Battle of the Scales.
1852	Adjustment of the primary triangulation completed – network named Principal Triangulation.
1854	Brevet Colonel L A Hall retires. Major H James appointed Superintendent.
1854	Photography used for the first time in map production.
1855	Abolition of the Board of Ordnance; control of Ordnance Survey transfers to War Office.
1855	Zincography begins to replace lithography as the main map production method.
1855	First Annual Report published.
1858	Royal Commission recommends map scales of 1:2500, 6-inch and 1-inch for national mapping. The end of the Battle of the Scales.
1858	Clarke deduces his first spheroid, the approximate shape of the earth.
1859	Photozincography invented.
1870	Mapping of England and Wales at 1-inch scale complete.
1870	Ordnance Survey transferred to Office of Works control.
1875	Major General Sir Henry James KCB, FRS retires. Major General J Cameron appointed Superintendent.
1878	Major General J Cameron CB, FRS dies. Colonel A C Cooke appointed Superintendent (first to use title Director General).
1883	Major General A C Cooke CB retires. Colonel R H Stotherd appointed Director General.
1886	Colonel R H Stotherd CB retires. Colonel Sir Charles Wilson appointed Director General.
1886	Approval given to the principle of map revision.
1886	Larger photographic negatives introduced enabling greater use of photozincography.
1887	1:2500 scale extended to Ireland.
1887	The Jubilee Book presented to Queen Victoria.
1888	Statement 'All rights of reproduction reserved', included on maps from this date.
1890	Ordnance Survey transfers to control of Board of Agriculture.
1892	Dorington Committee report lays down principles for map revision which influence policy for next forty-five years.
1894	Major General Sir Charles Wilson KCB, KCMG FRS retires. Brevet Colonel J Farquharson appointed Director General.
1896	Hayes Fisher Committee recommends that Ordnance Survey conducts its own wholesaling of maps.
1897	Publication of 1-inch maps in full colour commences.

Large-Scale
Main Map Series, 1800–1991

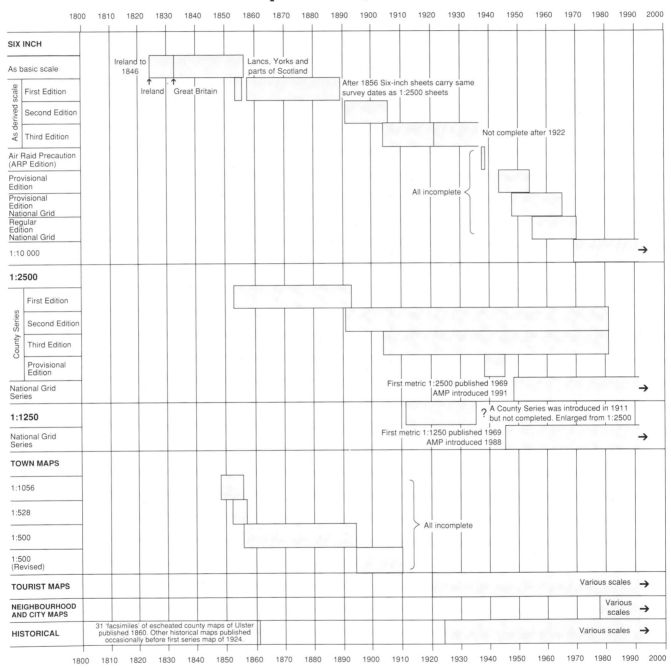

A Note on the Chart

Starting dates in the above chart indicate when a series became available to the public. Generally, starting dates are more precisely arrived at than end dates. The date (where known or arrived at by supposition) of the last printing of a map within a series is recorded by a vertical line within a shaded bar. In some cases maps within a series continued to be available until stocks ran out or were withdrawn, and this is shown by an open-ended extension of the bar. An arrow indicates that a particular series was still in print and available in 1991–2.

1899 Colonel J Farquharson CB retires. Brevet Colonel D A Johnston appointed Director General.

1899–1902 Start of the Boer War. Ordnance Survey produces maps of South Africa.

1900 Vandyke process introduced.

1902 Female labour first employed, for map mounting and colouring.

1902 Electricity installed throughout Southampton headquarters.

1903 First ½-inch map published (abolished as a national published series in 1961, last map at this scale was 'Snowdon', withdrawn 1990.)

1905 Colonel D A Johnston CB retires. Colonel R C Hellard appointed Director General.

1908 Colonel R C Hellard CB retires. Colonel S C N Grant appointed Director General.

1909 Lossiemouth base measured.

1911 Colonel S C N Grant CB, CMG retires. Colonel C F Close appointed Director General.

1911 Crown Copyright Act passed. Administration of Ordnance Survey copyright vested in the Controller of H M Stationery Office. 'Crown Copyright, reserved' added to all maps.

1912 Mean sea-level at Newlyn accepted as datum for levelling. Second geodetic levelling of England and Wales commenced (completed 1921).

1913 Magnetic survey of the British Isles commenced, in co-operation with the Royal Society (completed 1915).

1913 Ordnance Survey wins test copyright case.

1914 The Olivier Committee recommends improvement in presentation of small-scale maps.

1914 Telephones first installed at Ordnance Survey.

1914–18 First World War. Resources switched to production of maps for the war.

1918 Overseas Branch of Ordnance Survey (OBOS) set up at Wardreques near St Omer, France.

1919 Ellis Martin, a professional artist, engaged to design map covers and publicity material.

1919 H P L Jolly appointed first civilian Scientific Advisor.

1920 Departmental Whitley Council set up.

1920 First Tourist Map published (Snowdon).

1920 O G S Crawford appointed as first professional Archaeology Officer.

1922 Ordnance Survey Ireland passes to control of the new Irish Government. Ordnance Survey of Northern Ireland is established in Belfast.

1922 Geddes Committee introduce swingeing cuts in public expenditure. OS staff numbers cut to 1000.

1922 Colonel Sir Charles F Close KBE, CB, CMG, CB retires. Colonel E M Jack appointed Director General.

1923 End of copper plate engraving.

1924 First edition of map of 'Roman Britain' published.

1930 Brigadier E M Jack CB, CMG, DSO retires. Brigadier H St J L Winterbotham appointed Director General.

1935 Brigadier H St J L Winterbotham CB, CMG, DSO retires. Brigadier M N MacLeod appointed Director General.

1935 Interim report of the Davidson Committee recommends rapid revision of large-scale plans for town planning purposes and tighter control of copyright.

1935 Retriangulation of Great Britain commenced (completed 1962).

1936 Second geodetic levelling of Scotland commenced (completed 1952).

1937–8 Ridge Way base measured, Lossiemouth remeasured.

1938 Final Report of the Division Committee recommends 'overhaul' of national plans to be recast on national projection. Introduction of National Grid. Measurements to be in metres. Adoption of continuous revision; and the introduction of the new scale, 1:25 000.

1939–45 Second World War. Ordnance Survey resources turned to production of maps for the war.

Ten-mile, Quarter-inch and Half-inch Main Map Series, 1800–1991

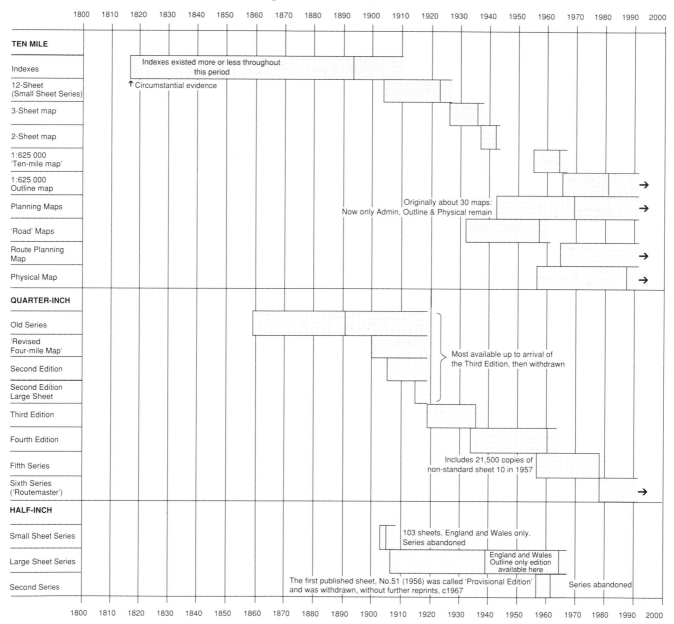

A Note on the Chart

Starting dates in the above chart indicate when a series became available to the public. Generally, starting dates are more precisely arrived at than end dates. The date (where known or arrived at by supposition) of the last printing of a map within a series is recorded by a vertical line within a shaded bar. In some cases maps within a series continued to be available until stocks ran out or were withdrawn, and this is shown by an open-ended extension of the bar. An arrow indicates that a particular series was still in print and available in 1991–2.

1940	Headquarters offices, London Road, Southampton, severely damaged in the blitz.
1943	Dispersal of headquarters to Chessington, Surrey.
1943	Major General M N MacLeod CB, DSO, MC retires. Brigadier G Cheetham appointed Director General.
1947	First 1:1250 scale maps produced.
1949	Major General G Cheetham CB, DSO, MC retires. Brigadier R Ll Brown appointed Director General.
1951	Third geodetic levelling of Great Britain commenced (completed 1958).
1952	Caithness base measured.
1953	Major General R Ll Brown CB, CBE retires. Major General J C T Willis appointed Director General.
1957	1:250 000 scale introduced to replace the ¼ inch (1:253 440).
1957	Major General J C T Willis CB, CBE, RI retires. Major General L F de Vic Carey appointed Director General.
1961	Major General L F de Vic Carey CB, CBE retires. Major General A H Dowson appointed Director General.
1962–3	The Estimates Committee recommends that the department should increase its revenue from sales.
1965	Major General A H Dowson CB, CBE retires. Major General R C A Edge appointed Director General.
1965	Ordnance Survey transfers to care of Ministry of Land and Natural Resources.
1965	First map in 1:25 000 Second Series published (Pathfinder series completed 1990).
1966	Outbreak of foot and mouth disease halts work in rural areas as surveyors denied access to land.
1967	Ordnance Survey transfers to care of Ministry of Housing and Local Government.
1969	Metrication of 1:25 000 and larger scale maps agreed.
1969	New headquarters opened at Maybush, Southampton, by Her Majesty Queen Elizabeth II accompanied by the Duke of Edinburgh.
1969	Major General R C A Edge CB, MBE retires. Major General B St G Irwin appointed Director General.
1970	Ordnance Survey transfers to care of Department of Environment which absorbs Ministry of Housing and Local Government.
1972	Publication of first Outdoor Leisure Map ('The Dark Peak').
1973	First large-scale digital map produced.
1973	Janes Committee report recommends that Ordnance Survey should adopt a more commercial approach.
1973	Supply of Unpublished Survey Information (SUSI) service introduced.
1974	Post of Director General no longer to be filled by a military officer. Major General B St G Irwin continues in post as a civil servant.
1974	1:50 000 scale mapping replaces 1-inch series (completed 1976).
1977	Major General B St G Irwin CB retires. Mr W P Smith appointed Director General.
1977	Microfilm service formalised as survey information on microfilm (SIM).
1979	The Serpell (Ordnance Survey Review) Committee report published. Recommends change to a 'marketing led' organisation.
1982	Joint ventures with co-publishers commence. (First book published: Pan/OS *Walker's Britain*.)
1983	Responsibility for archaeology archive transfers to the three Royal Commissions on Historical Monuments (RCHMs).
1983	Royal Engineers beat retreat from Ordnance Survey.
1984	Directorate of Overseas Surveys (DOS) merges with Ordnance Survey.
1984	Decision taken that Ordnance Survey will remain a vote-funded Civil Service department.

1985   Mr W P Smith CB, OBE retires. Mr P McMaster, Barrister, BSc, FRICS appointed Director General.

1986   First small-scale digital database marketed (1:625 000).

1987   Digital Field Update System (DFUS) introduced.

1987   Mission statement published giving direction for next decade.

1988   First 'paperless' fully digital office becomes operational at Milton Keynes.

1990   New national control network using the Global Positioning System (GPS) commenced.

1990   1:250 000 digital database produced.

1990   Large-scale Superplan becomes available in pilot areas.

1991   Digitisation of all 1:1250 maps completed.

1991   21 June: Ordnance Survey's bicentenary.

SELECT BIBLIOGRAPHY

The following are recommended as further reading.

J H Andrews, *A Paper Landscape: The Ordnance Survey in the Nineteenth Century – Ireland*. Oxford: Oxford University Press, 1975.

P Boyne, *John O'Donovan (1806–1861): A Biography*. Kilkenny, Ireland: Boethius, 1987.

J P Browne, *Map Cover Art*. Southampton: Ordnance Survey, 1991.

C Close, *The Early Years of the Ordnance Survey*. Newton Abbot: David & Charles, 1969

T Colby, *Ordnance Survey Memoir of Londonderry*. Limavady: North West Books, 1990.

J B Harley, *Ordnance Survey Maps – A Descriptive Manual*. Southampton: Ordnance Survey, 1975.

Ordnance Survey, *History of the Retriangulation of Great Britain*. London: HMSO, 1967.

Y O'Donaghue, *William Roy 1726–1790 – Pioneer of the Ordnance Survey*. London: British Museum Publications Ltd, 1977.

M M Reese, *Goodwood's Oak: The Life and Times of the Third Duke of Richmond, Lennox and Aubigny*. London: Threshold Books, 1987.

W A Seymour, *A History of the Ordnance Survey*. Folkestone: W M Dawson & Sons, 1980.

INDEX

Index by Anne Olerenshaw

Printed in the United Kingdom for HMSO
Dd 294210 C40 4/92